Sharon
KENDRICK

London's
Eligible Bachelors

MILLS &
BOON

$\mathcal{S}haron$
KENDRICK

COLLECTION

May 2015

June 2015

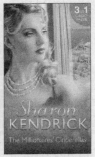

July 2015

August 2015

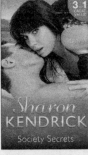

September 2015

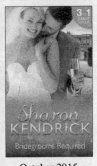

October 2015

Dear Reader,

I've known for a long time that I have the best job in the world—writing stories about powerful, complicated men and the women who love them—what's not to like? Some of these stories have stayed especially close to my heart and I'm delighted to announce that you can now read them for yourself if they're new to you—or maybe rediscover them if you loved them as much as I do.

I love them for different reasons. Sometimes because there's a heroine I can particularly identify with—like Rose in *Surrender to the Sheikh* or Sabrina in *The Unlikely Mistress*. Sometimes because I am unable to forget the hero—and I confess that they all have an unforgettable hero. I think about Dominic Dashwood in *Settling the Score* and all the fuss that book caused at the time. I think of the proud Russian, Nikolai, in *Too Proud to be Bought* and Ross in *One Husband Required*, who was a very different kind of hero. I can feel as if they're all in the room with me, urging you to read their stories, and I hope you will.

The collection runs from May through to October 2015, so please write or tweet me @Sharon_Kendrick and tell me which are *your* favourites.

Happy reading,

Love,

Sharon

Published in Great Britain 2015
by Mills & Boon, an imprint of Harlequin (UK) Limited,
Eton House, 18-24 Paradise Road, Richmond, Surrey, TW9 1SR

LONDON'S ELIGIBLE BACHELORS © 2015 Harlequin Books S.A.

The Unlikely Mistress © 2001 Sharon Kendrick
Surrender to the Sheikh © 2001 Sharon Kendrick
The Mistress's Child © 2001 Sharon Kendrick

ISBN: 978-0-263-25378-8

009-0615

Harlequin (UK) Limited's policy is to use papers that are natural, renewable and recyclable products and made from wood grown in sustainable forests. The logging and manufacturing processes conform to the legal environmental regulations of the country of origin.

Printed and bound in Spain
by CPI, Barcelona

The Unlikely Mistress

Sharon Kendrick once won a national writing competition by describing her ideal date: being flown to an exotic island by a gorgeous and powerful man. Little did she realise that she'd just wandered into her dream job! Today she writes for Mills & Boon, featuring often stubborn but always to-die-for heroes and the women who bring them to their knees. She believes that the best books are those you never want to end. Just like life…

CHAPTER ONE

SABRINA looked, and then looked again, her heart beating out a guilty beat while she tried to tell herself that her eyes were playing tricks on her. Because he couldn't possibly be for real.

He was standing close to the water, close enough for her to be able to see the carved symmetry of his features. Chiselled cheekbones and a proud, patrician nose. The mouth was luscious—both hard and sensual—a mouth which looked as though it had kissed a lot of women in its time.

Only the eyes stopped the face from being too beautiful—they were too icily cold for perfection. Even from this distance, they seemed to glitter with a vital kind of energy and a black, irresistible kind of danger...

Oh, Lord, thought Sabrina in despair. What am I *thinking* of? She was not the kind of woman to be transfixed by complete strangers—especially not when she was alone and vulnerable in a foreign country. And while Venice was the most beautiful place on earth—she was there on her own.

On her own. Something she was still having to come to term with. Once again, guilt stabbed at her with piercing accuracy.

But still she watched him...

By the edge of the water, Guy felt his body tense with a sense of the unexpected, aware of the unmistakable sensation of being watched. He narrowed hard slate-grey eyes as they scanned the horizon, and his gaze was suddenly arrested by the sight of the woman who drifted in the gondola towards him. Madonna, he thought suddenly. Madonna.

The pale March sun caught a sheen of bright red-gold hair, drifting like a banner around her shoulders. He could see long, slender limbs and skin so pale it looked almost translucent. She's English, he thought suddenly as their eyes clashed across the glittering water. And for one mad, reckless moment he thought about…what? Following her? Buying her a cup of coffee? His mouth hardened into a brief, cynical smile.

It was reckless to want to pick up a total stranger and he, more than most people, knew the folly of being reckless. Hadn't his whole life been spent making amends for his father's one careless act of desperation? The knock-on effect of impulsive behaviour was something to guard against. Resolutely he turned away from her distractions.

Sabrina felt something approaching pain. *Look at me*, she urged him silently, but her gondolier chose that moment to give an expert twist of his wrist to glide the craft into shore and he was lost to her eyes.

She pushed her guidebook back into her handbag and stood up, allowing the gondolier to steady her elbow, nodding her head vigorously, as if she understood every word of his murmured Italian. But she had paid him before the journey and didn't have a clue what he could be saying to her.

And then there was a shout behind her, a deep, alarming shout, and instinctively she knew that the voice belonged to the man with the dark hair. She automatically turned in response, just in time to feel a great whooshing spray of icy cold water as it splashed over her.

It jetted towards her eyes and the shock made her handbag slip from her fingers. She was aware of her gondolier shouting something furiously, and when she opened her eyes again she could see the zigzag of foam left in the wake of a small speedboat.

And the man with the dark hair.

He was standing on the shore right next to her, holding his hand out, and despite the look of icy anger on his face some instinct made her take it, losing herself immediately in the warmth of his firm grasp.

'Why the hell can't people control the machines they're supposed to be in charge of?' he said, in a voice as coolly beautiful as his face. He gave a brief, hard stare at the retreating spray of the boat, then narrowed his eyes as he looked down at the shivering woman whose fingernails were gripping painfully into the palm of his hand. Her face was so white that it looked almost translucent, and he felt a strange kick to his heart. 'You *are* English?'

Up close, he was even more devastating. Breathtakingly so. Awareness shimmered over her skin like fingertips. 'Y-y-yes, I am,' she replied, from between chattering teeth. 'How c-c-could you tell?'

He carried on holding her hand until he was certain that she was grounded. 'Because pale women with freckles and strawberry-blonde hair look quintessentially English, that's why,' he answered slowly as he allowed his eyes to drift irresistibly over her. 'And you're soaking.'

Sabrina looked down at herself, and saw that he wasn't exaggerating. She was wet right through—her T-shirt stained with dirty lagoon water, the pinpoint thrust of her nipples emphasising her plummeting body temperature as much as the chattering of her teeth.

'Not to mention freezing.' He swallowed as he followed the direction of her eyes, tempted to make a flippant joke about wet T-shirt competitions, then deciding against it. Not his scene to make remarks like that to a complete stranger.

Sabrina suddenly realised what was missing. 'Oh, my goodness—I've dropped my handbag!' she wailed.

'Where?'

'In the w-water. And it's got my purse in it!'

He went to peer over the edge of the lagoon, but the dark waters had claimed it.

'Don't!' Sabrina called, terrified that he would just disappear again, exit from her life for ever.

He turned round with a look of mystification. 'Don't what?'

'D-don't t-t-try and retrieve it!'

'You think I'm about to dive into the canal to hunt around for your handbag?' He smiled again. 'Princess, I'm not that much of a hero!' But the smile died on his lips as he saw that the edges of her mouth were turning a very pale blue. 'You know,' he observed slowly, unable to look away from the ice-blue dazzle of her eyes, 'you're really going to have to get out of those wet clothes before you catch pneumonia!'

The intimacy of his remark drove every sane response clean out of her mind. Sabrina opened her mouth, then chattered it shut again.

Guy frowned. He couldn't believe he'd said that. Crass, or what? 'Where are you staying?'

'M-m-miles away.' Naturally. Rooms this close to St Mark's Square tended to be beyond the reach of anyone other than your average millionaire.

Guy's mouth hardened as he read the unconscious appeal in her eyes. Pity she hadn't mentioned that *before* the gondola had sped away. If the driver hadn't been flirting with her quite so outrageously, then he might have been able to warn her about the speedboat in time. And the least he could have done to recompense would have been to give her a free ride back to her hotel.

Which left it up to *him*.

He had achieved what he had set out to do in Venice—had purchased a superb Italian old master for one of his more demanding clients. The price he had bartered had been better than expected and his client would be pleased.

He had planned a quiet day. Playing knight in shining armour hadn't been top of his agenda. But responsibility was etched deep into Guy's personality. He looked down into her heart-shaped face, and felt his heart kick-start again. She really was very beautiful... 'You can't possibly travel home in that state, but you can clean up at my hotel if you like—it's just around the corner.'

'Your *hotel*?' Sabrina swallowed, guiltily remembering the way she had been unable to tear her eyes away from him on the lagoon. She'd been certain that he hadn't seen her—but what if he had? And what if he'd then imagined that she was the kind of woman who allowed herself to be picked up in the most casual manner possible and taken back for a so-called siesta? 'I don't even know you—and I'm not in the habit of going back to strange men's hotel rooms!'

Guy's eyes glittered with unconcealed irritation. He was offering to do her a favour—did she really think that he was after something else? Desperate enough to make a pass at someone he didn't even know?

He supposed that he could have shrugged and said fine and walked away, but something about her defensive stance struck at his conscience. He forced his mouth into a smile. 'Then how about I introduce myself so I'm no longer a stranger?' He held his hand out. 'Guy Masters,' he said softly.

Something in the way he said it struck at Sabrina's heart like a hammer blow, as though she had been waiting all her life to hear just that name spoken aloud. She felt his hand still warming her frozen fingers, his grey eyes sending their icy light across her face, and tiptoes of some unknown emotion began to tingle their way up her spine. 'S-Sabrina Cooper,' she stumbled.

'Well, you'll be quite safe with me, Sabrina Cooper,' he assured her gravely. 'The alternative, of course, is that you travel halfway across Venice looking like that. It's up to you—I'm only offering to help. Take it or leave it.'

His grey eyes didn't stray from her face, which only seemed to reinforce where he *wasn't* looking. And he didn't really want to spell it out. That wet T-shirt did spectacularly draw the eye. Even if the sopping fabric was stretched over a pair of breasts which could in no way be described as voluptuous. On the contrary, he thought, they were small and neat and deliciously cuppable. She wouldn't be *safe* travelling back on her own, looking as beautifully sexy as she did right now.

Sabrina hesitated. Surely a man who looked like Guy Masters would have no need of ulterior motives. 'Why are you being so…?'

'Chivalrous?' he prompted, a cool fire dancing in his eyes. It amused him that she hadn't seen fit to leap at his offer. That didn't happen a lot, not these days. He shrugged. 'Because you're English, and so am I, and I have an over-developed sense of responsibility which just won't seem to go away. You're cold and wet and you've lost your purse. So what else can I do? Rip the clothes from my back in order to cover you up?'

She eyed the taut torso with alarm as her imagination gave her a disturbingly realistic picture of how he would look if he *did* remove that snowy-white T-shirt. What on earth was the matter with her? She had come to Venice in an attempt to make some sense of the tragedy which had transformed her life. And making sense of things did not involve feeling overwhelmingly attracted to men who had a dangerous air of inaccessibility about them.

'Er, no.' She swallowed. 'That won't be necessary. I'll

take up your offer of the bathroom. It's very…sweet of you. Thank you.' But 'sweet' did not seem an appropriate word to use about Guy Masters—he was far too elementally masculine for that.

'Come this way,' he said, and they began to walk through the narrow, dark streets of Venice with the slicking sounds of water all around them.

Sabrina felt the weight of heavy, wet denim chafing uncomfortably against her thighs. 'I don't know how I'm going to get my clothes dry.'

'Don't worry. The hotel will think of something.' Hotels like the Palazzo Regina always did, he thought wryly. Catering for each and every whim of their pampered guests, however bizarre. In life, Guy had realised a long, long time ago, you got what you paid for. And the more you paid, the more impressed the world seemed to be.

Sabrina was aware of the curious looks being cast in their direction, and couldn't decide whether that was because she looked half-drowned or because he looked so beautiful. She felt overpoweringly aware of him as he moved with a kind of restrained power by her side, every pore seeming to exude a vital kind of energy. It was as though that magnificent body had imprinted itself indelibly on every single one of her senses and she could feel the incessant pumping of her heart and the rapid little rush of her breathing as they walked.

'How much money was in your purse?' he asked.

'Only a bit. I've left most of it in my hotel safe, along with my tickets.'

'That's something, I guess. Imagine if you'd come out with your airline tickets.'

'Imagine,' she said faintly.

Something in the way she'd said it made him smile. 'We're here,' he announced, stopping in front of a large, impressive façade overlooking the waterfront itself.

Sabrina screwed her face up in disbelief. 'Here?' He was gorgeous, yes, but in his jeans and T-shirt he had seemed just like her—just another tourist. This couldn't be right, surely? His hotel couldn't be this central—not unless he was staying in some sort of museum or palace. Which was exactly what it looked like. 'You're staying *here*?'

Guy heard the incredulity in her voice and sizzled her a glance of mocking query. 'You think I don't know the way back to my own hotel?'

Sabrina compared it to the tiny, dark *pensione* she was staying in. 'It looks more like a palace than a hotel!'

'Mmm. I believe it was.' He glanced down and saw that the walk had removed that ghastly blue tinge from her lips, and smiled. 'A very long time ago.'

'How long?'

'Fourteenth century, would you believe?'

'Good heavens,' said Sabrina lightly, and the question came out before she had time to think about it. 'How on earth can you afford to stay in a place like this?'

Years of self-preservation against women with dollar signs in their eyes made Guy reply, without missing a beat, 'I'm lucky,' he said coolly. 'The company pays for it. Come on. You've started shivering again.'

As soon as they walked into a lavishly ornate foyer, she heard the faint buzz of comment. One of the men working at the reception desk, who looked handsome enough to be a movie star, fixed Guy Masters with an unctuous smile.

'Sir? I trust you have had an enjoyable morning.'

'Eventful,' Guy murmured. 'I'll just have my key, please, Luigi.'

'Certainly, sir, I'll have someone—'

'No, please, don't bother. I'll see myself up.'

In the mirror-lined lift, Sabrina saw how wet she really was.

The water of the lagoon was obviously much dirtier than

its colour suggested, because there were tiny spots of mud spattering her T-shirt. And unfortunately there were two damp circles ringing her breasts, drawing attention to the outline of her bra which was embarrassingly visible. And so, too, were her nipples, tight and hot and aching. Turned on by a man she had only just met...

Appalled by her dark and unwanted thoughts, she quickly crossed her arms and clamped them over her bust. 'That man at Reception gave me a very funny look.'

Guy felt a pulse flicker as he stared at her reflection in the mirror, noting the protective body language and working out for himself the reason for it. 'Well, you must admit you do look pretty spectacular,' he murmured. Like some glorious nymph who had just emerged from the water.

'Mmmm,' she agreed. 'Spectacularly drowned.'

He narrowed his eyes. Her voice was unusually soft. As soft as her lips. The lift pinged to a halt. 'Here's my suite.'

Suite?

Sabrina thought of her own small *pensione*, where she could never find anyone on duty. Like last night, for example, when the water coming from the tap had been nothing more than a dark, brackish trickle. With the aid of her phrasebook, she had been forced to laboriously construct a note to the *manager*, requesting that he do something about the hot water. What if she'd gone back today, dripping from head to toe in filthy lagoon water, to discover that nothing had been resolved?

Thank heavens for the chivalrous Guy Masters, she told herself—but she felt a mixture of nerves and excitement as he unlocked the door to his suite.

He pushed open the door to let her inside and Sabrina had to stifle a small cry of astonishment as she walked into a high-ceilinged sitting room. Because, yes, of course, she'd known that places such as these existed, but it was something so outside her own experience that it was like stepping into a parallel world.

The room was full of furniture which even an idiot could tell was very old. Antique, in fact. And priceless too, she imagined.

Sabrina looked around her. The light was muted because all the shutters were closed, but that made the contents of the room stand out even more.

Silken rugs in jewel-bright colours were scattered on the marble floors, on which stood spindly-legged chairs and tables. There was a faded sofa of crimson and gold and a couple of chairs which matched, all strewn with cushions of the same rich colours. She slowly turned to see an oil painting of a long-dead doge, set against the timeless Venetian backdrop, one of many paintings hung on the crimson walls.

'Oh, but it's beautiful,' she breathed. 'So beautiful.'

Guy watched her slow appraisal, her uninhibited pleasure making her look curiously elegant, despite the damp and dirty clothes.

'Isn't it?' he said softly, but he wasn't even looking at the painting.

And the lack of light was far too intimate, he decided suddenly, striding over to the window to push open the shutters, so the reflected light from the Grand Canal gleamed and glittered back into the room at them.

A view like that was worth a king's ransom, thought Sabrina, suddenly feeling as out of place as some scruffy urchin who had come seeking shelter from the storm.

It brought her quickly to her senses. She wasn't here to enjoy the view. Or to make small-talk. She had better just clean up and be on her way.

She cleared her throat. 'Could you show me—?'

He turned around, noting the sudden pinkness in her cheeks, the two high spots of colour making her look like some flaxen-plaited doll. 'Sure. The bathroom's that door over there.' He pointed. 'Take as long as you like. Oh, and throw your wet clothes out and I'll send them down and have them laundered.'

'Thank you.'

Sabrina was glad to lock the bathroom door behind her and peel off the freezing clothes from her shivering flesh. They smelt so *dank*!

The jeans were first, and then the T-shirt, and she dropped the sodden garments onto the marble floor. But her bra and panties were damp with canal water, too. Should she risk...?

Risk what? she asked herself impatiently. She couldn't keep sodden underwear on, and this pair of sensible cotton briefs was hardly likely to have him trying to beat the door down!

Sheltering behind the screen of the door, she picked the bundle up.

'Guy?'

'Leave them outside,' came a muffled sort of voice, and she did as he asked, quickly slamming the door shut and sliding the lock home before stepping into the shower, with its industrial-sized head.

Outside, Guy gingerly picked up the deposited items as if he were handling a poisonous snake.

Had it really been necessary for her to take *everything* off? he wondered uncomfortably, while asking himself why some women chose to wear knickers which looked as if they were armour-plated.

He knew almost nothing about Sabrina Cooper, and would never see her again after today, but what he *did* know was that she certainly hadn't come to Venice with seduction in mind.

Not unless she was intending to appeal to the type of man who got turned on by the frumpy gym-mistress look!

Biting back a smile, he wandered over to the telephone and picked up the receiver.

'*Pronto!*' he drawled for courtesy's sake, and then immediately switched to English, in which most of the staff were fluent. His Italian was passable—but in a case concerning a strange woman's underwear he needed no misunderstandings! 'How long will it take to get some clothes laundered?'

There was a short pause. 'Certainly within a couple of hours, sir.'

Guy frowned. That long? And just what were they supposed to do while Sabrina's jeans and T-shirt and bra and panties whizzed around in the washing machine? His time was precious, and his leisure time especially so. There were a million things he would rather be doing than being forced to sit and chat to someone with whom he had nothing in common other than that they both hailed from the same country.

Damn!

'Let's try for half that time, shall we?' he suggested softly. 'And can you have some coffee brought up at the same time?'

Bearing a tray of coffee, the valet came and collected the damp garments and Guy heard the sound of the shower being turned off. He walked over to the bathroom door.

'I'm afraid your clothes won't be back for an hour,' he called.

'An *hour*?' Sabrina's heart plummeted as she stood behind the locked door. What was she supposed to do in the meantime? Stay wrapped in a towel inside this steamy bathroom?

He heard the annoyance in her voice and felt like telling her that the idea pleased him even less than it did her. But he hadn't been forced to bring her back here, had he? No, he'd made that decision all on his own—so he could hardly complain about it now.

'Why don't you use that towelling robe hanging up on the back of the door?' he suggested evenly. 'And there's some coffee out here when you're ready.'

Squinting at herself in the cloudy mirror, Sabrina shrugged on a towelling gown which was as luxuriously thick and fluffy as she would expect in a place like this. She slipped it over her bare, freckled shoulders, and as she did so she became aware of the faint trace of male scent which clung to it.

Guy had been wearing this robe before her, she realised as an unwelcome burst of sexual hunger grew into life inside her. Guy's body had been as naked beneath this as her own now was. She felt the sudden picking up of her heart as the evocative muskiness invaded her nostrils, and she wondered if she might be going slightly mad.

How could a complete stranger—however attractive he undoubtedly was—manage to have such an incapacitating and powerful effect on her? Making her feel like some puppet jerked and manipulated by invisible strings. Was this what the death of her fiancé had turned her into—some kind of predator?

Guy glanced up as she walked in and his grey eyes narrowed, a pulse hammering at his temple. Maybe the robe hadn't been such a good idea after all, he conceded. Because wasn't there something awfully erotic about a woman wearing an oversized masculine garment like that? On him it reached to just below his knees—but on this woman's pale and slender frame it almost skimmed her ankles.

'How about some coffee?' he queried steadily.

'C-coffee would be lovely,' she stumbled, suddenly feeling acutely shy. She perched on the edge of a sofa on the opposite side of the room, telling herself that she had absolutely nothing to worry about. The circumstances might be bizarre, but for some reason she trusted this man. Men of Guy Masters's calibre wouldn't make a clumsy pass at a stranger, despite that brief, hungry darkening of his eyes.

He poured them both coffee and thought that conversation might be safer than silence. 'First time in Venice?'

'First time abroad,' she admitted.

'You're kidding!'

She shook her head. 'No, I'm not. I've never been out of England before.' Michael hadn't earned very much, and neither had she—and saving up to buy a house had seemed more important than trips abroad. Though a man like Guy Masters would probably not understand that.

'And you came here on your own?'

'That's right.'

He looked at her curiously. 'Pretty daring thing to do,' he observed, 'first time in a foreign country on your own?'

Sabrina stared down at the fingers which were laced around her coffee-cup. 'I've never done anything remotely daring before...'

'What, never?' he teased softly.

Sabrina didn't smile back. Hadn't she decided that life was too short to play safe all the time? 'So I thought I'd give it a try,' she said solemnly, and shifted her bottom back a little further on the seat.

Guy sipped his coffee and wished that she would sit still, not keep shifting around on the sofa as if she had ants in her pants. And then he remembered.

She wasn't wearing any.

Dear God. A shaft of desire shot through him, which was as unexpected as it was inappropriate, and he took a huge mouthful of coffee—almost glad when it scalded his lips. He risked a surreptitious glance at his watch. Only forty-five minutes to go. Less if he was lucky. Much more of this and he would be unable to move.

'So why Venice?' he queried, a slight edge of desperation to his voice.

'Oh, it's one of the world's most beautiful cities, and I—
I had to…to…'

Something in the quality of her hesitation made him stir
with interest. 'Had to what?'

She had been about to say 'get away', but that particular
statement always provoked the questions to ask why, and
once that question had been asked then the whole sad story
would come out. A story she was weary of telling. Weary
of living through. She had come to Italy to escape from
death and its clutches.

'I had to see St Mark's Square.' She smiled brightly. 'It
was something of a life's ambition. So was riding in a
gondola.'

'But not taking a bath in the Grand Canal?'

She actually laughed. 'No. Not that. I hadn't bargained
on that!'

He thought how the laugh lit up her face. Like sunshine
glowing from within. 'And how long are you staying?'

'Only a couple more days. How about you?'

He felt a pulse begin to beat insistently at his temple.
Suddenly Venice was getting more attractive by the minute—rather uncomfortably attractive, actually. 'Me, too,' he
said huskily, and risked another glance at his watch.

The room seemed much too small. Much too intimate.
Again Sabrina shifted self-consciously on the sofa.

'How old are you?' he demanded suddenly, as she
crossed one pale, slender thigh over the other.

Old enough to recognise that maybe Guy Masters wasn't
completely indifferent to her after all. The quiet, metallic
gleam in the cool grey eyes told her that. But that wasn't
the kind of answer he was seeking.

'I'm twenty-seven,' she told him.

'You look younger.'

'So people say.' She lifted her eyebrows. 'And you?'

'Thirty-two.'

'You look older.'

Their eyes connected as something primitive shuddered in the air around them.

'I know I do,' he murmured.

His words caressed her and Sabrina stared at him, unable to stop her eyes from committing every exquisite feature to memory. I will never forget you, she thought with an aching sense of sadness. Ever.

They sat in silence for a while as they drank their coffee. Eventually, there was a rap on the door and the valet delivered an exquisitely laundered set of underwear, jeans and T-shirt. Guy handed them over to her. 'There you go,' he said gravely.

She took them, blushingly aware that his fingertips had actually been touching the pressed cotton of her bra and panties. 'I'd better go and get changed.'

And if he'd thought that she'd looked exquisite before, that was nothing to the transformation which had taken place when she emerged, shimmering, from the bathroom. Guy didn't know what the laundry had managed to do with her clothes, but they now looked as if they were brand-new, and her hair had dried to a glorious strawberry-blonde sheen which spilled over her shoulders.

'You'd better take this,' he said as he dug deep into the pocket of his trousers and withdrew a wad of money, seeing her eyes widen in an alarmed question as he gave it to her.

'What's this?' she demanded.

'Didn't you drop your purse into the water?' he queried softly. 'And don't you need to get home?'

'I can't take your money,' she protested.

'Then don't. Think of it as a loan. Pay me back tomorrow if you like.'

Sabrina slid the notes thoughtfully into the back pocket of her jeans. 'OK. I will. Thanks.'

He went down with her in the lift to the foyer, telling himself that he would never see her again.

And wondering why that thought should make him ache so much, and so badly.

CHAPTER TWO

DESPITE telling herself that she was being crazy and unrealistic, Sabrina couldn't help the decided spring to her
step next morning as she set off to return Guy's money,
nor the flush of anticipation which made her cheeks glow.
And why had she dressed up for him in an ice-blue sundress
which very nearly matched her eyes and peep-toed sandals
which made her legs look longer than they really were?

Surely she didn't imagine for a moment that he would
take one look at her and decide that she was the woman of
his dreams?

She put the stack of lire in an envelope. He probably
wouldn't even be there, she reasoned. She would just have
to leave the money for him at Reception.

The buildings soared up all around her and the water—
which was everywhere—seemed to glimmer and glitter
with some unspoken promise. As her steps drew her closer
to Guy's hotel, she felt the slow prickle of nerves.

She told herself that even if he was there he would probably just take the money with that cool, enigmatic smile
and thank her. Then say goodbye, his faintly quizzical expression mocking her if she was foolish enough to linger
hopefully over their farewells.

Drawing a deep breath, she walked into the foyer, surprised that the man behind the desk with the movie-star
looks should raise his eyebrows in recognition the moment
he saw her. He quickly picked up the telephone and started
speaking into it.

By the time she had reached the desk he had finished his

call and was glancing down at a notepad in front of him. He smiled at her.

'Ah, Signorina Cooper,' he purred.

She raised her eyebrows. 'You know my name?'

The smile widened. 'But of course! Signor Masters asked me to telephone him the moment you arrived.'

Well, that was something. At least he hadn't imagined that she'd just disappeared into the sunset with his money.

She quickly took the envelope from her handbag. 'Can I just leave this here for him?' she said breathlessly. 'I won't stay. I'm—'

'Not planning on running away from me, are you, Miss Cooper?' came a deep voice from just behind her, and Sabrina turned round to find herself caught in the hard, grey crossfire of his eyes. And she was lost. Utterly lost.

'Hello, Guy,' she said weakly.

'Hello, Sabrina,' he mocked, his gaze running over her with pleasure, thinking that she had dressed up for him, and the rapid beat of his heart told him exactly what *that* meant.

'I brought your money back.' She held the envelope out.

'So I see.'

'I can't thank you enough for coming to my rescue. I don't know how I would have managed otherwise.' She swallowed down the constricting lump which was affecting her ability to breathe. 'Anyway, I'd better go—'

But he cut her words short with the restraining touch of his fingertips on her bare arm—a feather-light and innocent enough touch, but one which made sensation skate erotic little whispers all over its surface. He felt suddenly breathless. *Reckless.*

His eyes darkened. 'Why go anywhere?' he questioned softly. It's a beautiful day. We're both on our own. Why don't we go sightseeing together?'

'Together?'

He paused for a dangerous beat, giving her the unthinkable opportunity of saying no. 'Unless you'd rather be on your own?'

Well, that was why she had come to Venice, wasn't it? To get away and escape. To throw off the shackles of anxious eyes which followed her every move.

But Sabrina didn't want to get away. Not from Guy. She tried to keep her voice casual. 'Not especially.'

Guy almost laughed aloud at her lukewarm response. He wondered if she did this all the time—sent out these conflicting messages so that while that flushed look of anticipation and the bright sparkle of her eyes were like a sweet invitation to possess her, the somewhat indifferent responses to his questions were a slammed door in the face. Perplexing. And he hadn't been perplexed by a woman in a long time.

'So is that a yes or a no?'

It was an I'm-not-sure-whether-I'm-doing-the-right-thing, Sabrina thought, but she smiled anyway. 'It's a yes,' she said.

He watched the way she flicked her hair back over her shoulder. The movement made her breasts dance beneath the thin cotton dress, and Guy felt the primitive urge to take her somewhere and impale her and make her his. He hardened his mouth, appalled at himself.

'Why don't you tell me what you've seen already?' he suggested unevenly. 'And where you'd like to eat lunch?'

Sabrina noticed the sudden tension around his mouth, the way his eyes had darkened into a hungry glitter, and while she knew that she ought to be intimidated by the sheer potency of his masculinity she had never felt less intimidated in her life.

'I've seen the Basilica di San Marco,' she said. 'Of course! And the Golden House and the Doges Palace. But that's all. Lunch—I wouldn't have a clue about.' Her budget was tight and she'd been skipping lunch. But that had been no hardship.

Guy noticed the shadowed hollows beneath the high sweep of her cheekbones and wondered if she had been eating properly. 'Then let's go and find the rest of Venice,' he suggested softly.

But it took an effort for Sabrina to concentrate on her surroundings as they walked out into the sunshine. Yesterday the city had seemed like the most magical place on the planet, while today it was difficult to think about anything other than the man at her side.

At least she had some idea of what she was supposed to be looking at. She'd spent the preceding weeks reading every book about Venice that she could lay her hands on—it had been a good kind of displacement therapy—but Guy could more than match her.

'Did you know that the humorist Robert Benchley sent a telegram when he arrived in Venice?' Guy murmured. 'Saying, "Streets full of water. Please advise."'

Sabrina thought that his grey eyes looked soft, soft as the cream silk shirt he wore. 'No, I didn't know that. But Truman Capote said that Venice was like eating an entire box of chocolate liqueurs in one go.'

'Oh, did he?' He liked the quickness of her mind, the way her thoughts matched his own. Liked the fact that she'd researched the place so thoroughly. He felt his heart begin to pick up its beat as he stared down at her, at the strawberry-blonde hair which gleamed like bright gold in the midday sun and the slim, pale column of her neck. There was a fragility about her which was rare in a modern woman, he thought, and wondered what it would be like to take her in his arms. Take her to his bed. Whether she would bend or break...

He realised that they had spent the best part of two hours together and she hadn't asked him a single question about his life back in England. And he noticed that she'd been quietly evasive on the subject of her own life.

But why not? he thought with a sudden sense of liberation. Wasn't anonymity a kind of freedom in itself? Didn't he live the kind of life where people judged him before they had even met him, depending on what they'd heard about him?

The bell of San Marco rang out twice, and Guy looked at his watch. 'We'd better try and find a table for lunch while there's still time.'

Sabrina stared up into dark grey eyes and felt her skin prickle in heated reaction. 'I'm not hungry.'

'Is that why you're so thin?' he demanded. 'Because you skip lunch?'

'Thanks very much!'

'Oh, I'm not complaining,' he murmured, as his eyes drifted over her. 'Your cheekbones are quite exquisitely pronounced and your legs are just the right side of slender. I suppose you have to work at it, the same as every other woman.'

Sabrina let her gaze fall from his face, staring instead at the pink-tipped toes which peeped through her strappy sandals, remembering how she'd forced herself to paint them, telling herself that out of such small, unimportant rituals some kind of normal life would be resumed.

'Sabrina,' he said softly. 'What's the matter? It was supposed to be a compliment. Have I insulted you? Embarrassed you?'

She looked up again. Now would be the perfect time to tell him that the weight had simply fallen away after Michael's death. But tell him that and she would be back playing the unwanted role of the bereaved fiancée. Was it selfish of her to want to play a different part? To want to feel the sun warm and alive on her cheeks and see the unmistakable glint of appreciation in the eyes of the man who stood looking down at her? To feel *alive* again, instead of half-dead herself?

She shook herself out of her reverie and forced a smile which, to her suprise, felt as if it wanted to stay on her mouth. 'By telling me I'm thin? Come on, Guy—did you ever hear of a woman who was offended by that?'

Her smile was like the sun nudging out from behind a cloud, he thought. 'I guess not.' Come to think of it, he didn't have much appetite himself, and certainly not for conventional fare.

Instead, he found himself wondering how her lips would taste and what the scent of her breath would be like against his. He shook his head to dispel the sensual imagery. 'Why don't we have coffee and a pastry at one of these cafés in the square?' he suggested steadily. 'It's warm enough to sit outside in the sunshine.'

They found a vacant table and ordered pastries with their coffee, the lightest and most beautiful cakes imaginable, and Guy thought that they tasted like sawdust in his mouth. And saw that Sabrina had taken exactly two mouthfuls herself.

'It must be the heat.' She shrugged in response to the mocking question in his eyes.

'So it must.' He echoed the lie, knowing that their lack of hunger had nothing to do with the temperature.

He marched her through the city like a professional tour guide, as if determined that he should show her everything. Sabrina wondered what had provoked this sudden, relentless pace, but she was too bewitched by him to care.

They stood side by side on the Bridge of Sighs and stared into the dark waters beneath.

'Look down there,' said Sabrina suddenly. 'And think of the thousands of tourists who have stood here like this and been affected by this amazing city.'

His heart missed a beat as enchantment washed over him. 'You mean the way it's affecting us now?'

'Yes.' She told herself it wasn't *that* remarkable for him to have echoed her thoughts, but still her voice trembled. 'That's exactly what I mean.'

He wanted her, he thought. And she wanted him. 'Are you going to have dinner with me tonight, Sabrina?' he asked suddenly.

She didn't even stop to think about it, or bother to wonder whether she'd made it too easy for him. 'You know I am.'

He nodded, the thrill of anticipation making his heart pick up speed. 'Tell me where you're staying and I'll pick you up at eight.'

'You don't have to do that.'

Her reluctance sharpened an appetite already keenly honed. 'Oh, but I insist,' he contradicted softly.

But pride made her match his determination. He must be some kind of hot-shot to be staying at that hotel. She didn't want him seeing her humble little *pensione*, emphasising how great the differences between them. Just now they were as close to equal as they would ever be and she wanted to hold onto that. 'I'll meet you in the square. Honestly, Guy, I'm an independent woman, you know!'

'Well, sometimes a man doesn't want an independent woman,' he ground out. He couldn't believe he'd just said that, but he had. Or that he'd caught her by the arm to feel the soft tremble of flesh where his fingers burnt so delectably against her bare skin. 'Are you always this damned stubborn?'

Something in the heated frustration of his question made Sabrina's blood sing with a glorious inevitability, and she had the sense of being led towards something which defied all logic. It was liberation at its most intense and powerful, and she was no longer heartbroken, bereaved Sabrina. For one enchanted moment she stood poised on the brink of something magical.

She smiled. 'Only if I need to be.'

There was a long and dangerous pause. 'But I'm used to getting my own way,' he told her steadily.

'I know you are. It shows.'

She looked down at his tanned fingers which still lay against her white skin, and he let his hand fall, perplexed by his own actions. He was a man whose reputation hinged on being in control—so why was he acting as if he were auditioning for the leading role in a Western movie?

'Was I being unbearably high-handed?' he asked her, missing the satin feel of her skin beneath his fingertips.

She took one last look at him as she stepped into the water-taxi which had slid to a halt beside them. Not unbearably anything, she thought. You wouldn't know how to be. 'Only a little.' She shrugged. 'I'll see you tonight at eight.'

And Guy was left staring at the back of her bright blonde head, his heart thundering with a mixture of admiration and frustration.

CHAPTER THREE

SABRINA was twenty minutes late. Guy had never had a woman keep him waiting in his life and he couldn't decide whether to be irritated or intrigued. He glanced down at his watch for the umpteenth time and actually began to wonder whether he'd been stood up.

But then he saw her crossing the square, wearing some slinky little silver-grey dress with a filmy silver stole around her pale shoulders, her legs looking deliciously long in spindly, high-heeled shoes.

Sabrina spotted his tall, brooding figure straight away, as if he had been programmed to dominate her whole horizon. He was wearing a pale grey unstructured suit which did nothing to disguise the hard, muscular body beneath. And, outwardly at least, he looked completely relaxed, but as she grew closer she could see a coiled kind of tension, which gave him the dark, irresistible shimmer of danger. He looked completely relaxed, but there was no mistaking the watchful quality which made his grey eyes gleam with subdued promise.

She had very nearly not come tonight, lifting the telephone to ring Guy's hotel more than once, telling herself that this was fast turning into something she hadn't planned. Something she wasn't sure if she could handle.

Or stop.

But something had prevented her cancelling—something she couldn't quite put her finger on. Maybe it was the memory of that first, glorious sight of him. Leaving behind the knowledge that if she were never to see him again, then the world would never seem quite the same place.

His smile widened as she approached, but he made no move towards her. Let her come to me, he thought. He wanted to watch the way she moved—her hips unconsciously thrusting forward, the fluid sway of her bottom. He imagined those hips crushed beneath the hard contours of his own, and swallowed. *Come to me, baby*, he thought silently. *Come*.

'Hello,' Sabrina said breathlessly, but something in the darkening of his eyes seemed to have robbed her of the ability to suck air into her lungs.

'Hello.' So. No blurted little excuses for being late. No shrugged or coy reasons. Her carelessness sharpened his desire for her even more intensely and he felt his senses clamour into life. 'Where would you like to eat?'

There was a new, dangerous quality about Guy tonight, Sabrina thought. A danger which should have frightened her, but instead filled her with a sense of almost unendurable excitement. And inevitability. 'You know the city far better than I do,' she said huskily. 'You choose.'

'OK,' he said easily, and for a moment felt the penitent shimmer of guilt. As if he hadn't just spent an hour under the hammering power of the shower, deciding exactly where he wanted to take her. He had opened his mouth to the torrent of water which had beaten down on him, his body growing hard with frustration as he remembered that Sabrina had stood naked beneath these same icy jets.

Except that he doubted whether *she* had needed an ice-cold shower to ward off a desire which was stronger than any desire he could remember.

The restaurant was close by and its menu was famous. It was private and discreet but not in the least bit stuffy; he wondered whether she would comment on its proximity to his hotel, but she didn't.

And it wasn't until they were seated in the darkened alcove he had expressly requested that he relaxed enough to expel a long, relieved breath. She was here, he thought exultantly. Sabrina was *here*. Her hair was all caught back in a smooth pleat at the back of her head and he wanted to reach out and tumble it all the way down her back.

'You look beautiful,' he said slowly.

The way he was looking at her made her feel beautiful. She savoured the compliment, held onto it and tried it out in her mind. 'Why, thank you,' she said demurely.

'I thought you weren't coming.' He couldn't believe he'd just said that either. Hadn't the hard lessons of his childhood meant that he'd spent his whole life striving for some kind of invulnerability?

'I nearly didn't.' Oh, God, she thought, please don't ask me why. Because I might just have to tell you that I knew, if I came, where I might end up spending the night.

'What changed your mind?'

'I was hungry.'

He laughed as the waiter came over with the menus, and Sabrina took hers with hands which had begun to tremble. She wondered whether Guy had noticed.

He had. But he hadn't needed to see her fingers shaking to know that she was working herself up to a fever pitch of sexual excitement which almost matched his own. That was evident enough from the soft line of colour which suffused the high curve of her cheekbones and the hectic glitter of her eyes. The way her lips looked all swollen and pouting, parting moistly of their own volition, the rosy pink tip of her tongue peeping through. And the way the buds of her tiny breasts pushed like metal studs against the silvery silk of her gown.

His grey eyes glittered into hers as she stared unseeingly at the menu. 'Want me to order for you?'

Strange she should be so grateful for a question which would normally have left her open-mouthed with indignation. 'Yes, please.'

His eyes scanned the menu uninterestedly. About the only things he felt like eating right now were oysters, followed by a great big dish of dark, juicy cherries—and it didn't take a great stretch of the imagination to work out why that was.

Guy shifted his chair a little, relieved that the heavy white damask of the tablecloth concealed the first heavy throbbing of desire. Another first, he thought wryly, unable to remember a time when he'd been so exquisitely aroused by a woman without any touch being involved.

He ordered *Brodetto di pesce* followed by *moleche*. Dessert he would take an option on. He had his own ideas for dessert...

The waiter brought over a bottle of the bone-dry Breganze *bianco*, but Sabrina felt intoxicated just by the lazy promise of his smile.

'I don't know if I need any wine,' she admitted.

'Me neither.' He shrugged, but he poured them half a glass each and signalled for some water.

Sabrina sipped at her drink, feeling suddenly shy, not daring to look up, afraid of what she would see in the grey dazzle of his eyes. Or what he might read in hers...

'You know, we've spent nearly the whole day together—and I don't know a single thing about you,' he observed softly. 'I'm not used to women being quite so mysterious.'

Sabrina put her glass down. Here it came. The getting-to-know-you talk. A talk she most emphatically did not want to have. She'd been touched by a tragedy which had left her tainted, simply by association. People treated you differently once they found out and she didn't want Guy to treat her differently. She wanted him to carry on exactly as he was.

She forced a lightness into her voice. 'What exactly do you want to know?'

Guy narrowed his eyes. Women usually loved talking

about themselves. Give them an opener like that and you couldn't shut them up for hours. 'It isn't supposed to be an interrogation session,' he informed her softly, and then he leaned across the table, dark mischief dancing in his eyes. 'Why? Have you got some dark, guilty secret you're keeping from me, Sabrina? Don't tell me—in real life you're a lap-dancer?'

His outrageous question lifted some of the tension, and Sabrina found herself smiling back. 'Much more exciting than that! I work in a bookshop, actually,' she confided, and waited for his reaction.

'A bookshop?' he repeated slowly.

'That's right.' Now it was her turn for mischief. 'You know. They sell those things consisting of pages glued together along one side and bound—'

'And why,' he said, with a smile playing at the corners of his lips, 'do you work in a bookshop?'

She took a sip of her wine. 'Oh, all the usual reasons— I love books. I'm a romantic. I have a great desire to exist on low wages. Do you want me to go on?'

'All night,' he murmured. 'All night.' But then their fish soup arrived and Guy stared at his darkly, wishing that he had known her longer. Wishing that she was already his lover so that he could have suggested that they leave the food untouched and just go straight home to bed. 'And where exactly is this bookshop?'

Sabrina nibbled at a piece of bread. 'In Salisbury. Right next to the Cathedral. Do you know it?'

'Nope. I've never been there,' he said thoughtfully.

She studied the curved dip at the centre of his upper lip and shamelessly found herself wanting to run her tongue along its perfect outline. 'How about you? Where do you live? What kind of work do you do?' She thought of the man she had first seen, in jeans and T-shirt. 'It must be something pretty high-powered for your company to pay for a hotel like that.'

Guy hesitated. When people said that money talked, they didn't realise that it also swore. It sounded ridiculous to consider yourself as being *too* highly paid, but he'd long ago realised that wealth had drawbacks all of its own. And when you were deemed rich—in a world where money was worshipped more than any of the more traditional gods—then lots of people wanted to know you for all the wrong reasons.

Not that he would have put Sabrina into that category. But he liked the sweet, unaffected way she was with him. He hadn't been treated as an equal for a very long time. And if he started hinting at just how much he was really worth, might she not be slightly overawed?

'Oh, I'm just a wheeler-dealer,' he shrugged.

'And what does a wheeler-dealer do?'

He smiled. 'A bit of everything. I buy and sell. Property. Art. Sometimes even cars. Houses occasionally.' But there was no disguising the dismissiveness in his voice as he topped her wine up. 'All pretty boring stuff. Finish your soup.'

'I have finished.'

She'd barely touched it, he noticed as the waiter removed their plates—but, then, neither had he. And he was still aroused. So aroused that...

Sabrina saw the dark colour which had flared over his cheekbones and suddenly she felt weak. Across the table they stared at one another, and the sounds of the other diners retreated so that they might have been alone in the crowded room.

'G-Guy,' she stumbled, through the ragged movement of her breathing.

'What is it?' he murmured.

'The waiter is w-waiting to give us our main course.'

Guy looked up to find the waiter standing beside the table, holding two plates containing crayfish and barely able to contain his smile.

'*Grazie,*' said Guy tightly.

'*Prego.*' The waiter grinned.

Sabrina smoothed her fingers over her flushed cheeks. She didn't speak until the waiter was out of earshot. 'Did you see his face?' she whispered.

'We're in Italy,' he remarked, with a shrug. 'They're used to couples displaying...' he lingered over a wholly inappropriate word '...affection. Now eat your crayfish,' he urged softly.

Like two condemned prisoners eating a last meal, they both silently spooned the crayfish into their mouths. It was fine food, meant to be savoured and enjoyed, but they both ate it quickly, without tasting it. In fact, Guy only just re-frained from shovelling it down as if he were on a ten-minute lunch-break.

Sabrina wondered why she didn't feel shy. Or embar-rassed. Why being with Guy in an atmosphere so tense with expectation seemed to feel so right. Something she needed more than anything in the world. She put her knife and fork down with a shaky hand and saw that Guy had mirrored her movements.

'Shall I call for the bill?' he queried.

She forced herself to try and respond normally, even though she knew what he meant by his question. 'Don't you want dessert? Or coffee?'

His mouth curved. He heard the delicious thunder of the inevitable. 'I thought we could try somewhere else for cof-fee.'

'Yes,' she agreed with nervous excitement, because she knew exactly what he meant—and wouldn't a well-brought up girl be frightened by that? Or outraged? 'I guess we could.'

In a daze she allowed him to drape the wrap around her shoulders, feeling the negligent brush of his fingertips against her bare flesh as he did so, and she felt the breath catch in her throat like dust.

He took her by the hand and led her outside into the starry night, looking down at her with soft, silver light gleaming from his eyes.

'You're shivering,' he observed quietly, tracing a thoughtful fingertip down the slim, pale column of her neck and seeing her tremble even more. 'Again.'

'Y-yes.'

He took his jacket off and draped it around her shoulders; the broad cut of it almost swamped her slender frame. 'Here, take this...'

'You'll get cold yourself,' she objected.

'I don't think there's any danger of that,' he said softly, and, sliding his arms around her waist, he bent his head to kiss her.

Her heart was blazing as her mouth parted to meet the first sweet touch of his lips. She ignored the half-hearted voice of her conscience telling her to stop this, because who could have stopped *this*?

He was breathing life into her, bringing warmth flooding back into her veins. As though she had been some cold, bloodless statue and now...now...

'Oh, Guy,' she whispered, in a distracted plea. 'Guy.' But the words were lost against the honeyed softness of his mouth.

Desire shafted through him like an arrow. 'Oh, God, yes, Sabrina,' he ground out, on a sultry note of hunger. 'Yes, and yes, and yes.' He brought her closer into his body, up to the cradle of his hips, where the hard, lean power of him was unmistakable. And now it was Guy's turn to make a harsh little sound. He broke the kiss off with a supreme effort, tearing his mouth away to look down with frustrated perplexity into her disappointed eyes.

'This is all threatening to get out of hand,' he groaned, sucking in a shuddering breath which scorched the lining of his lungs. 'I haven't engaged in such a public display of passion for a long time.' He had always liked beds—clean sheets and clinical comfort—so why was he having to swallow down the primitive urge to lead her to the nearest narrow, dark alleyway, pin her up against some ancient wall and do it to her right there…?

She felt no fear, and no shame. Only an overwhelming need to be near him. She trickled a questing fingertip down the proud, hard lines of his face. 'M-me neither.'

He forced himself to bite out the question, even though it was the most difficult thing he had ever had to say. 'Do you want me to take you back to your hotel, or would you like to…?' The word trailed off temptingly.

'To what?' she asked softly.

'To come back with me? We could have that dessert. Coffee. What do you think? Would you like that, princess?'

'Yes,' she whispered, knowing that he didn't want coffee any more than she did.

He took her hand and led her through the darkened streets. She felt dizzy with the sense of his proximity but she was so disorientated that he could have been leading her to the ends of the earth for all she knew. Or cared.

It wasn't until they found themselves back in the grand elegance of his suite, with the hazy gleam of the lamps falling like moonlight on her flushed cheeks, that something of the enormity of what she was about to embark on began to seep into Sabrina's consciousness. She ought to stop this, she told herself, and stop it right now.

Yet the longer she stared into the mesmerising glitter of those dark-lashed eyes, the harder it was to listen to reason.

Because reason was a weak component in the presence of raw need.

And Michael had taught her that nothing was certain. His death had brought the frailty of life crashing home in a way that nothing else could have done. Why, she could walk out of this room right now and something could happen to ensure that she would never see Guy Masters again. And never know the warmth of his embrace, or taste the luxury of his kiss.

She turned her face up to his, but her half-felt protest became a moan of surrender as he drove his mouth down on hers with a hungry kiss which splintered her senses.

He reached out to remove the clip from her hair, murmured his warm pleasure as it fell in a red-blonde gleam around her shoulders. 'See how your hair glows like fire against your skin. And how your eyes sparkle like pure, clear aquamarines.'

She had never been seduced by words before, had never known their sweet, wanton power. 'G-Guy,' she said shakily.

His eyes gleamed like silver and onyx. 'I want to see you, to see your flesh glow in the moonlight. I want to undress you.' He moved his hand distractedly to find the zip of her dress, before sliding it down with unsteady fingers, kissing her neck as the silky material parted for him.

She gasped as she felt the touch of his fingers against her burning skin and the weight of his hands as they moved down to possessively cup the curve of her bottom. Her head fell helplessly against his shoulder as she felt her dress begin to slide down over her thighs.

'God, princess, you're driving me *crazy*,' he ground out on a shudder as the dress pooled with a silken whisper at her feet. He lifted his head to gaze at her, taken aback by the sight of her frivolous underwear.

It was the last thing he had been expecting—she looked

like a centrefold. A pure white lace bra through which her nipples peaked rosy and hard, and a matching wisp of a G-string through which he could distinctly see the red-gold blur of hair. And then there was the outrageous little suspender belt, onto which were clipped the sheerest stockings he had ever seen.

He very nearly lost control. What had happened to the plain cotton functional garments she'd been wearing the other day? The ones which he'd sent to the laundry whilst thinking that she was obviously of the gym-mistress persuasion?

He gazed at the slender curves of her body, his hand unsteady as it followed the path of his eyes. 'You wore these for me?' he questioned shakily, his fingers splaying over the barely perceptible curve of her belly.

'Yes.'

'Sweet, sweet torment. You look…wonderful.' He swallowed. 'Quite the most exquisite thing I've ever seen.'

She found herself blushing under that passion-glazed scrutiny. The underwear had been bought as part of her trousseau, for the honeymoon she'd been fated never to have.

Her worried mother had persuaded her to pack them. 'Good underwear always makes a woman feel better about herself,' she'd urged her. 'And it seems such a pity to waste such beautiful lingerie.'

Not wanting a row, Sabrina had weakly agreed to take them and had stuffed them into the bottom of her suitcase, knowing that she would never have the heart to wear them. And yet some instinct had urged her to slide them onto her scented and freshly bathed body before dressing to meet Guy this evening… Had she secretly been imagining that shining look of delight as he looked at her?

He dipped his head and dropped a soft kiss on her mouth. 'Get into bed,' he ordered unsteadily, 'while I undress.'

She slid between the linen sheets immediately, thankful that he wasn't expecting her to undress *him*. Why, her hands were shaking even more than his.

She watched as he slowly began to unbutton his silk shirt, and in a reflex action her fingers slid up to clutch at her throat, their tips colliding with the thin gold chain from which hung a ring.

Her engagement ring!

Guy had bent to remove one of his shoes, and Sabrina took the opportunity to pull the sheet right up to her chin and to unclip the chain without him seeing. She was about to place it unobtrusively on the floor beside her when he glanced up to see her shrouded in the sheet, with only her face and bright hair showing, and he gave a lazy smile.

Maybe he was more old-fashioned than he gave himself credit for—because it pleased him to see that she was a little shy. 'You look sweet,' he murmured. 'Very, very sweet.'

'D-do I?' Whereas he looked the antithesis of sweet. He looked strong and dark and very, very aroused. Maybe she should have been frightened by his hard, masculine body, but she was in too deep now. Too enthralled by him—too chained by the honeyed flutterings of desire.

His shirt fluttered to the ground and he left it where it lay with arrogant disregard. But when he turned his attention to the belt that was holding up his trousers, Sabrina surreptitiously allowed the chain to slither like a slim gold snake onto the carpet.

He kicked his trousers off and Sabrina hastily shut her eyes, only to open them to find him looking down at her, a kind of bemused tenderness on his face.

'You *are* shy,' he observed softly.

'A little,' she answered truthfully.

'I like it.'

'Do you?'

'Mmm. But, then, I think I like everything about you. Your golden hair spread all over my pillow. Your skin as white as milk.' Wearing only a pair of dark, silken boxer shorts, he lifted back the sheet and climbed into bed beside her. 'Come here,' he said softly, pulling her into the warm cradle of his arms.

She felt the shock of sensation as they tangled their limbs, his bare, warm flesh pressing against hers, and she gasped with a heightened sense of recognition.

He dipped his mouth to brush against a tiny, puckered nipple. 'I find myself in the curious position of not knowing where to begin,' he murmured. 'Like a starving man being presented with the most fantastic banquet and being completely spoilt for choice.'

'Guy,' she stumbled helplessly, her eyes huge and dark. 'So, do I kiss you?' he mused. 'Yes, I think so.' His lips brushed lightly over hers, there and gone in an instant, leaving her mouth moistly open and expectant. 'Or touch you here?' A feather-light flicker of finger to nipple which made her shiver. 'Yes, you like that, don't you, my sweet torment?'

'Y-yes,' she gasped.

'Or here?' The tantalising graze of that same finger over the moist, warm centre of her panties and Sabrina gasped aloud. 'You like that, too, don't you?'

He looked down, losing himself in the black distraction of her eyes, and felt himself grow so hard that he thought he actually might explode. He struggled to rein in his feelings and then kissed the tip of her nose.

'On second thoughts,' he said thickly, 'we've got all night.'

Guy awoke to the clear tinge of early morning. He narrowed his eyes in the direction of the unshuttered windows to see the first rose-gold shaft of the new sun. The very early morning.

He didn't stir. By his side, Sabrina lay sleeping, her arms spread out in careless abandon across the rumpled bed. He had no wish to wake her—and not just because they'd fallen into a passion-sated slumber only a couple of hours back. No, he needed a little time to come to terms with what had just happened.

Well, he knew exactly what had happened. He felt his mouth dry. They had spent a whole night indulging every single sexual fantasy he'd ever had—and a few more besides. As if there were infinite variations and dimensions to the act of making love that he had never discovered before.

As if the world were about to end and they had greedily needed to discover every sensual pleasure known to man. Or woman.

He swallowed, his heart beginning a rapid drumming at the slow, inevitable stir of arousal. No, if he woke her now it would happen all over again—and, much as he wanted it to happen, he also needed to think.

Because, if he were being brutally honest, he'd behaved in a way that he'd never imagined he could. Had just spent the night making love to a stranger. To a woman who was beautiful, intelligent and engaging—but a stranger nonetheless.

He gazed again at the sky, which was now being pierced by a soft apricot light, and his mouth hardened. He was old enough and experienced enough to know that what had happened between them last night was rare. And yet he'd been reckless, out of control. He'd enjoyed it, yes, but that didn't mean he approved of his actions.

'Mmm!' Beneath the sheet, Sabrina stretched her body sleepily.

Guy felt his heart rate increase as he looked down at the

perfect outline of her slender body and felt the stirrings of desire spring into full and vibrant life. 'And "mmm" to you, too,' he said softly.

Sabrina opened her eyes and felt impaled by that lancing glance of steel-grey as seductive memories of the night danced tantalisingly through her mind. But reality brought with it disbelief. She had given herself to him, no holds barred. So now what? 'What time is it?' she said uncertainly.

'Early.' He leaned over her, his lean, hair-roughened torso just crying out to be touched. 'Is that all you've got to say for yourself?' he teased.

Her doubts fled with the warm reality of his proximity. 'That depends.' Sabrina gave in to temptation and reached one finger up to touch a hard, flat nipple. He groaned, dipping his head to kiss her while one hand trailed down over her flat belly, to where she was hot and moist and ready.

He raised his eyebrows mockingly as he moved to lie over her, dropping tiny kisses on the flutter of her eyelashes and her lips. 'Do you always wake up so pleasingly compliant in the morning?' he murmured, reaching down the side of the bed to open another packet of contraceptives. His fingers came into contact with something hard and metallic and he impatiently shoved it aside until he found what he was looking for.

She could feel the hard tip of him nudging against her and her instant warm, sweet response. Last night he had not only brought her back to life, he'd made her feel his equal. There was nothing she could have done or said that would have shocked him, nor he her.

Sabrina was not about to start making odious comparisons, but she'd never known that lovemaking could be so free or so uninhibited. That it could have so many faces, and so many forms.

With a newly learnt and slumberously provocative pout, she took the condom from him.

'Shall I deal with this for you?' she whispered.

He gave a low laugh of delight, but the laugh was tinged with a certain amount of apprehension. Right then she could do what she liked with him, and he suspected that he would just lie there like a puppy and grin with pleasure. What the hell had happened to his habitual dominance? His need to orchestrate?

'Deal away, princess,' he drawled.

She pushed him to lie back against the pillow, and knelt over him, her long, bare thighs straddling him. 'Quite appropriate, really,' she said breathily, as she slowly inched the sheath down over the hard, silken length of him. 'As you're a dealer.'

'Oh, God,' he moaned. 'God! Why are you taking so long?'

Her fingernails lightly teased at the delicate protection. 'But it's all your fault, Guy—you shouldn't *be* so long,' she teased.

He let her torment him until the condom was firmly in place and then he swiftly lifted her up and laid her on her back. Again he moved above her, but this time there was an inexplicable mixture of emotions on his face, his eyes so dark that Sabrina didn't have a clue what was going on inside that head of his.

'You know,' he mused, and now it was his turn to tease her, the full tip of him nudging against her, 'I always thought that girls who worked in bookshops would be so timid. So demure.'

'And aren't I?'

He smiled, but there was an odd edge to the smile. 'No, you're not,' he groaned. 'You're a very bad girl indeed and you leave me no alternative than to do *this* to you…'

He thrust into her with such power that stars exploded

behind her eyes, and he'd barely moved inside her before she could feel the first slow glimmerings of release. Drowning in honeyed sweetness, she turned her head distractedly from side to side on the pillow as wave upon wave of pure sensation left her shuddering and helpless in their wake.

Guy tried to make it last, but he was lost. This must be some kind of record, he thought as he felt the first sweet tug of his own release.

It was one of the best orgasms of his life, but it left him feeling curiously empty, as though she had taken something from him he had not intended to give. He slowly withdrew from her to find her watching him with dazed disbelief, and his smile was wry as he kissed her.

'Go to sleep now,' he urged. 'Go to sleep.'

And only when her breathing became steady did he slip silently from between the sheets.

CHAPTER FOUR

WHEN Sabrina opened her eyes again, the space on the bed beside her was empty. She gazed around the room, listening out for the sounds of activity in the bathroom, but there was only silence.

She sat up in bed and yawned, noticing that Guy's clothes were gone. She ran her fingers back through her tousled hair and wondered where he was. Rubbing her eyes, she picked up her watch. Ten past seven. Very early. So where could he be?

She clambered out of bed and went into the bathroom, where she found most things she needed, including a courtesy toothbrush, still wrapped in its Cellophane paper.

She wandered back into the bedroom just as the phone started ringing, and she picked it up with a smile on her face.

'Guy?' she said, thinking how pampered she sounded.

But it wasn't Guy. The voice was female—a husky voice which was edged with suspicion.

'Who is this, please?'

Sabrina wondered fleetingly whether she should give her name. No, better not. 'This is a friend of Guy's,' she answered.

'A friend?' The voice sharpened. 'And where is he, please?'

'He's gone out.'

'Where has he gone?' asked the voice impatiently.

Suddenly Sabrina had had enough. The woman was speaking to her as if she were a chambermaid! 'Who would like to know?' she asked softly.

The voice acquired a sudden brittle ring. 'This is one of Prince Raschid's representatives. The Prince is keen to learn whether Mr Masters has managed to acquire the painting he was so anxious to secure.'

Sabrina very nearly dropped the phone. 'I really have no idea where he's gone,' she said slowly, still reeling from the fact that Guy Masters was doing deals for *princes*. 'I'm sorry.'

'The Prince is paying Mr Masters an extremely large commission—for which we would obviously expect him to be instantly accessible,' said the voice icily. 'And whether or not he chooses to jeopardise that commission by using his time in Venice to concentrate on his love affairs, instead of paying attention to the work in hand, is obviously something which the Prince will be very interested to hear about.'

Sabrina drew in a deep breath, trying to remember that the customer was always right. 'Isn't there someone else who can deal with your query?'

There was silence. 'The Prince will only deal with the owner of the company. Not his minions. Goodbye,' said the woman, and put the phone down.

The owner of the company? The company that paid for this hotel room? Sabrina stared down at the receiver, then walked over to the desk, which was covered with neat sheaves of paper.

She hunted around until she found what she was looking for—a letterheaded sheet of business notepaper stating, 'Guy Masters. Dealer in fine art', and an address in what was probably one of the most famous and exclusive streets in London.

Sabrina felt dizzy. Sick. He had lied. Just a little lie— but a lie all the same. What else had he lied to her about? she wondered as she hunted distractedly around the room for her discarded panties. All those things he'd said. He'd implied...

She drew in a deep, unsteady breath as she clipped up her bra. She remembered his words as she'd gazed up with wide-eyed admiration at the hotel's beautifully faded façade. 'The company pays for it.'

He had deliberately played down his wealth and his influence—which begged the question why? Did he think that if she found out just how rich he really was, he might never get rid of her? And was that why he had disappeared so conclusively this morning, despite knowing that she would probably be feeling vulnerable?

She had just slithered into her panties when the phone rang again, and she snatched it up without thinking.

'Signor Masters, please,' said an Italian-accented voice.

Feeling that she'd already been down this road, Sabrina sighed. 'He isn't here.'

'Could you please give him a message?' asked the voice.

Curiosity overrode caution. 'OK,' said Sabrina tentatively.

'This is Air Executive at Venice Airport. We need him to confirm his seat on this afternoon's flight out to London. A water-taxi has been booked for two-thirty, as requested.'

A flight out *today*?

'I'll tell him,' said Sabrina in a dazed and hurt voice, then replaced the receiver.

The bastard! The cheating, lying bastard! Another lie! How many more would she discover? He had told her that he was staying for a few days—just as she was. Maybe he had always planned to leave just as soon as he had taken her to bed—he probably hadn't reckoned on her falling into it quite so quickly.

She felt the sickening plummet of her stomach as the reality of what she had done began to sink in. She had slept with a stranger. It had been the most heart-stoppingly beautiful night, yes, but Guy hadn't even been able to face her this morning. And that was how much he cared about her. At least he was allowing her to make the decision to leave herself, rather than having to eject her.

Face it, she told herself with a bitter pang of regret, you've been used. The classic one-night stand. But what had she expected? No woman would ever receive courtesy and consideration from a man like Guy Masters—not when she had ended up in bed with him on a first date.

Her heart racing, Sabrina slithered the silvery-blue dress over her head and located first one shoe, and then the other.

She looked around at the sumptuous fittings of the room, feeling more out of place with each second that passed. This was not her kind of world. Guy was not her kind of man. Get out now, she told herself—now while you still have some pride left.

He was probably downstairs on the lookout in the huge marble foyer, waiting until she had gone back to her own hotel and the coast was clear for him to return to his suite.

Pausing only to brush through the tangled strands of her hair, she quietly left the room and located the lift, steadfastly ignoring the rather curious expression of a beautiful young Italian woman until it had reached the ground floor.

Stealthily slinking out, she peeped around one of the giant marble pillars to see, to her absolute horror, that Guy was sprawled out on one of the silk sofas, talking into a mobile phone.

He looked, Sabrina thought, completely businesslike. Miles away. Worlds away. Worlds apart. He'd shaved, put on a suit and smoothed down the hair which she had ruffled with her greedy, frantic fingers during the night. He didn't look remotely like a man who had spent the whole night making mad, passionate love to her. Maybe that had been put in the out tray, she thought, her heart thundering like a cannon in her ears.

She waited until he turned his head, giving her a glimpse of that hard, beautiful profile as he gestured for a coffee.

Moving with a quiet and guilty step, Sabrina quietly left the hotel.

Guy opened the door to his suite, wondering whether Sabrina would still be in bed, telling himself that he would not join her there. After recklessness came reason.

But still a slow rise of colour begin to flush its way along his cheeks, and he moved quietly towards the bed and stared down at it with slowly dawning disbelief. Empty.

He stood very still. 'Sabrina?' he called softly, but even as he said her name he knew that it was futile.

She had gone.

He ripped the covers back, as if they were somehow concealing her, as if her slender frame could be hidden away, but there was nothing other than the lingering musky traces of sex marking the sheets.

His mouth twisted as he dropped the sheet as abruptly as if it were contaminated, his grey eyes growing steely as they travelled around the room.

Her clothes had gone. The discarded panties and stockings had disappeared.

Gone, just as if she had never been there.

A slow pulse began to throb unsteadily at his temple, his gaze not missing a thing as he walked round to the other side of the bed. His eyes scanned this way and that for the note which logic told him she had not left. And at first the glint of gold which gleamed so palely against the silken rug held no interest for him.

Until he realised that she had left *something* behind.

He bent and retrieved the delicate chain and stared down at it with dawning realisation as it glittered in the palm of his hand.

And his mouth twisted into a slow, cruel smile as his fingers closed over it and he dropped it deep into the pocket of his trousers.

CHAPTER FIVE

THE old-fashioned bell on the bookshop door clanged loudly as Sabrina stepped in out of the rain. The shop was empty save for a mild-looking man with glasses who glanced up, his face brightening into a smile of welcome.

'Sabrina!' he said in delight. 'Welcome back!'

Sabrina tried to match his smile, and wondered if it looked as lopsided as it felt. 'Thanks, Paul,' she said, and slowly began to unbutton her raincoat, brushing off the drops of rain as she did so. 'It's great to be back!'

'So, how was Venice?'

Sabrina quickly turned to hang the dripping garment on the peg, hoping that he wouldn't see the sudden defensive set of her shoulders. Or the swift shiver of memory which had her biting her lip in consternation. How could you ache so badly for a man you barely knew? she wondered. A man who had given you his body, but not his honesty?

But by the time she turned round again she had managed to compose her face into the kind of dreamy post-holiday smile which Paul would be expecting.

'Venice? Oh, it was...' She swallowed as recollections of mocking grey eyes and a hard, lean body swam unwillingly into her mind. 'It was lovely!' she finished lamely.

'Lovely?' echoed Paul, pulling a face. 'This is the place that you wanted to visit more than anywhere else on earth and you describe it as "lovely"? What happened in Venice, Sabrina?' He laughed. 'Did you leave your descriptive powers behind?'

'I'm a bit tired after all the travelling, that's all. I went to see my aunt in Scotland as soon as I got back.' She sat

51

down at the desk and began to flick through the morning's post.

'Yes.' Paul frowned. 'You look a little pale. Like some coffee?'

'I'd love some. I'll make it.'

But Paul Bailey shook his head. 'No, you won't. I'll do it. You look bushed. Sit down and I'll bring you something hot and restorative.'

'Thanks, Paul,' said Sabrina gratefully. She dropped a discarded envelope into the bin and looked around.

It was hard to believe that she was back. That everything was just as she'd left it. And nothing had changed.

She bit her lip again and stared down at the pile of manila envelopes on her lap.

Except her. *She* had changed. In the course of those few days in Venice she had discovered some unbelievable things about herself—things she wasn't sure she liked at all.

And now she was having to come to terms with the knowledge that she was the kind of woman who was able to have a passionate fling with a man who was little more than a stranger to her. A stranger who had left her heart breaking for him.

Paul came back into the room, carrying a tray with two steaming mugs of coffee, one of which he deposited in front of her, together with a chocolate bar.

She shook her head. 'You can have the biscuit. I'm not hungry.'

Paul tutted, sounding torn between concern and impatience. 'I thought that one of the reasons behind you going to Italy was to try and tempt yourself back into eating.' His voice softened, along with his eyes. 'Come on—you can't keep pining for Michael for ever, you know, Sabrina. He wouldn't want that.'

Sabrina quickly put down the coffee, terrified that she

might drop it. For what would the decent and honourable Paul say if he knew how little she had been pining for Michael? She tried to imagine his reaction if she told him the truth about her holiday, and paled at the thought of how his opinion of her would be reversed if only he knew.

'In fact,' said Paul gently, 'I thought you were going to come back from Venice a new woman—wasn't that the plan?'

She lifted her head. 'And I haven't?' she teased him. 'Is that what you mean?'

He shrugged awkwardly. 'Just as slim and even paler— what *did* you do out there?'

'What does everyone do in Venice?' she asked lightly, as she tried not to remember.

Paul grinned. 'You travelled in a gondola, right?'

Sabrina forced a smile in response. 'You bet I did!' And that was how the whole damned thing had started—blinded by a man with night-dark hair and a body which had stirred a deep, primitive response in her. And she couldn't blame Guy for that. She had set the wheels for that in motion herself. Unless she was planning to blame him for his physical beauty and impact. 'Anyway, that's enough about me, Paul. How has business been?'

Paul shrugged. 'So-so. March is slow, as you know, but it'll be Easter soon. Interestingly enough, I had a phone call yesterday from a man trying to track down a rare first edition.'

Sabrina sipped her coffee. 'Oh?'

'That's right. You must have served him. He asked for you. I told him you weren't due in until today.'

'Really?' she questioned absently.

Once she had drunk her coffee, Sabrina forced herself to get back into the slow and rhythmic pattern of her working day and found it comforting. She would put the whole affair down to experience and not let it get out of hand in her imagination. After all, lots of people had holiday romances which ended badly.

If only Guy Masters wasn't such an unforgettable man. If only she hadn't lost her head. But 'if onlys' wouldn't change a thing—they never did.

Fortunately, work soon took over. Maybe that was because she had become an expert in pushing away disturbing thoughts. She settled down to some long-overdue ordering and soon became immersed in that.

She heard the sound of the shop door clanging open and flourished her signature in the order book before looking up and blinking, her polite smile freezing into disbelief on her lips.

It couldn't be him, she thought, even as her heart responded with an instinctive surge of excitement. But the delight ebbed away as quickly as it had come, to be replaced by a sudden wariness when she saw the dark, forbidding expression on his face.

It couldn't be him. But it was.

She was aware of the fact that Paul was working in the storeroom, and composed her face accordingly.

'Hello, Guy,' she said, her voice sounding astonishingly calm considering that the thundering of her heart was threatening to deafen her. 'This is a surprise.'

'Is it?' He leaned over the desk and the male scent of him reached out to her senses, sending them spinning out of control as she registered his closeness. 'So you *do* remember me?' he drawled silkily. 'Wow—*that's* a relief.'

Sabrina blushed at the implication behind his insulting question. 'Of course I remember you! I… We…'

'Had a night of no-holds-barred sex before you did a runner in the morning?' he remarked insolently.

'You were the one who did a runner, and will you *keep your voice down*?' she hissed furiously.

'Or what?'

'Or I'll have you thrown out of the shop!'

Guy's gaze swivelled to where Paul was busy flicking through a card index, and he raised a laconic eyebrow. 'Oh, really?'

She knew just what he was implying. For a man of similar age to Guy, Paul was no weakling, but comparing him to the angry specimen of manhood who stood just inches away from her would be like comparing a child's chug-chug train to a high-speed express. But even so...

Sabrina raised a stubborn chin to him. No matter what had happened between the two of them, he couldn't just march in here like some autocratic dictator and start jeopardising her very livelihood. Not when he'd already taken out her heart and smashed it into smithereens...

'Yes, really!'

He cocked an arrogant eyebrow at her. 'Going to start talking, then, are we, Sabrina?'

'I can't talk to you now,' she stated levelly. 'I'm working.'

'Then when?'

'I don't know,' she prevaricated.

The grey eyes narrowed. 'What time is your lunch-hour?'

'I don't usually take lunch.'

'House rules?' he drawled.

'No, my rules,' she answered stiffly.

'Then change the rules, baby,' he commanded, with a cool arrogance which infuriated her almost as much as it reminded her of his consummate mastery in bed. 'And change them now.'

Sabrina tried to imagine the worst-case scenario. What if she agreed to meet him for lunch—in a city where she had lived all her life and where she was known? She wasn't the same woman here as he had met in Venice. Not by any stretch of the imagination. But what if he managed to reduce her to that same mindless being who just cried out for his touch?

And it wasn't difficult to work out how he might go about that. Surely he would only have to take her in his arms again. Just as he'd done before. She couldn't guarantee that she wouldn't succumb, and how could she possibly come back in here after *that* and spend the afternoon working, as if nothing had happened?

'I eat my lunch here,' she told him resolutely.

He rubbed a thoughtful forefinger over his chin, and the movement was accompanied by the unconscious thrust of his hips. 'Then I guess I'll just wait here until you've finished,' he told her softly, and then deliberately raised his voice. 'Perhaps you could point me to the section on erotic literature?'

'Don't you *dare*—'

'Is something wrong, Sabrina?' Paul came through from the storeroom, pushing his spectacles to the back of his nose, looking with distrust at the tall, dark man who was towering over his assistant's desk.

Sabrina sent a look of appeal up at Guy but was met with nothing but an uncompromising glitter. She knew then that he wouldn't be going anywhere until he got what he'd come for. And that there was no way she could get out of this meeting. She swallowed down her reservations and forced a brittle smile.

'Guy is a friend…' She hesitated on the inappropriate word before continuing, seeing the brief, hard twist of his mouth as he registered it, too. 'A friend of mine. Who has dropped into town unexpectedly—'

Guy fixed Paul with a bland smile. 'And I was hoping to persuade her to come to lunch with me, but—'

'Well, we usually eat a sandwich here—but you go to lunch if you want, Sabrina!' said Paul immediately. 'It'll make a nice change.'

Sabrina shook her head and sent Guy a furious look. How dared he be so manipulative in order to get his own way? 'No, thanks, Paul. I've agreed to meet Guy...after work.' She managed to get the words out—even though they almost choked her in the process.

'Yes, she has. I can *hardly wait*.' Guy gave her another wintry smile, but the hungry look of intent which had darkened his eyes told its own story. 'I'm taking you out for dinner, Sabrina.'

That was what he thought! 'Just a drink will be fine,' she said stiffly. 'My mother will be expecting me home for supper.'

'Your mother?' A frown of disbelief criss-crossed his forehead. Surely she didn't still live with her *mother*?

Sabrina read the disappointment in his eyes, and pride and fury warred inside her like a bubbling cauldron. What had he expected? A reenactment of that night in Venice? A half-finished meal and she would fall back into bed with him?

'Yes,' she said, with a demure flutter of her eyelashes. 'I live with my mother.'

'And what time do you finish?'

'Five-thirty.'

'I'll be here,' he promised, on a note of silky threat. 'Waiting.'

'I'll look forward to it,' she responded furiously.

Guy forced himself to give his cool, polite smile as he left the shop. But inside he was raging. *Raging*.

He should have just forgotten all about her. That was what he had told himself over and over on the plane coming back from Italy. He didn't know what had possessed him to track her down like some kind of amateur sleuth. Because, yes, there were a few questions he would like a few honest answers to—but common sense had told him just to cut his losses and run. She was trouble, and he couldn't for the life of him work out why.

He should have just posted her the chain and the ring with a cynical note attached saying, 'Thanks for the memory.'

And left it at that.

But he had been driven by a compulsion to see her again and to challenge her—a compulsion he was certain was driven by nothing more than the fact that she had given him the best sex of his life.

But maybe that had been *because* she'd been a stranger, not *in spite of* that fact. Because she'd had no expectations of him. Or any knowledge. She'd judged him as a man—a well-paid employee, true, but not as a man with megabucks. She had responded to him in the most fundamental way possible, and he to her. It had left him shaken, seeking some kind of explanation which would enable him to let the memory go.

She had been honest and open and giving in his bed—so why the secrets? The hidden chain and a ring which was almost certainly an engagement ring. Why the sudden and dramatic exit—like something out of a bad movie?

Guy walked around Salisbury dodging the showers—but not dodging them accurately enough. So that by the time he arrived at Wells Bookstore at twenty-five minutes past five his thick, ruffled hair was sprinkled with raindrops which glittered like tears amidst the ebony waves.

Sabrina glanced up from her desk and her heart caught in her throat at the sight of his rain-soaked frame. He would, she thought, be all too easy to fall in love with. Women must fall in love with him all the time. Leave me alone, Guy Masters, she urged him silently. Go away and leave me alone.

Paul, who was standing a little space away, followed the troubled direction of her eyes.

'Your friend is waiting,' he said carefully. 'You'd better go.'

Sabrina turned to him, her eyes beseeching him. 'I know what you're thinking.'

Paul shrugged. 'It's not my place to say anything about your private life, Sabrina—but it *is* very soon after Michael, isn't it? Just take it easy, that's all.'

Guilt smote at her with a giant hand. 'He's just a friend.'

Paul gave her an awkward smile. 'Sure he is,' he said, as though he didn't quite believe her. 'Look, it's none of my business.'

'No.' She picked up her coat from the hook. 'I'll see you in the morning, Paul. Goodnight.'

Through the window Guy watched her shrugging her raincoat on, unable to stop himself from marvelling at the innate grace of her movements. She moved like a dream, he thought—all long, slender limbs and that bright, shiny hair shimmering like sunlight in the grey of the rainy afternoon.

He remembered the way she had straddled him, her pale, naked thighs on either side of his waist, and he felt the first uncomfortable stirrings of desire—until he reminded himself that that was not why he was here.

Sabrina pushed the door open and thought how chilly Guy's grey eyes looked, and how unsmiling his mouth. She told herself that this would be one short evening to get through and then she need never see him again. He had lied to her, she told herself bitterly.

'Where would you like to go?' she questioned.

'You live here.' He shrugged. 'How the hell should I know?'

'I meant do you just want coffee—or a drink?'

He remembered that night in Venice and the lack of interest with which he'd greeted the wine. Yet tonight he could have willingly sunk a bucketful of liquor. 'A drink,' he said abruptly.

Me, too, she thought as she led the way across a cobbled courtyard to one of the city's oldest pubs.

Inside, a log fire blazed at each end of the bar and the warmth hit her like a blanket.

'Go and find a seat,' he instructed tersely. 'What do you want to drink?'

'B-brandy.' She shivered violently, despite the heat of the room.

She found a table far away from the others. She suspected that their conversation wouldn't be for general consumption. Then she slipped her coat off and sat there waiting for him, her knees glued primly together—like a girl who had just been to deportment lessons.

He brought two large brandies over to the table and sat down opposite her, aware of the way that she shrank back when their knees brushed.

'Oh? So shy, Sabrina? Don't like me touching you?' He held his glass up in a mocking toast. 'Isn't that a little like shutting the stable door after the horse has bolted? You weren't so shy in my bed, were you, my beauty?'

She gulped down some brandy, the liquid burning welcome fire down her throat, and her cheeks flushed with indignant heat. 'Did you bring me here just so you could insult me?' she demanded. 'Is that what you'd like, Guy?'

He shook his dark head and sipped his own drink more sparingly, surveying her over the rim of his glass with eyes which gave nothing away. 'Not at all.' But he bit back the unexpectedly explicit comment about what he *would* like.

She put the glass down, feeling slightly dizzy with the impact of the burning liquor on an empty stomach. 'What, then?'

He dipped his hand deep into his trouser pocket, aware that her eyes instinctively followed the movement. Aware, too, that she certainly wasn't immune to him either. He watched with fascination as her eyes darkened and he could sense that she was resisting the desire to run her tongue over her lips.

'Recognise this?' he asked casually, as he withdrew the thin gold chain with the pretty little ring and dropped it on the polished surface of the table in front of her.

Sabrina's heart pounded with guilt and shame. 'Don't insult me even more by asking me questions like that!' she said bitterly. 'Of course I recognise it! It's mine—you know it's mine! I left it in your bedroom!'

It lay like an omen before them.

'Then why hide it from me?'

She opened her mouth to deny it, but could not. He knew. He was an intelligent man. She was cornered, and she reacted in the same way that all trapped creatures reacted. She attacked. 'You lied to me, too!' she accused.

His eyes narrowed. 'When?'

'You implied that you were *employed* by the company—you didn't tell me you owned it!'

He nodded and his eyes took on a hard, bright glitter. 'Yes, I heard about your discussion with Prince Raschid's emissary.'

'She insulted me!'

'So I believe.' His lips flattened into a forbidding line.

'She was jealous,' said Sabrina slowly, as she recognised now the emotion which had made the woman's voice so brittle. 'Jealous that I was in your bedroom.'

'Yes.' His gaze didn't waver.

'Have you slept with her, too?'

'That's none of your business!' he snapped, but something about the dark horror written in her eyes made him relent. 'Of course I haven't slept with her! She's a business acquaintance I've met on barely half a dozen occasions!'

'And you met me once,' said Sabrina hollowly.

'That's different!' But he didn't pause to ask himself why.

'So why did you lie to me about owning the company?'

He paused deliberately and met her eyes with a bitter challenge. 'I wanted to be sure that it was me you were turned on by, and not all the trappings.'

'As though I'm some kind of cheap little gold-digger, you mean?' Sabrina glared at him. 'And you lied to me about when you were leaving Venice, too!' she accused.

He raised a dark, arrogant eyebrow. 'Did I?'

'You know you did! You told me you were staying for a few days, yet the airport said you had a flight booked out that afternoon!'

He gave her a look of barely concealed impatience. 'Oh, *that*!' he said dismissively. 'So what? Flights can usually be changed.'

'And if they can't?' she challenged.

'Then you buy another ticket.' His eyes glittered. 'A small price to pay under the circumstances.'

The cool, arrogant statement told her in no uncertain terms his true opinion of her, and Sabrina stared at him with hurt and anger in her eyes. 'These particular circumstances being sex with a stranger, you mean?'

He smiled. He certainly preferred her fighting and spitting to that lost look of despair she'd worn when they'd first walked in here. 'You were there, too, Sabrina. That's what we did—had sex.'

'Yes,' she said bitterly, thinking that he didn't even respect her enough to dress up what had happened by calling it lovemaking.

'And you still haven't answered my question,' he observed coolly. 'About the ring.'

Shakily, she grabbed her glass from the table and drank from it.

He wondered whether she was aware that her tiny breasts

moved with such sweetness beneath the fine sweater she wore. A pulse began to beat insistently at his temple and he jabbed an angry finger at the chain. 'So why hide it from me, Sabrina?'

She stared down into the trickle of brandy left in her glass and started to feel nervous. 'Can I have another drink, please?'

'No, you bloody well can't!' He didn't take his gaze from her downcast head. 'Sabrina? I'll ask you again. *Why hide it from me?*'

'I d-don't know.'

'Oh, yes, you do.' He sucked in a deep, painful breath. 'Is it an engagement ring?'

Well, now he would know what type of woman she really was. 'Yes. Yes, it is. You know it is!'

He nodded, unprepared for the jerking pain of jealousy. And a bright, burning anger—as fierce as anything he had ever experienced. It pierced like an arrow through his heart. He tried to stay calm, but it took every shred of self-restraint he possessed. 'I see.'

There was something so wounding about the way he said those two empty words that Sabrina looked at him with a question in her eyes.

'Now I understand,' Guy said heavily. He pushed the chain across the table towards her and gave a hollow, humourless laugh. 'You must have had a lot of explaining to do.'

She stared back at him in genuine confusion. 'Explaining?'

He leaned back in his chair a little, as if close proximity to her might taint him. Or tempt him. 'Well, yes. Hell, I know you're a *liberal* woman, Sabrina—you certainly proved that—but surely your fiancé would be a little jealous if he found out about your little *lapse*?' His mouth curved. 'Though maybe not. Maybe you're the kind of couple who play away.' He lowered his voice into a sexy, insulting whisper. 'Then get turned on by telling each other all about it. There are couples like that, or so I believe.'

The blood left Sabrina's face and she stared at him in horror, scarcely able to make any sense of his words. She would have risen to her feet and walked out there and then, except that her legs felt so unsteady she didn't think she would be able to stand properly. 'How d-dare you insult me?' she whispered.

'You're honestly asking how I dare?' His eyebrows disappeared into the still damp strands of his ebony hair. But now it was his turn to look outraged as he leaned forward, his voice little more than a harsh, accusing whisper. 'Quite easily, actually. When you meet a woman and she does what you did to me that night, it's kind of *disappointing* to discover that she's got some poor sucker of a fiancé waiting on the sidelines.'

His mouth twisted as his anger drove him on remorselessly. 'Maybe you were bored with him, huh? Or were on the lookout for someone a little more…*loaded*.'

He deliberately gave the taunt two meanings, and his dark gaze flickered insultingly in the direction of his lap, seeing her flinch as her eyes followed his. And then he shifted in his seat, angry and uncomfortable, realising that he was starting to get turned on. What the hell did she *do* to him? 'Was that it?' he snarled. 'Were you looking for someone with a little more to offer than your home-spun boy?'

Sabrina felt sick and she shook her head, unable to speak. But he didn't seem to be expecting an answer because he ploughed on, a hard, clipped edge of rage to his voice.

'So what did you tell him? Did you describe in full and graphic detail the things I did to you? The things you did to me? Just what *did* you tell him, Sabrina?'

The unwitting inappropriateness of his question brought

her a new kind of strength, and she wanted to reach out and to wound him, just as he had wounded her.

'Nothing!' she choked out. 'I didn't tell him anything! I couldn't, could I? Because he's dead, you see, Guy! Dead, dead, *dead*!'

And the spots which danced before her eyes dissolved into rainbows, and then, thankfully, into darkness.

CHAPTER SIX

GUY knew that Sabrina was going to faint even before the great heavy weight of her eyelids flickered to slump over her eyes. The colour blanched right out of her face and she swayed, slender and blonde as a blade of wheat.

He caught her just before she slid to the ground, pushing her head down to her knees while with his other hand he reached round to undo the top button of her shirt. He felt her wriggle beneath his fingers.

She groaned. 'Guy—'

'Don't try to say anything.' His words were controlled and clipped as he rubbed the back of her neck, while inside his mind raced. A dead fiancé. His eyes narrowed. Why the hell hadn't she told him that right at the beginning?

Sabrina felt dizzy, dazedly aware that the other customers must be staring at her and knowing that the last thing she wanted was to attract more attention to herself. She needed to get out of here. And fast. But Guy's fingers were distracting her so. She tried ineffectually to shrug off the fingertips which massaged so soothingly at the nape of her neck.

He felt her flinch beneath his touch and his mouth hardened. 'Don't worry,' he ground out agitatedly. 'I'm not going to hurt you.'

How could he hurt her any more than she had been hurt already? As if his words had not wounded her and left her smarting. She felt the salty trickle of a tear as it meandered its way down her cheek and she sucked in a choked kind of sob. As if she were listening through a cotton-wool cloud which had dulled all her senses, she heard Guy talking to someone else. And then he was easing her head back and dabbing at her damp temples with some deliciously cool cloth.

She opened her eyes with difficulty, startled by the flickering gleam of concern which had briefly softened the hard eyes. 'I'm OK.'

'You are not OK,' he contradicted her, crouching down so that his face was on a level with hers. 'Do you want me to take you home?'

In this state? Why, her mother would start fretting about her—and hadn't she had enough to worry about over the last few months? 'Can we wait here for a little bit?' she asked weakly.

Guy made a slow, glittering appraisal of all the curious faces that were turned in their direction and frowned. 'Or somewhere less public? There are rooms upstairs. Why don't I see if we can use one—at least until you recover.'

Sabrina stared at him in undisguised horror. Surely he didn't imagine for a moment that…that…

'Oh, I see.' Guy gave a low, hollow laugh. 'Is that what you think of me, Sabrina?' he questioned. 'So governed by my libido that I'd take any opportunity to pounce on the nearest woman, even though she's only half-conscious?'

'I didn't say that.'

'No, you didn't have to,' he said grimly. 'The accusation was written all over your face. But don't worry, princess— that's not really my thing.'

Sabrina let her head fall back against the rest. 'I don't want to stay here.'

'You don't have to. Come on, let's go upstairs,' he said, and his arm was strong at the small of her back as he helped her to her feet.

The temptation to just lean back and lose herself in the warm haven of his arms was overwhelming, but Sabrina feebly pushed his guiding hand away from her. Touching him in any way at all was too much like trouble.

'I can do it myself,' she said stubbornly.

He looked as if he didn't believe her, but didn't argue the point, just walked right behind her in case she stumbled and fell.

Gripping the bannister with a grim kind of determination, she was glad when they reached the top and he pushed open the door of one of the rooms.

It was as different from his suite in Venice as it could have been—clean and middle-of-the-road, with a mass of chintz and swagged fabrics—and Sabrina heaved a small sigh of relief. She certainly didn't need reminders in the way of vast, luxuriously appointed beds or priceless paintings.

She flopped down onto the flower-sprigged duvet and heaved a sigh of relief.

Guy stood beside the bed, looking down at her, his face impenetrable as a disturbing thought nagged at his conscience. 'So why the hell did you faint?'

Reproach sparked from her eyes. 'Why do *you* think I fainted, Guy? Don't you imagine that the things you accused me of would make most women feel ill?'

But he shook his head. 'Harsh words are not normally enough to make a healthy young woman pass out.' His eyes threw her a cold, challenging glitter. 'You're not pregnant by any chance, are you?'

She supposed that he had every right to ask her, but that didn't make answering any easier. Especially not when the look of abject horror on his face told her *exactly* what he would think of that particular development.

'No, I'm not.' She lifted her head. 'And please don't imply that that was something in my game plan. We took precautions, remember?'

He wished she hadn't reminded him, though maybe he

only had himself to blame—he had been the one who had brought the subject up. But her defiant words only painted the most gloriously explicit picture of the way she had made the putting on of those damned condoms into some of the single most erotic moments of his life.

He forced himself to express the harsh truth. 'And precautions fail. Everyone knows that.'

Sabrina stared at him as life and energy began to warm their way around her veins once more. And anger. 'Then you should have given more thought to that *before* we made love, shouldn't you?'

'Yes,' he said bitterly. 'Maybe I should—only I wasn't thinking too straight at the time.'

'And just how would you be coping now if I told you that, yes, I *was* pregnant?'

He glittered her a chilly look. 'I'm in the fortunate position of being able to support a child—'

'Financially, you mean?' she challenged. 'Certainly not emotionally, by the sound of it.'

'Anyway, you're not pregnant, are you, Sabrina?' he snapped. 'So it's academic!'

But the nagging and worrying thought was that she *could* have allowed herself to get pregnant, and then never seen him again. Because Guy was right. Precautions *did* fail. Yet falling pregnant had been the very last thing on her mind. 'Maybe we both acted like the world's two biggest fools!'

He didn't agree with her blurted declaration, just continued to subject her to a cool, steady scrutiny. 'So, if pregnancy is not the reason for you fainting, what else could it be? Have you been eating properly?'

'I…yes…no,' she admitted eventually. 'Not really.'

'For how long?' he clipped out.

'It's obvious, isn't it? Since Michael died, I guess.'

Guy felt the flicker of a muscle at his cheek, unprepared

for the sharp kick of unreasonable jealousy. So the fiancé
had had a name, had he? 'And how long ago was that?'

There was no way to answer other than truthfully, but
mentally Sabrina prepared herself for his disapproval. 'Four
months,' she told him baldly.

There was silence. 'Four months?' he said heavily, as
though he must have misheard her.

She didn't look away. 'That's right. I expect I've
shocked you,' she said. 'Haven't I?'

He gave a bitter laugh. 'One way and another, I've done
a pretty good job of shocking myself lately.' Four *months*?
His mouth hardened. It threw what had happened into a
completely different perspective. He had wondered about
her spectacular and uninhibited response in his arms.

So had he just been a substitute for the man who had
died? A warm, living body filling her and reminding her of
what life should be?

'You didn't waste much time, did you?' he said flatly.

'And here comes the condemnation,' she said in a low
voice.

'It was an observation.' He walked over to study an un-
imaginative little hunting print and resisted the temptation
to punch his fist against the flowered wallpaper. When he
turned around to face her, Sabrina could see the fire and
the fury that sparked from his eyes. 'Why the hell didn't
you tell me about it before?'

She bit her lip, willing her eyes not to fill with tears.
'Why do you think?' she said tremulously, before she had
had time to think it through.

Guy stilled, his eyes narrowing perceptively. 'Because I
wouldn't have made love to you,' he said slowly. 'Because
even if it had killed me—' and he suspected that it might
have gone some way towards doing that '—there is no way
that I would have taken a vulnerable woman to bed and
seduced her over and over again! But you wanted me badly,

didn't you, Sabrina?' he concluded arrogantly. 'So much that you weren't prepared to risk not getting what you wanted! *That's* why you didn't tell me!'

Sabrina shook her head, and it felt as though it were filled with lead. 'You wanted it, too.' She bit her lip guiltily. 'You make me sound passive—and I wasn't. We both know that. We both wanted it...'

'Badly,' he put in softly, seeing the answering colour which flooded her cheeks. 'Very, very badly. Yes, we did.' He shook his head in a gesture which was the closest he had ever come to confusion. 'The question is *why* we both wanted it—so much that it drove reason and sane behaviour clean away.'

'We were sexually attracted,' she said shakily. But it had been much more than that. She forced herself to forget the warm glow of recognition she had experienced the very first time she had set eyes on him. As if she had known him all her life. Or longer. She stared at his handsome face and tried to sound coolly logical. 'I'm sure that kind of thing happens to you all the time, Guy.'

He shook his head in anger. 'But that's just the point, dammit—it doesn't! Oh...' He shrugged as he saw her disbelieving face. 'Women come on to me all the time, sure...'

Sabrina's smile turned into a grimace, wondering if he had any idea how much he had just insulted her.

'But usually it leaves me cold,' he reflected thoughtfully. 'I haven't had casual sex since I was a teenager.' And never like that, he thought achingly. Never like that.

Sabrina flinched. '*I* don't remember coming on to *you*,' she objected, but more out of a sense of pride than conviction. 'I thought it was *you* coming on to *me*!'

He threw her a look of mocking query. 'It was pretty mutual, Sabrina. You're not going to deny that, are you?'

No, she wasn't going to deny it. She looked down at her

lap, as if the knotted fingers lying there would provide some kind of inspiration.

'I'm still waiting for an answer, princess.'

The resolve which had deepened his voice made Sabrina frown at him in alarm. 'That sounded like a threat!'

He shook his head. 'Of course it isn't a threat,' he said patiently. 'But surely you aren't deluding yourself that we don't need to talk about what happened.'

She bit her trembling lip. 'C-can't we just call it history, and forget it ever happened?' she croaked.

'No,' he said flatly. 'Of course we can't. I think you owe me some sort of explanation, Sabrina.'

'I owe you nothing!'

He wanted to know. He *needed* to. 'Why did you run away the next morning?'

'Why do you think?' She shuddered as she remembered waking up all warm and replete in his bed. 'Because I realised what I had done! And it was never going to be any more than a one-night stand, was it, Guy? Besides, you lied to me—so how could I trust you?'

'And wouldn't it have been more sensible to have thought all this through before it actually happened?' he demanded. 'I didn't drag you back there with me! You weren't drunk!'

His condemnation was like a slap in the face and Sabrina flinched beneath his accusing stare.

'So what was I?' he demanded. 'A substitute? Did you close your eyes and pretend it was Michael?' He ignored her look of pain, remorselessly grinding the words out. 'Any man would have done for you, wouldn't he, Sabrina? I just happened to come along and press the right buttons.'

She met the dark, accusing fire in his eyes. 'You honestly think that?'

'I don't know what to think. It's not a situation I've ever found myself in before. Thank God.' His gaze narrowed

into a piercing grey laser, and then he saw her white, be-
wildered face and felt a sudden slap of conscience. 'You
look terrible,' he said bluntly.

'Thanks.' She sat up a bit and sucked in a breath. 'I'm
feeling a bit better, actually.'

'Well, you don't look it. 'I'm going to ring down for
some soup for you. You can't go home in that state.'

'Guy, no—'

'Guy, *yes*,' he countered, reaching out to pick up the
phone, completely overriding her objections.

Soup and sandwiches arrived with the kind of speed
which suggested to Sabrina that he might have already ordered them. Had that been the muffled conversation with
the landlord she had overheard?

She told herself that she felt too weak to face food, but
the stern look on his dark face warned her that if she refused to eat, he didn't look averse to picking up the spoon
and actually feeding her!

Guy sat and watched her. The thick broth sent steam over
her pale features, but gradually, as the bowl emptied, some
of the roses began to creep back into her cheeks. He saw
her half-heartedly bite into a sandwich and then look at it
with something approaching awakening—as if she had only
just learnt how good food could taste when you were hungry.

Sabrina wiped at her lips with a napkin and sighed, aware
of the glittering grey eyes which were following her movements with a steely kind of fascination. He hadn't, she realised, eaten a single thing—he'd just sat there and watched
her like a hawk.

She flicked him a questioning look. 'You're not hungry?'

'No, I'm not hungry,' he said flatly. 'And I think it's
time I got you home.'

She shook her head. He was too potent a presence, who
had demonstrated the depth of his contempt for her. She

didn't want him invading any more of her space. She didn't need any more aching reminders of just how devastating he really was.

She had blown it with Guy Masters by being too greedy. She should have given him her telephone number and gone back to her own hotel that night.

But nothing could change the fact that she had been desperate for him, driven on by an unrecognisable hunger she'd been unable to control.

Well, it was too late now. What man wouldn't be filled with contempt at what she had allowed to happen, and so soon?

'Why don't you just call me a cab?' she said tiredly. 'I don't need you to come with me.'

'I'm taking you home,' he said firmly. He saw her open her mouth and shook his head with the kind of dominance that brooked no argument. 'Oh, no, Sabrina,' he said softly. 'This has nothing to do with independence, or pride. You're in no state to go home on your own—'

'Yes, I am!' she protested.

'You are not,' he contradicted impatiently. 'And you can sit there arguing with me all night long, but it won't change a thing. I'm not budging on this—I'm taking you home.'

But her ice-blue eyes looked so helpless as she stared up at him that he found himself unable to resist the temptation to brush a stray strand of hair away from her cheek, feeling its warm tremble beneath his fingertip.

His grey gaze burned into her and for one heart-stopping moment she thought that he had relented. She saw the sudden, impulsive softening of his mouth and the way that his eyes had now brightened to glittering jet and thought that he was about to kiss her.

But all he did was open the door. 'Come on,' he said abruptly. 'Time we were out of here.'

He made her sit down while he went to settle up with

the landlord, gently placing her against some cushions as if she really *were* pregnant. And Sabrina bit her lip as an inexplicable yearning to carry his black-haired baby washed over her.

Outside the pub was no ordinary taxi—somehow he had managed to magic up a long, low limousine from somewhere. Sabrina registered the gleaming bodywork with a disbelieving blink as Guy opened the door of the car. She supposed that Salisbury did *have* vehicles like this for hire—it was just that she had never encountered them before. Not in her world.

'Here, put this on,' he said, as he slid into the back seat beside her and buckled up her seat belt, still playing the guardian angel.

'Where are we going?' asked the driver.

'Wilton Street,' she responded quietly.

The driver half turned in his seat and shot a quick look in Guy's direction. 'Wilton Street?' he asked in surprise. 'Are you sure?'

'Of course she's sure!' snapped Guy, and flicked shut the glass partition, immediately distracted by the sweet perfume of her hair.

Sabrina felt the bitter ache of emptiness as the huge car negotiated its way into a tiny road, where the houses were small and boxy, each one looking exactly the same. She stole a glance at the stony perfection of his profile, knowing that she would never see him again after tonight.

And maybe it was best that she didn't. They weren't just from different worlds—more like different universes.

The driver flipped the glass partition open. 'What number Wilton Street?'

'Number th-three,' she stumbled.

Guy heard the tremble in her voice as the car pulled to a halt in front of a tiny house and frowned.

'You're crying!' he exclaimed softly.

'N-no, I'm not.' She gulped, but took the crisp, white handkerchief which he offered her and buried her nose in it.

'Why are you crying? Because I spoke so harshly?'

She heard the self-recrimination which had hardened his voice and shook her head wordlessly as she tried to bring the gulping sobs under control. How could she tell him that she didn't really know why she was crying? That maybe her tears were for Michael—maybe just for herself. Or maybe she was mourning a golden relationship with Guy Masters which had been doomed from the very outset.

He waited until the shuddering of her breathing had slowed down in something approaching calm and then he got out of the car and went round to open the door for her.

'Wait here for me,' he said to the driver.

He led Sabrina up the narrow front path and rang the doorbell. Moments later the door was opened by a woman who was unmistakably Sabrina's mother. She had an amazing pair of identical ice-blue eyes and her hair was still bright—apart from the occasional touch of grey. And Guy had a sudden powerful vision of what Sabrina would look like in her fifties.

Mrs Cooper's eyes flew open in alarm as she saw her daughter's pale and tear-stained face. 'Sabrina, darling!' she exclaimed. 'Whatever is it?' She looked up at the tall, dark man who was supporting her. 'Who are you? What's happened to her?'

'Nothing at all has happened to harm her.' Guy injected calm into his voice as Sabrina shook off his restraining hand and sat down abruptly at the foot of the staircase. 'She's a little upset,' he said. 'Although I suppose that's understandable, under the circumstances.'

Mrs Cooper nodded. 'So she's told you about Michael?'

Again Guy felt the sharp spear of unreasonable jealousy. 'Yes, she has.'

Sabrina wondered why they were talking about her as if she wasn't there. Or why her mother was staring up at Guy with trust rather than suspicion.

'My name is Guy Masters,' he said. 'Sabrina and I met in Venice.' He took a business card from his coat pocket and gave it to her. 'Will you give this to your daughter in the morning?' he said, moving to the staircase and bending his head down so that it was almost touching Sabrina's.

'Ring me if you need to talk,' he said grimly.

And then he was gone and the hall seemed suddenly so empty—so lacking in the strength and vitality generated by that dark, mocking face and that beautiful, strong body.

Mrs Cooper shut the door behind him, and turned to her daughter. 'Are you going to tell me what happened, darling?'

Sabrina shook her head wearily. 'It's too complicated to explain. I'm OK now.'

'Are you sure?'

Sabrina nodded, and slowly rose to her feet. 'Positive.'

Mrs Cooper cocked her head in the direction of the front door. 'He seems very considerate, dear,' she commented curiously, 'your Mr Guy Masters. Are you going to ring him?'

'No.' But Sabrina actually managed a wan smile. *Considerate?* She could think of about a hundred adjectives which would describe Guy Masters.

And considerate wouldn't even make the list.

CHAPTER SEVEN

RING me if you need to talk. Those had been Guy's last words to her a week or so ago.

Sabrina opened her eyes and stared at the blank white space of the ceiling. What woman would want to admit to being needy? And what could she possibly say if she picked the phone up to ring him? *Hello, Guy, it's me, Sabrina. Remember me? I'm the woman you had the one-night stand with in Venice?*

And then what?

No. There was no point in ringing him. No point in anything really, other than trying to get through each day the best way she could.

'Sabrina?'

Sabrina turned over and yawned as she focussed her eyes on the clock on the locker. Nearly ten o'clock. She loved her Sunday morning lie-ins. 'Yes, Mum?'

'You've got—' there was a rather odd note in her mother's voice as she called up the stairs, Sabrina thought '—a *visitor*, dear!'

Some sixth sense warned her. Sabrina sat bolt upright in bed, her baggy Minnie Mouse nightshirt almost swamping her.

'Who is it?' she demanded hoarsely.

'It's Guy,' called her mother.

Her heart did a somersault. 'Guy M-Masters?'

'Why, how many others do you know?' came a shockingly familiar voice.

'I'm still in bed!' she shouted down, feeling the shiver

of nerves beginning to trace chaotic pathways over her skin. There was a split-second pause, and then a sardonic reply.

'Don't worry. I'll wait.'

She told herself that there was no way of getting out of seeing him, even if she'd wanted to. And that was the most disturbing thing of all.

She didn't want to.

Sabrina felt the powerful acceleration of her heart as she quickly showered and dressed.

Instinct told her not to go over the top with her choice of clothes, while pride nagged at her to make *some* sort of effort. If he was simply calling by to check on her welfare—then she refused to have him wondering what he had ever seen in her.

But she was actually shaking as she dressed—in a warm woollen dress which she'd bought at the market, its ice-blue colour matching her eyes exactly. And her knee-high leather boots—absolutely ancient now, but lovingly polished and cared for, so that they had entirely justified their original high price-tag.

Sabrina went downstairs, expecting—no, *hoping*—to feel nothing for him. But she wondered who she had been trying to fool, because the moment she walked into the sitting room and saw him she was incapacitated by his sheer physical beauty.

He looked, she thought with a sharp edge of despair, absolutely wonderful—as wonderful as the first time she had seen him. He was wearing a pair of faded jeans which clung to every millimetre of the longest, most muscular legs she had ever seen. The denim emphasised the jut of his hips and the flat planes of his stomach. And he was wearing a beautiful cashmere sweater in a shade of grey just darker than his eyes. A dark jacket lay heaped over a chair.

There was nothing she could do to stop the primitive

leap of pleasure in her heart. But at least she could keep it from showing. 'Hello, Guy,' she said calmly.

He thought how fine and how translucent her skin was—so fine that you could quite clearly see the shadowed definition of her amazing cheekbones. He had not meant to come here today—he had been waiting for a phone call which had never materialised. He had expected her to ring, the way women always did. And he had been unable to get her out of his mind. Out of a determination to forget her had grown a need to know that she was OK. Well, she certainly *looked* OK. More than OK.

'Hello, Sabrina,' he said slowly. 'How are you feeling?'

'Better,' she told him truthfully. 'Much better.'

They stared at one another, like two people meeting for the first time. Well, maybe not quite like that, thought Sabrina. She knew too much about him to ever be like that. The top button of his shirt was open to reveal the tiniest jagged scar which ran alongside his Adam's apple. A scar she distinctly remembered running the tip of her tongue along, so that his big body had writhed with a kind of reluctant pleasure.

'Would you like coffee, or something?'

He looked at the luscious tremble of her lips and the ice-blue dazzle of her eyes. 'No, I'll tell you what I'd really like,' he said slowly.

It was so like something he had murmured at the most intimate point of their lovemaking that Sabrina felt her cheeks begin to burn.

'I've got the car outside,' he said evenly. I thought maybe you could show me something of the city. I'll park close to the centre, and we can walk.'

Sabrina looked around her, at her sweet mother who could never be accused of being uptight. But the house was small, no, tiny, and it would be impossible to do anything other than stumble out pleasantries that neither of them meant.

'I'll go and get my coat,' she said.

'Wrap up warmly, Sabrina,' said her mother. 'It may be sunny outside, but it's bitterly cold in that wind.'

Guy helped her on with the coat, which had a collar of fake fur. Her hair was loose and spilled into the fur, giving her a faintly glamorous appearance, he thought.

His fingers brushed lightly over her shoulders and he felt the dark lickings of temptation scramble at his senses. He remembered how translucent her skin had been, and that his tongue had followed the fine blue tracery of the veins which laced her tiny breasts.

She looked at him, a question darkening the blue of her eyes. 'Where's the car?'

'It's a little way along the street.' He omitted to say that the street was way too narrow for such a powerful car.

'Not the limousine, I hope?' she asked faintly.

He heard the trace of mockery, and gave a wry smile. So she wasn't particularly impressed by status symbols. 'No, not the limousine.' They began to walk up the road together. 'The landlord of the pub ordered that car, not me. He obviously took one look at me and made an assumption about what my requirements were. I wasn't intending to make quite such a statement,' he added drily.

'Well, you did,' Sabrina remarked as they drew alongside a more sedate, but equally luxurious car. 'My mother said that all week the neighbours have been dying to know who the visitor was.'

He paused in the act of unlocking the door, his grey gaze steady and imperturbable. 'And what did you tell them?'

She managed to return his look, though it wasn't easy— not when it took her mind back to how she had seen it when he'd been in her arms. Stripped of all pretence, darkened and glazed with…lust, she reminded herself painfully. That was all it had been. Lust.

'I said that you were…' She hesitated and now the gaze became laser-sharp, lancing through her. 'A friend.'

His mouth twisted into a cool smile as he held the door open for her. 'A friend?' he mocked.

'What should I have said, then? A lover?'

'That certainly would have been more accurate, wouldn't it?'

'I don't think so, Guy. It's in the past tense now.'

She slid her legs into the car. Actually, she had wanted to say 'acquaintance', because that had seemed more accurate than 'friend', though it hadn't really seemed appropriate either—not in view of what had happened. 'Acquaintance' implied that you didn't know somebody terribly well, and yet she knew Guy Masters exceedingly well. Sabrina swallowed. In certain respects, anyway.

She kept her eyes fixed straight ahead while he drove into the city and parked. And in the dim, ugly light of the concrete car park he looked down at her.

'You haven't asked me why I'm here,' he said suddenly.

'Maybe I'm afraid of what your answer will be.' She lifted her shoulders a little. 'Why *are* you here?'

'That's just it.' He gave a short laugh and shook his head as he locked the car doors. 'I don't know!'

With a chill wind blowing in their faces, they walked right into the centre of the city, with the cathedral spire dominating the skyline and drawing them in like a magnet.

'Want to go inside?' she asked softly.

He glittered her a dark smile. 'You know I do.'

Yes, she had known that, just as she instinctively knew that he didn't want a guided tour, not today. The stiff set of his shoulders said, *Stay away*, quite clearly.

So she walked around the huge empty cathedral with him, quickly turning away when he paused to stare up at the altar and an indescribable sadness seemed to harden his beautiful face into stone.

And that was grief, she recognised painfully, a grief too bitter to intrude into.

Outside, the wind whipped her hair into ribbons which curled over her cheeks and Guy found his fingers itching to brush them away.

'I'll drive you home,' he said abruptly.

She felt the sinking sensation of disappointment. 'OK,' she agreed.

But as he drew up at the end of her street he made no move, taking the key out of the ignition and turning to look at her.

'So what happened?' he asked quietly. 'To Michael?' he persisted softly. 'How did he die?'

There was silence.

'It was a car crash,' she said eventually. 'He wanted to go out for the evening, and I didn't. We were supposed to be saving up. He tried to change my mind, but I wouldn't. He…' This bit was hard, but she forced herself to continue. 'He said that I was a control freak.'

His eyes narrowed with interest. 'A control freak?' he echoed softly. 'Is that so?'

She supposed that he didn't believe her, and how could she blame him? She hadn't exactly behaved like that around him, had she? 'Well, that's the most peculiar thing—I *do* like to be in control, yes. Normally.'

'And so do I,' he said, his voice as bitter as the recrimination in his eyes. 'Perhaps we just bring out the worst in each other.'

And the best, she thought suddenly. The very best.

'We had a row,' she remembered, her voice slowing painfully. 'A blazing row. And Michael got angry and he stormed out, and…and…that's when he crashed. He was killed instantly.'

Guy nodded, his grey eyes narrowing perceptively. 'Oh, I see,' he said slowly. 'So you carry all the guilt, as well as the grief, do you, Sabrina?'

'If only I hadn't been so rigid,' she said bitterly. 'If I'd gone with him then it might not have happened.'

'And it just might. That's a pretty heavy burden to carry, you know, Sabrina. What with that and our little fling you could soon find that feeling guilty becomes too much of a habit.'

She unclipped her seat belt angrily. 'I don't have to stay here and listen to—'

The truth?' he drawled, and something in the way he said it stopped her in her tracks.

'Do you think I feel good about myself?' she demanded. 'Letting a man who was virtually a stranger make love to me, and so soon—'

And so thoroughly, he thought longingly. 'Yeah, yeah, yeah,' he interrupted coolly. 'I thought we'd already done the regret trip, Sabrina.'

'*We?*' she queried. 'You mean you feel bad about what happened, too?'

'What do *you* think?'

Sabrina looked down at her lap. So now she knew.

'I don't know anything about you,' she realised aloud, but he shook his head.

'Oh, yes, you do,' he said softly. 'You haven't seen my flat, or met my family, or seen where I work—but none of that is important. You've seen me at my most—' He bit the word out as if he didn't like it very much. 'Exposed.'

'Like every woman you've been to bed with, you mean?'

He shook his head. 'That night was something outside my experience. Like you, Sabrina, I like to be in control— and on that occasion I most definitely wasn't.'

'Guy,' she said suddenly, and something in the way she said it made his eyes narrow.

'What?'

'Who were you thinking about—back there in the cathedral?'

He stilled. Usually he would have blanked such an intrusive question, but hadn't he just been asking her questions just like that?

'I was thinking about my father,' he said slowly, feeling her suck the admission from him. 'He died a long time ago,' he said, and then his face hardened. 'But we're not here to talk about me, are we?'

'Apparently not.' She shrugged listlessly.

'What you need to face up to now is that it *happened*! Everything. Michael died and we made love all night long, and however much you might want to unwish that—you can't. Fact. End of story. The important question is where do you go from here?'

'I don't know,' she admitted brokenly.

His mouth tightened as he saw the dark shadows thrown onto her pale skin by her sharpened cheekbones. 'I'm taking you out to lunch,' he said grimly.

She shook her head, more tempted than she should have been. 'I can't. I usually have lunch with my mother on Sundays.'

'Then bring her along.'

'Are you sure?'

'Why not? She eats lunch, doesn't she?'

Sabrina nodded, surprised and pleased. Michael wouldn't have dreamed of issuing such an invitation—he'd seen parents as nothing but authority figures, just hell-bent on stopping you enjoying yourself. 'I'm sure she'd be delighted,' she said truthfully.

'Then let's go and find her,' he said, still in that same grim voice.

Sabrina's mother was as pleased by the invitation as her daughter had anticipated, especially when Guy chose a restaurant on the very edge of the city, one which neither of the two women had ever visited before.

'Oh, we couldn't possibly—it's much too expensive!' protested Mrs Cooper.

'No, it's not,' said Guy patiently.

'And we'll never get a table,' put in Sabrina.

The grey eyes glittered. 'Want to bet?'

And of course he got a table—how could she have ever doubted for a moment that he wouldn't? Men like Guy Masters always got tables.

Sabrina tried very hard to eat her shrimp salad and lobster with some element of appetite, but it was unbelievably difficult to concentrate on the food when there was such a distraction on the other side of the table.

Her eyes kept straying to the dark gleam of Guy's hair as he sat and chatted to her mother. The top two buttons of his shirt were undone and she could just see the faint shadowing where the dark hair began.

She wiped a damp palm over the napkin which lay on her lap. What on earth would her mother say if she had any idea that the man who was chatting to her so companionably had ravished her daughter more than she'd believed it possible for a woman to be ravished.

Guy studied her from over his wineglass, suddenly registering her tense silence. 'You're very quiet, Sabrina,' he observed.

'Oh, she's quiet like that a lot of the time,' said Mrs Cooper. 'Can't seem to snap out of it, can you, darling?'

'I don't think Guy particularly wants to hear, Mum,' said Sabrina warningly.

But Mrs Cooper was only just warming to her subject. 'I'm dreadfully sorry that Michael is dead—of course I am—and it's hit her very hard, as you would expect.'

Sabrina didn't dare meet Guy's eyes for fear of the de-

rision she might find there. Grief-stricken people didn't
tend to behave in the way she had behaved.

'I know what it's like myself,' said Mrs Cooper, and she
reached over and patted Sabrina's head. 'After my husband
left me, people always saw me just as a divorcee—not as
Maureen Cooper in her own right.'

Guy nodded. So Sabrina had no father either.

'No one will give the poor girl a chance to get over it.
And the trouble is that this is where she grew up. Everyone
knows her, and everyone knew Michael—and she can't escape from their memories. I think she should get out and
have a little fun. That's why I persuaded her to go to
Venice—she'd always wanted to go there—but when she
came back she looked worse than ever.'

'Have you quite finished, Mum?'

'Can't you get away somewhere?' queried Guy thoughtfully.

'Like where?' She met the stormy challenge of his gaze.
She had tried fleeing to Venice and look where *that* had
got her.

'How about London? That's where most people want to
go.'

'London's expensive,' said Sabrina defensively. 'And I
don't earn very much. And, besides, I don't really feel like
going into a city where I don't know anyone.'

'But you know me, Sabrina,' came the surprising response.

She violently began spearing at a piece of lobster.

'You know you can always come and stay with me.'
He'd spoken the words aloud before he'd realised their implication.

For a second Sabrina froze, and then slowly lifted her
head to gaze at him in disbelief. 'What did you say?' she
whispered.

'I have a flat,' he said. 'A big flat—plenty big enough

to accommodate another person. Come and use the spare room for a while.'

She thought of sharing a flat with him, even temporarily, and her heart began to bang against her ribcage—until she forced herself to quash the hopeless dream and replace it with reality. 'It's a crazy idea,' she said woodenly. 'I don't have a job to go to.'

'So find one.' He shrugged.

'It isn't as easy as that, Guy,' said Mrs Cooper gently.

Sabrina found herself thinking that Wells did have another branch, in the capital, but loyally she found herself confirming her mother's words. 'No, it isn't.'

Guy stirred his coffee, as if he didn't really care, and Mrs Cooper got up from the table and beamed. 'Will you excuse me for a minute?'

Guy rose to his feet until Mrs Cooper had disappeared, and Sabrina thought what impeccable manners he had. She stared across the table at him as he sat back down. 'It's very…kind of you, Guy, but you know very well I can't accept your offer.'

He coolly returned her stare. 'Do I?'

She narrowed her eyes in frustration. 'Don't be so obtuse.'

'Then don't be so damned evasive—and come right out with what it is you want to say!'

Surely he wasn't really expecting her to say it out loud. But, from his unhelpful silence, he clearly was. Reminding herself that they had already been as intimate as any couple could be, Sabrina drew in a deep breath.

'How could I come and stay with you, not knowing—' she met his gaze without flinching '—whether we…we…'

'Oh, for God's sake!' he snapped, as the meaning of her words became clear to him. 'Do you really think that I'm about to start extracting rent in the form of sexual favours?'

'That wasn't what I said!'

'That's what you meant, though—isn't it?'

She shook her head, but without conviction.

He leaned back in his chair and looked at her speculatively. 'You told me you like to be in control, didn't you? Is that why you're afraid to come? Afraid that you'll lose it again around me? Scared to risk it?'

She met the challenge in his eyes. 'Do you think you're so irresistible?'

'I don't know. Maybe that's something we should both find out. Maybe we both need this opportunity to redeem ourselves.'

She stared at him in confusion. 'Redeem ourselves?'

'Sure. This is the perfect opportunity to demonstrate that we're not completely ruled by our hormones—'

'That's a very nice way to put it!'

'Sabrina, there isn't,' he told her bluntly, 'a *nice* way to put it.'

'So you're saying that the relationship will be platonic?'

'No, that's not what I'm saying at all,' he countered. 'I'm not promising anything.'

Sabrina began to get a glimmering of understanding about what he meant. Put two people who were sexually attracted to each other in a flat, and in the end it all came down to who cracked first. And who didn't. Control, that was what this was all about. Power and control. But she said nothing more as her mother had begun to walk back towards the table.

Nothing more was said on the subject during the drive back to her house, and Sabrina felt an unwilling sense of emptiness as Guy said goodbye to her mother, then turned to her, his enigmatic grey eyes glittering darkly.

'Goodbye, Sabrina.'

'Goodbye, Guy. Thanks for lunch.'

He gave a brief hard smile before climbing into his car.

Sabrina and her mother stood and watched the powerful car move away.

'You aren't going to go, are you, darling?' asked Mrs Cooper. Sabrina carried on looking, even though the tail-lights had long since disappeared.

'I don't know, Mum,' she said honestly. 'I just don't know.'

CHAPTER EIGHT

SABRINA'S pulse was hammering as she punched out the number, and it hammered even more when the connection was made and a rich, deep voice said, 'Guy Masters.'

She opened her mouth but no words emerged.

The voice sounded impatient now. 'Guy Masters,' he repeated irritatedly.

'Guy. It's me—Sabrina.'

There was a two-second pause which seemed like an eternity.

'Sabrina Cooper,' she rushed on. 'Remember? We met—'

'Yes, of course I remember you, Sabrina. How are you?'

For a moment she was tempted to hang up and forget the whole stupid idea, but she had spent the last few weeks changing her life around. She couldn't back out now.

'I've managed to get a transfer!' she said, and then, in case he had completely forgotten his proposal, rushed on, 'To the London branch of Wells. They've said I can work there for six weeks. The bookshop,' she added, just in case he had forgotten *that*.

'Oh.' There was a pause. 'Good. So, when are you coming to stay?'

He *did* remember. Thank God. 'I can start first thing on Monday.' Sabrina crossed the fingers of her left hand and pulled a ghastly grimace at herself in the mirror. 'If it's all right with you, I thought I'd come on Sunday afternoon.'

'*This* Sunday?'

'If that's a problem—'

'No.' The deep voice sounded thoughtful. 'No, that shouldn't be a problem.'

She thought he might make the effort to sound a little more convincing. Or pleased about it. 'Are you sure?'

'Have you got a pen?' he asked tersely. 'I'll give you directions how to get here.'

She scribbled down his home address, instantly noting that it was in Knightsbridge. So she would be staying in one of London's most affluent areas.

'What time will we see you?'

'We?' she questioned, feeling suddenly frozen by nerves.

'I'm having a few friends for brunch—but they'll probably have gone by teatime.'

'Then I'll come at teatime,' she promised hoarsely.

She struggled onto the train on Sunday with her two suitcases and then onto the tube, where she had to stand for the entire journey because it seemed that the whole world and his brother were heading for Knightsbridge and the museums.

So by the time she reached the outrageously exclusive address which Guy had given her she felt as grimy and bedraggled as a cat which had been left out in the rain all night.

His flat was situated in a quiet square, several streets back from the main thoroughfare of Knightsbridge. In the centre of the square was a gated garden, and Sabrina put her suitcases down and peered in through the railings.

Beneath the trees, daffodils waved their sun-yellow trumpets, and she could hear the sound of birdsong. And despite her misgivings, Sabrina felt a sudden sense of freedom. Picking up her cases with a renewed determination, she walked up the steps of the house, rang the doorbell and waited.

Sabrina glanced down at her watch as she waited. Four-thirty. Most people's idea of teatime, surely? What if the unthinkable had happened and Guy had forgotten that she was coming? What would she do if he wasn't in?

She lifted her finger to the doorbell once more and just at that moment the door opened and there stood Guy. She swallowed down the lump which had risen in her throat.

His dark hair was ruffled, and he wore an old pair of jeans with the top two buttons left undone, revealing a pro-vocative downward arrowing of dark hair. He had clearly just dragged on a black T-shirt which clung to every per-fectly defined muscle of his chest. He looked, Sabrina thought with a sudden stab of anxiety, as if he'd just got out of bed.

His eyes narrowed with an unmistakable look of surprise as he stared down at her, and then he said, very steadily, 'Sabrina!'

Her heart thumped faster. 'You *had* forgotten I was com-ing.'

He didn't miss a beat. 'Of course I hadn't forgotten.' He stole a glance at his watch, which gleamed gold against the faint blur of hair on his wrist, and frowned. Hell, was *that* the time? 'It's later than I thought. Come on in. Let me take your cases. We're just finishing brunch.'

'At this time?'

'Why not?' he said softly. 'It's Sunday. No deadlines.'

'If you're busy I can go away and come back later,' she said, although as soon as the words were out of her mouth she realised how ridiculous they sounded—because where on earth would she go on a late spring afternoon in a city where she knew nobody?

He smiled as he took the suitcases from her, thinking how cold she looked. How she always looked as if she needed protecting. His protection. 'Don't be silly,' he said softly. 'Come on in. You look frozen.'

Well, she was shivering, yes, but that had more to do

with the reality of seeing him in the glorious, living flesh. Of hearing his rich, deep voice. It had only been a few weeks, but it seemed like a whole lifetime since she had last seen him. How could she have so easily forgotten the impact he had on her—as compelling now as when she had first set eyes on him?

She followed him inside, but her nerves were jangled even further when she saw just how amazing his home was—all light and space and breathtakingly big windows.

The walls were painted in some pale, cool colour with modern paintings which might have looked out of place in a period building but looked as though they had been designed to hang just there.

He gestured towards a sweeping staircase. 'I'll show you your room in a minute. Come on up and meet the others first.'

Oh, lord, and here she was looking all grubby and windswept. And whilst Guy looked pretty ruffled himself, he managed to look extremely sexy into the bargain.

There was no time to do anything except hastily smooth down her hair, and she followed him upstairs, trying to look anywhere but at the denim which hugged his narrow hips as he walked.

She could hear the muffled notes of lazy laughter—feminine laughter—and the chinking of glasses, and a sense of apprehension washed over her, even though she forced herself to pin a smile onto her lips. They can't eat me, she told herself. They're Guy's friends.

Guy glanced down at her as he put the cases down. She looked bushed. And fragile. And yet…yet…

A pulse began a slow, heavy dance at his temple as he pushed the door open.

'Come on in and say hi. This is Sabrina,' he announced, as three faces looked up. 'Sabrina Cooper.'

The first thing that registered was that two of the three

occupants of the room were female. And that one of them was a heart-stoppingly beautiful brunette who was stretched out on a huge lemon sofa, painting her toenails and wearing a lazy smile.

She had on a pair of jeans which had been carefully constructed to emphasise every curve of her delectable bottom. As did the teeny-weeny T-shirt which came to just above her smooth brown navel. So, did she, wondered Sabrina with an unsteady thump of her heart, belong to Guy?

'This is Jenna Jones.' Guy smiled.

Jenna gave a polite smile. 'Hi,' she said shortly.

The other sofa was occupied by a man who was looking at Sabrina with interest. At his feet sat the second woman, her hair twisted into a topknot, and they were both drinking champagne out of long, frosted flutes.

'And this is Tom Roberts, my cousin,' said Guy. 'Our mothers are sisters.'

Sabrina looked at Tom, trying to see any family resemblance, but she couldn't. But, then, Tom's face was neither so haughty nor so aloof as Guy's. 'Hello.'

Tom crinkled her a smile. 'Hello, Sabrina.'

'And Trudi Herley—his fiancée.'

'Come and sit down and have some champagne, Sabrina,' said Trudi. 'Have you eaten?' She pointed to the remains of what Sabrina assumed had been brunch, which lay on trays scattered in the centre of the room.

At least they seemed friendlier than Jenna, who hadn't moved and was staring at Sabrina with a decidedly moody look on her face. She looked over at Guy.

'You haven't told us about Sabrina, Guy, darling.'

'Haven't I?' For no good reason, Guy suddenly resented the implication that he *should* have done.

He poured out a flute of champagne and handed it to Sabrina, putting his hand in the small of her back and propelling her towards one of the chairs. 'Go and sit down over there.'

Feeling a little like a marionette, Sabrina obeyed, gulping nervously at the glass of bubbly as he lowered his long-legged frame into a chair opposite her.

Who *were* these people? And who was Jenna, for goodness' sake? That possessive look she was currently slanting at Guy suggested that the two of them were more than just friends. He hadn't brought *that* into the equation when he'd suggested she come and stay with him.

'So where did you two meet?' persisted Jenna.

Ice-grey eyes glittered coolly in Sabrina's direction. 'We met in Venice,' Guy said slowly, seeing her body stiffen in recollection and feeling his own slow, answering response.

Sabrina studied her glass of champagne intently, feeling as naïve as it was possible to feel. Why had she said she would come here? Because there was a part of her which had been secretly hoping that they might fall into each other's arms again? Why hadn't she considered that he had a life she knew nothing about? With other women and other friends? Who obviously were not about to welcome her with open arms. Not if Jenna's reaction was anything to go by.

'Venice?' echoed Tom, and threw him a curious look. 'When you flew over to buy that painting?'

'That's right,' said Guy succinctly, and drained his glass.

'But I thought you never mixed business and pleasure?'

'I don't,' came Guy's smooth retort. 'Not usually.'

Sabrina saw Tom raise his eyebrows in surprise.

'And what were *you* doing in Venice, Sabrina?' asked Jenna.

'I was there on holiday.'

'On your *own*?'

Sabrina saw Guy frown at the question, and something

in the quality of the brief, hard look he sent her gave her the courage to be truthful. Just for once she allowed herself to focus on the pleasure of their lovemaking, instead of the guilt, and a dreamy smile curved her mouth. 'That's right,' she said softly. 'It's the most wonderful place to explore on your own—you never know what you might find there.'

Guy's eyes were arrowed in her direction, their dark glitter telling her that he shared the erotic memory.

'So where *exactly* do you live?' persisted Jenna.

'In Salisbury.'

'Really? Are you on an awayday, or something?'

'Er, not exactly…'

'Sabrina's going to be…' Guy paused, as if seeking an elusive word. 'Staying…with me for a while.'

'*Staying* here?' Jenna's mouth fell open as if he had just confessed to murder. 'You mean she's going to be *living* here?'

'Sure.' He shrugged, and gave a lazy smile. 'Why not?'

Sabrina couldn't miss the swift look of amazement that crossed Trudi's face before she narrowed her eyes, then slowly stood up and nudged Tom with her bare foot. 'Good heavens,' she said faintly. 'Right. Time we were going, I think. Thank goodness Jenna is driving, and not me! Come on, Jen!'

Sabrina drew a deep breath and raised her head, her gaze drawn to the unfathomable grey of Guy's eyes, knowing that she needed to get out of there. Because if Jenna *did* belong to Guy, then she couldn't bear to endure a tender farewell scene between the two of them.

'Could you show me where I'll be sleeping, please, Guy?'

'Would that be the main bedroom, Guy?' Jenna smiled spikily. 'Or the junk room you call the spare?'

There was a brief, frozen silence and then Guy stood up,

his mouth tightening with an unmistakable look of irritation.

'If that was intended to embarrass Sabrina, Jenna, then you've succeeded with honours,' he said shortly. 'This way, Sabrina.'

There was a rather stunned silence as the two of them left the room. He picked up her suitcases, a thoughtful glint in his eyes as he observed her set expression.

Neither of them said a word until he threw open a door right at the end of the corridor to reveal a small room cluttered with a desk, a filing cabinet, an exercise bike and, hardly visible beneath a heap of skiing clothes, a narrow, single bed.

Sabrina turned to face him. 'You weren't expecting me,' she observed, and tried to keep the disappointment from her voice as she took in the general chaos.

He gave a half-apologetic shrug. He was letting her have the room, for heaven's sake—was she expecting red-carpet treatment into the bargain? 'I was snowed under when you rang last week, and I just didn't get around to asking my cleaning lady to sort the place out. Let me go and see the others out, and then I'll come and help you tidy up.'

'I can do it myself!'

'You don't know where to store things,' he said evenly, and walked out of the room before she had a chance to reply.

Unable to do anything until he came back, Sabrina went and stood over by the window, gazing out at the darkening sky, at the city lights which were just beginning to flicker on. She thought of how her life had changed, and was changing still, in ways she had never imagined would happen to a girl like her. And there wasn't, she realised, a single thing she could do to stop it. So, was that fate, or destiny?

She was still standing there when he returned, and as he

walked into the confined space she suddenly became stupidly aware of the fact that he had now done up the top two buttons of his jeans.

And that they were alone.

'What did your friends say?' she asked him.

Guy's mouth twisted. 'Let's just say that they wanted to know more than I was prepared to tell them.'

She dreaded having to ask, but she needed to know. 'And is Jenna your...your...girlfriend?'

He stared at her in disbelief. 'You really think I'd invite another woman to stay with me, without telling her, if she was?'

'I don't know, do I? That's exactly why I'm asking!'

The challenging look was replaced by one of faint irritation. 'I tend to go for a little more communication in my relationships than that,' he said coldly.

'So you don't have one at the moment?'

'One what, princess?' he mocked.

Suddenly she was aware that they were in a bedroom, and that the space between them yawned like a great, gaping chasm. It was the antithesis of the eager way they had fallen into each other's arms back in Venice... No. She wasn't going to put herself through that kind of torture.

'Relationship,' she said doggedly.

God, but she was persistent! 'No, Sabrina,' he said deliberately. 'I do not have a relationship at the moment.'

She realised then that there was something else she needed to know, something which she really ought to have established before she'd come here.

'And won't I...' she lifted her face to his '...cramp your style?'

He looked down at her, momentarily disorientated by that fierce little look of pride. He frowned. 'What are you talking about?'

Her heart was in her mouth as she said it, but she managed to keep her voice steady. 'Well, if you haven't got a relationship, then presumably you're in the market for one—'

'Why, is that an offer?' he questioned silkily, but the surge of blood to his loins made him wish he could take the question back again.

'It most certainly is not!'

'Pity. Actually, I'm *not* ''in the market'' for a relationship, as you so delightfully put it.'

Was that a note of warning colouring his tone? A polite but efficient way of telling her not to start concocting any little fantasies of her own?

'You might meet someone else,' Sabrina rushed on. 'And prospective girlfriends might be put off by the presence of another woman. Particularly one with whom…whom…'

'With whom I've already had a relationship?' he challenged coolly.

She felt oddly defiant. 'Do you really think that what we had could be called a relationship, Guy?'

'Well, how would *you* like to describe it?' he mused.

As the most wonderful night of her life, that was how *she* would describe it, but tell Guy that and she would see his gorgeous face freeze with fastidious horror. Men judged events differently. A little light passion. No, scrub that. Very heavy passion.

'Things just got out of hand,' she said, trying not to think about the way he'd smiled a secret kind of smile as he'd bent his dark head to kiss her. 'That's all.

As a blow to his sexual pride, it was quite the most exquisite thrust, and Guy very nearly smiled. But not quite. 'They sure did,' he agreed in a sultry murmur, watching with dark interest as the nipples of her tiny breasts sprang into glorious life beneath the sweater she wore. Almost as if they were reaching out to touch him.

He leaned over the bed and scooped up an armful of ski

clothes. 'I'll pack these away,' he groaned. 'And then I'll think about throwing together some supper.'

Guy's idea of 'throwing together some supper' was not what Sabrina understood by the term. For a start, the contents of his fridge could have kept the most dedicated hedonist going for at least a week. Sabrina could see fancy chocolates, champagne and enough different cheeses to stock a delicatessen.

'Do you like smoked salmon?' he asked.

'Er, love it.'

He looked up at her, and frowned. 'Well, do you or don't you?'

'I said yes, didn't I?'

'You sounded unsure.' He gave a little click of irritation. 'Look, Sabrina, let's just get a couple of things straight, shall we? I don't want you agreeing with me for the sake of it—just because it's my flat.'

'OK,' she agreed. 'And while we're on the subject of house rules—'

'Rules?' he interrupted, with a sardonic elevation of his dark brows. 'Goodness me, how very schoolmistressy of you! Are we talking firm and unbending rules, I wonder, or very, very *flexible* ones?'

Sabrina felt a mixture of fury and frustration as she stared into eyes which mocked her. He could stop that right now! 'Oh, do, please, spare me the innuendo!' she snapped.

Guy gave a reluctant smile. Had he actually been worried that all the fire had gone out of her? Not all of it, no. 'OK,' he said slowly.

'I meant rules about things like paying you rent—'

'The rent doesn't matter.'

'It *does* matter,' said Sabrina stubbornly. 'I can't stay here for nothing—and before you tell me that you can afford it—'

'You know very well I can—'

'That's not the point.'

'Then just what is the point?' said Guy steadily, hooking his thumbs into the waistband of his jeans.

The movement distracted her, and suddenly she found his proximity disburbing. More than disturbing. Had she really thought that she would just be able to ignore that blatant sex appeal? 'I'd just like to make a contribution while I'm here.'

Their eyes met.

'Oh?' questioned Guy softly.

She saw the swift darkening of his eyes. 'I'll contribute food,' she told him shakily.

'Food?' Guy queried dazedly.

'Towards the running of the household,' she elaborated.

'Yeah,' he agreed distractedly. 'Whatever you say, Sabrina.'

CHAPTER NINE

SABRINA was woken by a banging on the door, and her eyes flickered open for a few dazed moments before reality clicked in from unconsciousness. Her gaze drifted upwards. A high ceiling. A beautiful flat. Guy's flat.

'Sab*rina*!'

Guy's voice!

'What is it?' she answered groggily.

'Are you awake?'

'I am now.' She yawned and picked up her wristwatch, which was lying on the locker. Six-thirty? What time did he call this? She had never been the best early morning person in the world. Still in the warm haze of sleep, she felt too lazy to be inhibited.

'Why have you woken me up?' She yawned again.

'I wondered why you weren't up. Did you set your alarm? We don't want you to be late on your first day, now, do we, Sabrina?'

That teasing little lilt set her senses fizzing. 'Of course I set my alarm! I don't have to be at work until nine!'

'That late?' he drawled. 'I'll have been at my desk for at least two hours by then.'

'I'll have a medal minted for you, Guy!'

He sounded amused. 'I'm just off now—you'd better come out while I show you how the security system works.'

Sabrina was out of bed and pulling a face at her tousled reflection in an instant. She raked a brush through the unruly locks, pulled on her dressing gown and opened the door.

He was wearing the most beautiful dark pinstriped suit

with a matching waistcoat and pure silk tie. The snowy shirt emphasised the blackness of his hair, the faint tan of his skin and the almost indecent length of his legs.

Sabrina couldn't stop her heart from racing at just the sight of him—but it was with pure delight rather than desire, as if seeing Guy in the morning was the most perfect way to start a day. Even though her fingers flew automatically to her chest to clutch together the gaping blue satin of the robe.

Guy didn't miss the movement, nor the tantalising glimpse of pale breast it obscured. He swallowed. 'Let me show you how to set the alarm.'

'Right.' Sabrina tried to listen carefully to what he was saying, but it wasn't easy. It seemed bizarre, crazy, stupid—*tantalising*—for her to be standing half-naked beside him, concentrating fiercely on which numbers his fingers were punching out on the alarm system and not on the delicious lemon and musk scent which drifted from his skin.

'Now, this key,' he told her, deliberately leaning a little bit away from her, because it was more than distracting being this close to the butting little swell of her breasts as they jutted against the slippery satin of her robe, 'is for this lock here. The longer, thicker key…' Oh, God, he thought despairingly, what was she *doing* to him? 'That locks here.' He swallowed. 'Got that?'

'Could you show me again?' She had hardly heard a thing he was saying, and she wished he would just go. But the last thing she needed was for all his expensive paintings and books and furniture to suddenly 'walk'—just because she hadn't had the sense to lock up properly.

'Do you want me to write it down for you, step by step?' he questioned sarcastically.

'That won't be necessary!'

This time she listened as if her life depended on it.

'Understand now?'

'Perfectly, thank you very much.'

He shot a glance at his watch and gave a small click of irritation. 'You've made me late now. I haven't been late in years.'

'Well, you could have shown me all this last night, couldn't you?'

Yeah, he supposed he could have done—it was just that they had opened a bottle of wine during dinner and had then sat and finished it in the sitting room. Bad idea. And Sabrina had kicked her shoes off in front of the fire, perfectly innocuously, but Guy had been riveted by the sight of those spectacularly slender ankles and had found it difficult to tear his eyes away from them. He had never quite understood why the Victorians had considered the ankle such an erogenous zone, but last night the reason had suddenly hit him in a moment of pulse-hammering insight.

He usually did paperwork on Sunday evenings, but last night it had lain neglected. And now he was late.

He glowered. 'I'll be home around seven.'

She looked at him expectantly. 'Will you be eating supper? Or going out?'

He had said that he would meet up for a drink with Philip Caprice—the man who was now working for Prince Raschid—but he couldn't really leave her alone on her first full day in London, could he?

He sighed. 'No, I won't be going out.'

'Then—' she suddenly felt ridiculously and utterly *shy* '—maybe I could cook *you* supper tonight. I'll buy the food and everything—as I said, that can be my contribution towards my upkeep.'

He hid a smile, unwillingly admiring her persistence, as well as her independence. 'OK,' he agreed gravely. He suspected that she would conjure up some bland but rather noble concoction of pulses or brown rice or something. He repressed a shudder. 'I shall look forward to it.'

After her shower, Sabrina went back to her room to get dressed. At least now it looked slightly better than when she had first arrived. Guy had cleared away the clutter on the desk, and had pushed the filing cabinets back against the wall. The exercise bike had been moved from its inconvenient position located slap-bang in the middle of the room. It could do with some decent curtains, she decided suddenly, instead of those rather stark blinds.

She shook her head at herself in the mirror. She was here on a purely temporary basis—she certainly shouldn't start thinking major redecoration schemes!

She dressed in black trousers and a warm black sweater and took the tube to where the London branch of Wells was situated, close to St Paul's Cathedral.

It was an exquisite jewel of a Georgian building, set in the shadow of the mighty church. Sabrina had been there twice while negotiating her transfer and had met the man she would be working for.

Tim Reardon was the archetypal bookshop owner—tall, lean and lanky, with a fall of shiny straight hair which flopped into his eyes most of the time. He was vague, affable, quietly spoken and charmingly polite. He was single, attractive—and the very antithesis of Guy Masters.

And Sabrina could not have gone out with him if he had been the very last man on the planet.

'Come on in, Sabrina.' Tim held his hand out and gave her a friendly smile. 'I'll make us both coffee and then I'll show you the set-up.'

'Thanks.' She smiled and began to unbutton her coat.

'Where are you staying?' he asked, as he hung her coat up for her.

It still made her feel slightly awkward to acknowledge it. 'In Knightsbridge, actually.'

'*Knightsbridge?*' Tom gave her a curious look which clearly wondered how she could afford to live in such an expensive neighbourhood on her modest earnings.

'I'm staying with a...friend,' she elaborated awkwardly.

'Lucky you,' he said lightly, but to her relief, he didn't pursue it.

It was easy to slot in. The shop virtually mirrored its Salisbury counterpart, and after she and Tim had drunk their coffee they set to work, opening the post and filing away all the ordered books which had just come in.

The shop was quiet first thing in the morning, and it wasn't until just after eleven that the first Cathedral tourists began to drift in, looking for their copies of William Shakespeare and Jane Austen.

During her lunch-hour Sabrina managed to locate a supermarket and rushed round buying ingredients. Never had choosing the right thing proved as taxing. She wanted, she realised, to impress Guy.

When he arrived back home that evening, he walked in on an unfamiliar domestic scene, with smells of cooking wafting towards him and loud music blaring from the kitchen.

He moved through the flat in the direction of the noise, pausing first at the dining-room door, where the table had been very carefully laid for dinner for two.

And when he walked into the kitchen, Sabrina didn't notice that he was there, not at first. She was picking up something from the floor, her black trousers stretched tightly over the high curve of her bottom, and Guy felt his throat thicken.

'Hello, Sabrina.'

Half a lemon slid uselessly from her fingers back to the floor as she heard the soft, rich timbre of his voice. She turned round slowly, trying to compose herself, to see him still wearing the beautiful dark suit, the slight shadowing around his chin the only outward sign that twelve hours had elapsed since she had last seen him. Oh, sweet Lord, she thought despairingly. He is *gorgeous*.

'Hi!' she said brightly. 'Good day at—'

'The office?' he put in curtly. 'Yes, fine, thanks.'

'Shall I fix you a drink? Or would you prefer to get changed first?'

His mouth tightened. 'Any minute now and you're going to offer to bring me my pipe and slippers.'

Sabrina stiffened as she heard his sarcastic tone. 'I was only trying to be friendly—'

'As opposed to coming over as a parody of a wife, you mean?'

'That was certainly not my intention,' she told him primly.

The glittering grey gaze moved around the room to see that his rather cold and clinical kitchen had suddenly come to life. 'This looks quite some feast,' he observed softly.

'Not really.' But she blushed with pleasure. 'And if you're planning to get out of your best suit, could you, please, do it now, Guy? Because dinner will be ready in precisely five minutes.'

Neglected work. Late. And now she was telling him to get changed!

Guy opened his mouth to object and then shut it again. What was the point? And she was right—he didn't want to eat in his 'best' suit, which was actually one of twenty-eight he had hanging neatly in his wardrobe. He sighed. 'Five minutes,' he echoed.

He took slightly longer than five minutes, simply because, to his intense exasperation, he realised that she had managed to turn him on. Had that been her bossiness or her presumption? he wondered achingly as he threw cold water onto his face like a man who had been burning up in the sun all day. Or maybe it had something to do with the fact that he hadn't been with a woman since that amazing night with Sabrina in Venice. Hadn't wanted to. Still didn't want anyone. Except her.

Now, that, he thought, was worrying.

The meal began badly, with Guy frowning at the heap of prawns with mayonnaise which Sabrina had heaped on a plate.

'You don't like prawns?' she asked him nervously.

'Yeah, I love them, but you really shouldn't have gone to all this trouble.'

'Oh, it was no trouble,' she lied, thinking about the beef Wellington which was currently puffing up nicely in the oven. 'Do you want to open the wine? I bought a bottle.'

He shook his head, remembering last night, the way it had loosened him up so that he had spent a heated night tossing and turning and wondering what she would do if he walked just along the corridor and silently slipped into bed beside her. 'Not for me thanks,' he answered repressively. 'You can have some, of course.'

'I'm fine, thanks.' As if she would sit there drinking her way through a bottle of wine while he looked down that haughty and patrician nose of his.

Guy saw the beef Wellington being carried in on an ornate silver platter he'd forgotten he had and which she must have fished out from somewhere.

'Sabrina,' he groaned.

Her fingers tightened on the knife. 'Don't tell me you don't like beef Wellington,' she said, the slight note of desperation making her voice sound edgy.

'Who in their right mind wouldn't?' He sighed. 'It's just that you must have spent a fortune on this meal—'

'It was supposed to be a way of saying thank you—'

'And I've told you before not to thank me!' he said savagely, feeling the sweet, inconvenient rush of desire as her lips trembled in rebuke at him. 'Look, Sabrina, I don't expect you earn very much, working in a bookshop—'

'Certainly nowhere in your league, Guy,' she retorted.

'And I don't want you spending it all on fancy food!'

'I'm not here to accept charity—especially not yours!'

'Sabrina—'

'No, Guy,' she said stubbornly. 'I want to pay my way as much as possible.'

He took the slice she offered him and he stared down at it with grudging reluctance. Pink and perfect. So she could cook, too. He scowled. 'Do that,' he clipped out. 'But this is the last time you buy me steak! Understood?'

That was enough to guarantee the complete loss of her appetite, and it was only pride which made Sabrina eat every single thing on her plate. But by the time they were drinking their coffee his forbidding expression seemed to have thawed a little.

'That was delicious,' he said.

'The pleasure was all mine.'

He heard the sarcasm in her voice, saw the little pout of accusation which hovered on her lips. Maybe he *had* been a little hard on her. 'I'm not used to sharing,' he shrugged.

'It shows.' She risked a question, even if the dark face didn't look particularly forthcoming. 'Have you got any brothers and sisters?'

'One brother; he's younger.'

'And where is he now?'

He sighed as he saw her patient look of interest. These heart-to-heart chats had never really been part of his scene. 'He lives in Paris—he works for a newspaper.'

'That sounds interesting.'

He blanked the conversation with a bland smile. 'Does it?'

But Sabrina wasn't giving up that easily. What were they *supposed* to talk about, night after night—the *weather*?

'So, no live-in girlfriends?' she asked.

The eyes glittered. 'Nope.'

'Oh.' She digested this.

'You sound surprised,' he observed.

'I am, a little.'

'You see me as so devastatingly eligible, do you, Sabrina?'

Her smile stayed as enigmatic as his. 'That's a fairly egotistical conclusion to jump to, Guy—that wasn't what I said at all. I just thought that a man in your position would yearn for all the comforts of having a resident girlfriend.'

'You mean regular meals.' His eyes fell to his empty plate. 'And regular sex?'

Sabrina went scarlet. 'Something like that.'

'The comfort and ease of the shared bed?' he mused. 'It's tempting, I give you that. But sex is the easy bit—it's communication that causes all the problems. Or rather the lack of it.' His voice grew hard, almost bitter.

Sabrina looked at him and wondered what he wasn't telling her. 'You mean you've never found anyone you could communicate with?'

'Something like that.' No one he'd ever really *wanted* to communicate with. 'Or at least, not unless we both happened to be horizontal at the time.' He looked at her thoughtfully as she blushed. 'But I have a very low boredom threshold, princess,' he added softly.

He was telling her not to come too close—it was as plain as the day itself. And it was the most arrogant warning she had ever heard. 'More coffee?' she asked him coolly.

CHAPTER TEN

'So how has your first week been?'

Guy looked across the sitting room to where Sabrina was curled up like a kitten with a book on her lap—she was always *reading*, though he noticed that not many pages had been turned in the past hour. Snap, he thought with a grim kind of satisfaction. He hadn't made many inroads into his *own* reading.

Sabrina met the piercing grey gaze and repressed a guilty kind of longing. How could she possibly concentrate on her book when she had such a distraction sitting just across the room from her?

'I've enjoyed it,' she told him truthfully. Well, most of it, anyway. It wasn't easy being around him, being plagued by memories of a time it was clear that both of them wished forgotten—but at least she had done her utmost not to show it. She forced a smile. 'How do you rate me as a flatmate?'

Guy thought about it. She was certainly less intrusive than he would have imagined. She kept out of his way in the mornings. She didn't drift around the place in bits of provocative clothing—and she didn't leave panties and tights draped over the radiator, which he understood was one of the major irritations when sharing with a woman.

'Seven out of ten,' he drawled, his smile not quite easy. 'And how's the bookshop surviving with its newest member of staff?'

Sabrina wished he wouldn't stretch his legs out like that. 'The shop is f-fine,' she stumbled. 'In fact, it's very similar to the Salisbury branch—'

'So living in the big city doesn't scare you, Miss

Cooper?' he mocked softly, cutting right through her stumbled reply.

'I don't scare easy,' she said, raising a glittering blue gaze, and thinking that it was all too easy to be scared. Scared of her susceptibility to Guy Masters—especially when he looked at her like *that*. Scared of what might happen if he should happen to lazily make a pass at her—because surely *most* men who had already slept with a woman *would* make a pass. Even if they'd said that they wouldn't.

But Guy, of course, hadn't.

In fact, he'd spent the last five evenings behaving as though he had a piece of radioactive equipment in the room with him—keeping a wary and observant distance and occasionally glancing her a look from beneath those sensationally long black lashes. But tonight he seemed edgy.

'Do you want to go out for a drink before supper?' he asked suddenly.

Sabrina snapped her book shut with nervous fingers. 'What, now, tonight?'

He shrugged. 'It's Friday night—it's what people do.'

Anything would be better than having to spend another whole evening watching while she managed to turn reading a book into a very erotic art form indeed. It was all getting a little too cosy for comfort. And Guy had found that leafing through art-world journals had lost most of its allure when he had the infinitely more distracting vision of Sabrina flicking that bright red-gold hair back over her slim shoulders.

But it was a challenge he had set himself and Guy thrived on challenges. He was determined to resist her—and resist her he damned well would. Unwittingly he had taken advantage of her once before, but once had been enough. 'How about it?' he asked.

She thought about the fine wines he had crowding the

vast rack in the dining room. Maybe he wanted to go out because he was bored, just sitting here alone with her night after night. And it was just politeness which had made him invite her to go with him.

'You go out if you like,' she offered. 'I'll stay in. You don't have to have me tagging along with you.'

'You can't sit in here all on your own,' he objected.

She forced a smile. It would do her good. After five evenings she was beginning to enjoy his company a little *too* much. 'Go on! You go, Guy—I'll be fine here. I'll probably have an early night.'

Guy felt an infuriating urge to stay home, yet he hadn't been out a single night this week—and this from the man who was the original party animal. 'Sure?' he asked reluctantly.

'Who else is going?'

'Tom is, and a couple of guys who work with him. Oh, and I expect that Trudi and Jenna might turn up.'

Jenna. Sabrina's smile didn't slip. 'I think I'll pass, if you don't mind. Honestly, Guy, I'm tired.'

Guy rose to his feet, strangely reluctant to move. 'Maybe we should go out for dinner some time?'

She felt a little stab of pleasure, until she reminded herself that it wasn't a date. He was simply making sure that she wasn't bored.

'Dinner?' she asked casually.

'Yeah. There are a couple of clients I need to take out— you might as well come with me.'

'Oh. Right,' she said, her heart sinking despite her intention not to let it. No, it definitely *wasn't* a date—he couldn't have phrased it more unflatteringly if he'd tried. The token female at a client dinner!

He paused by the door and shot her a quick glance. 'Any plans for tomorrow?'

'Not really. I'm working. I work every third Saturday.'

He nodded. 'Me, too. Well, actually, I work *most* Saturdays.'

Sabrina stared at him. 'Why?'

He frowned. 'Why what?'

'Why do you work on Saturdays?' She gave him a slightly waspish smile. He left at the crack of dawn each morning and didn't put in an appearance until at least eight o'clock. Even after five days she had decided that he drove himself too hard. 'You do happen to *own* the company, don't you, Guy?'

'Yes, I do, and I like to make sure that I stay one step ahead of my competitors,' he retorted softly. 'And the only way to do that is to work hard. Number-one lesson in life. Build yourself so high that no one can knock you down. Ever.'

She lifted her eyebrows. He sounded almost *ruthless*. 'Try to be invincible, you mean?'

There was an unmistakable flicker of tension around his mouth. 'It's an achievable goal,' he answered, in a voice which was suddenly harsh.

She was tempted to tell him that he was already top of the heap. And that it didn't look as if anyone was going to knock him anywhere, least of all down, but there was a distinctly warning glitter hardening his slate-grey eyes.

She thought of him as polished and sophisticated, a man who had everything, with his dark good looks and his enormous flat and wealthy lifestyle—and that wasn't even taking into account his consummate skill as a lover. Yet something just now had frozen his face into granite. Had made him look almost savage. Was Guy Masters a man of never-ending ambition—and, if so, then why, when he seemed to have more than most men could only dream of?

'What's so good about being invincible?' she queried softly.

Guy's face tightened. Because it was the opposite of how

his father had operated, with his easy come, easy go attitude to life and all the devastation that attitude had brought in its wake. But he had never shared that devastation with any woman and he wasn't about to start now. Even with Sabrina Cooper and her warm, trusting smile and tantalising blue eyes which the devil himself must have given her.

'It all comes down to personal choice,' he said coldly. 'And that's mine.'

Sabrina could recognise a brush-off when she heard one—and more than a reluctance to open up. From the daunting expression in those dark, stormy eyes, it was more like a *refusal* to talk.

Tactically, she retreated.

'Have a nice time,' she said placidly. 'I think I'll have a bath and that early night.'

Guy had to stifle a groan as some of the tension he'd been feeling was replaced by a new and different kind of tension. Images of her long, pale limbs submerged beneath the foaming bubbles of his bathtub crept tantalisingly into his mind as his photographic memory recalled them with breathtaking accuracy. Did she really need to share something like *that* with him?

'Yeah,' he clipped out. 'Do that.'

'Shall I leave you some supper?' she asked. 'I thought I'd make some risotto—I got some amazing oyster mushrooms cheap at the market.'

Guy scowled. Just five days and she seemed to have taken over most of the cooking and most of the shopping—and she insisted on shopping around to save him money—*even when he'd told her that she didn't need to.* With her, it seemed pride as much as parsimony—and she could be so damned *stubborn.*

'You don't have to cook for me every night,' he said shortly. 'I told you that.'

'But it's no trouble if I'm cooking for myself—'

'I'm perfectly capable of fixing myself some eggs when I get home!' Guy snapped, and turned and walked out of the room, because that hurt little tremble of her mouth was enough to crumble a heart of stone.

Sabrina could hear him slamming around in his room; then the telephone began to ring. She waited to see whether Guy would answer it, but it carried on ringing and so she picked it up.

'Hello?'

There was a pause, and then a rather flustered-sounding woman's voice said, 'I'm sorry—I think I must have got the wrong number.'

'Who did you want to speak to?' enquired Sabrina patiently.

'Guy Masters. My son.'

'Your *son*? Oh, I'm sorry, Mrs Masters, I didn't realise— I'll just get him for you.'

'No, no, wait a minute—just who might *you* be?'

Sabrina cleared her throat. 'I'm Sabrina,' she said. 'Sabrina Cooper.' And then, because the voice seemed to be waiting for some kind of clarification, she added, 'I'm staying here. With Guy.'

'*Are* you now?' enquired the voice interestedly.

'Er, just a minute, I'll get him for you,' said Sabrina hastily, but when she looked up it was to find Guy standing in the doorway, his face a dark and daunting study.

Wordlessly, he came and took the phone from her, and Sabrina quickly left the room, but not before she heard his first responses.

'Hi, Ma. Mmm. Mmm. No, no. No—nothing like that.'

A few minutes later, he came and found her in the kitchen, chopping up her mushrooms.

'Don't do that again!' he warned.

She put the knife down. 'Do what?'

'Answer my phone—especially when I'm *around*.'

'I'm sorry,' she said stiffly. 'I didn't realise I was breaking some unwritten rule, but of course it *is* your flat.' His
flat, his territory, his control.

But he didn't appear to be listening. 'And now my
mother's asking me eight hundred questions about you.
Move a woman in and suddenly everyone's thinking rice
and confetti!'

'Well, I can assure you that I'm not,' she told him acidly.

'Me, neither!' he snapped.

She turned her back on him and heard him go out, slamming the door behind him, and she viciously decapitated a
mushroom. He was bad-tempered and unreasonable, she
told herself. And she must have been crazy to agree to
come here.

Guy walked into the Kensington wine-bar where his friends
had been congregating on Friday evenings for as long as
he could remember, surveying the dimly lit and crowded
room with an unenthusiastic eye. He asked himself why he
had bothered to come out to fight his way to the bar for a
glass of champagne when he could have drunk something
colder and vastly superior at home. And maybe given
Sabrina a glass, too.

He shook his head. What the hell was he thinking of?
He *always* went out on a Friday night!

'Guy!' called Tom Roberts, from the other side of the
room, and Guy forced himself to smile in response as he
wove his way through the crowded room.

'It's obviously been a bad day!' joked his cousin, as Guy
joined him.

'On the contrary.' Guy took the proffered glass of champagne and gave it a thoughtful sip. 'I think I may have
negotiated a deal on that old schoolhouse over by the river.
It's going to make someone a wonderful home.'

'So why the long face?' teased Tom.

'I guess I'm just tired,' said Guy, and that much was true. Sleep didn't come easily when all you could think about was moon-pale flesh and banner-bright hair and a naked body in the room just along the corridor.

Tom topped up his glass. 'So how's the new flatmate working out?' he asked casually.

Guy could recognise a leading question when he heard one. 'Sabrina?' he stalled, equally casually.

Tom smiled. 'Unless you've moved another one in.'

'I must have needed my head examined!' groaned Guy.

'That bad, is it?' Tom threw him a sympathetic glance. 'She seemed sweet.'

'Yeah, she is.' Too damned sweet. Sweet as honey. That night in his bed—all clinging and sticky like honey. A honey *trap*, he thought with a sudden heat, and drained his glass in one. 'Where's Trudi tonight?' he asked.

'She's on a sales conference in Brussels,' explained Tom. 'She's not coming back until tomorrow.'

Guy nodded. Good. Good. 'Fancy going out for a meal in a while?' he asked.

'Oh!' Tom started grinning. 'Diversionary tactics to keep you out of the flat, you mean?'

'I don't know what you're talking about.' Guy shrugged.

'Oh, we've all been there, mate,' said Tom obscurely. 'There's bound to be a woman sooner or later who gets underneath your skin. It's about time it happened to you!'

'Sorry.' Guy's voice was cool but firm. 'You've lost me.'

Tom put his glass down and narrowed his eyes. 'And you still haven't told me anything about Sabrina Cooper...'

'What do you want to know?'

'The obvious. Like, is she a friend, or is she a lover?'

Guy opened his mouth and then shut it again. What was the point in trying to explain the whole bizarre situation, even to a man who had known him nearly all his life?

Sabrina's reputation wouldn't emerge from it unscathed. And neither, he realised grimly, would his own.

'We're men, Tom,' he said flippantly, 'so we never talk about things like that, right?'

In Guy's high-tech kitchen, Sabrina unenthusiastically cooked her risotto, and then picked at it without interest. She had made plenty. Enough for two...just in case. But Guy still wasn't back. Should she pop the rest into the fridge and cover it with clingfilm? Or would Guy go mad if she did that? Probably. He'd blanched with horror when she'd suggested frying up some leftover potato for breakfast.

After supper she forced herself to relax in a long, deep bath, and when she came out she looked at the clock to see that it was getting on for ten. So, his 'quick' drink was taking longer than he'd anticipated.

She put her bedroom light out and tried to sleep, but sleep infuriatingly refused to protect her with its mantle of oblivion. In the end she gave up trying and snapped on the light and tried reading her book.

'Tried' being the operative word. The words danced like tiny black beetles in front of her and all she could think about was that it was now nearly midnight and all the bars would be closed.

And Guy still wasn't back.

She pulled on her dressing gown and went to pace up and down the sitting room.

By twelve she was getting frantic, and by one she was just about to pick up the phone and call the hospital when she heard the sound of a key being turned in the lock. She flew out into the hall to find Guy with his back to her, shutting the door with exaggerated care and hanging up his overcoat with the other hand.

Sabrina didn't even stop to think about it. She just blazed

right in there. 'Where the hell have you *been*?' she demanded.

He turned round, the grey eyes narrowing to cold chips of slate as he saw Sabrina in her satin dressing gown, her tiny breasts heaving, a look of complete fury on her face. 'I *beg* your pardon?'

That frosty little question should have been enough to stop her in her tracks, and normally it would have done, but, then, this didn't feel normal. None of it did. Surely 'normal' would have meant a complete numbing of her senses until she was properly over Michael?

'You told me you were going out for a quick drink!' she stormed, her breathing coming through in great ragged bursts.

Guy felt torn between incredulty and irritation. 'And?'

'And it *wasn't*, was it? Not quick at all. It's way past midnight—what *time* do you call this?'

'It's none of your damned business what time it is!' he roared. 'I'll live my own life, the way I always have done! I'll go out *when* I want and *where* I want and with *whom* I want—and I'll do it *without* your permission, thank you, princess!'

Through her shuddering breaths Sabrina stared at him, realising just how preposterous she must have sounded. And realising that if she didn't get away from him pretty quickly, she risked making even more of a fool of herself.

'I'm sorry,' she said tightly. 'I spoke out of turn.' She half ran along the corridor and into her room and then pressed her forehead to the door, her eyes closed, her breath still shuddering.

He'd seen the awful whitening of her face and the brief glimpse of terror which had iced the blue of her eyes, and in an instant he'd begun to comprehend just what had motivated her reaction.

'Damn!' he swore softly. Swiftly following in her footsteps, he went and banged his fist on the door. 'Oh, damn!'

Behind the door, Sabrina froze. Just keep quiet, some instinct of preservation told her. Keep very quiet and just don't answer and he might go away.

'Sabrina! Open the damned door. We both know you can't possibly be asleep.'

She shook her head. 'Go away.'

'I'm not moving from this spot until you open the door and come out and talk to me. That way neither of us will get to sleep and that means we'll both be bad-tempered at work tomorrow.'

You and your precious *work*, thought Sabrina, trying to concentrate on something—*anything*—other than how she wanted to open the door and fall into his arms, and…and…

'Alternatively, I could kick it down,' he promised in a voice of silky intent.

It was such an outrageous proposal that Sabrina very nearly smiled. 'You wouldn't do that,' she sniffed.

'Not unless you make me,' he agreed mockingly. 'So, are you going to open the door now? Or not?'

Slowly, she complied, her fingers clutching onto the handle as if they were petrified, gearing herself up to withstand Guy's fury at her presumptuous behaviour. But when she dared to look up into his face it was to see a look of bitter regret written there, and Sabrina felt the trembling approach of tears. If she weren't careful, she was in terrible danger of exposing all her desperate insecurities to him.

'I'm s-sorry,' she said shakily. 'I had no right—'

'No.' He shook his head. 'I'm sorry. It was the most stupid and insensitive thing to do and, oh, God, Sabrina…' His voice deepened to a caress as he saw her face crumple. 'Princess, don't cry. Please, don't cry.'

'I'm n-not c-crying,' she sobbed quietly, trying simultaneously to push him out of the room and close the door after him, and failing miserably to do either.

Saying something that she couldn't quite make out, Guy just grabbed her by the hand and steered her into the sitting room.

'What do you think you're doing?' she spluttered.

'What does it look like? I'm taking you somewhere where we can talk.' Somewhere that didn't involve a bed. 'I'm damned if I'm going to have you fainting on me for a second time!'

'I'm not going to faint. I want to go to bed,' she said plaintively.

'Well, we need to talk,' he said grimly. 'Or, rather, *you* need to talk, princess.'

He pushed her down very gently on the sofa and covered her with a cashmere throw, which was as light as a feather and as warm as toast.

'That's nice,' she said automatically.

It was also vital, in his opinion, that she cover up. If he wanted to talk to her—or, rather, have her talk to *him*— then he needed to concentrate. And it would be damned nigh impossible trying to concentrate on anything—other than an urgent need to possess her—when that silky robe was clinging like honey to the sweet swell of her limbs and moulding the perfect outline of her tiny breasts.

He sat down next to her and stared into the pale heart of her face. 'It was thoughtless of me. I should have telephoned—told you I was going to be late.'

'It doesn't matter.' She shook her head. 'I had no right to expect—'

'You had every right to expect consideration,' he refuted heatedly. 'And at least a *modicum* of understanding.' There was a grim kind of pause and his grey eyes glittered with self-recrimination. 'And I showed you neither.' He had deliberately stayed out tonight—and he still wasn't sure why—without thinking through the consequences of his actions. 'Neither,' he finished bitterly.

'It doesn't matter,' she repeated, and even managed to raise her shoulders in a shrug, as if it really *didn't* matter, but he shook his head like a man who was onto something and wouldn't give up.

'Why don't you tell me,' he said slowly, 'about the night Michael died? Is that what happened? Were you waiting for him and he never came?'

Something in the burning intensity of his eyes pierced right through the barriers she'd built around herself. She'd pushed the memories of that night to the far recesses of her mind. Deliberately. It had been a defence mechanism to shield her from the bitter pain, and the guilt. She'd refused counsellors and her mother's faltering requests that she open up and talk to someone.

But something in Guy's face completely disarmed her, and her words of defiance and denial died on her lips.

'OK, I'll tell.' She nodded her head slowly. 'I'll tell you everything.' There was a pause while she struggled to find the right words. 'Like I said, Michael wanted to go out that night and I didn't, and it was more than about the fact we couldn't afford it. It was a filthy night. The weather was awful…snow and ice.'

She took a slow, shuddering breath and stared at him as she forced herself to face up to the truth for the first time. 'Just awful. I said that it wasn't a good night to be out driving…but he wouldn't listen… He just wouldn't *listen*!'

Guy nodded as the strands of her story began to be woven together, beginning to make some sense of her guilt.

'I told him to be sure and ring me when he got to the pub, only the phone call didn't come, and I wasn't sure if he was sulking because he was angry with me…and…'

'And?' His voice was soft. Too soft. How could you resist a voice that soft?

'And when I rang the pub...' Sabrina bit her lip '...they said they hadn't seen him. So I thought he must have changed his mind about going there, never dreaming...never dreaming—'

'Never dreaming that the inconceivable had happened,' he said carefully, 'and that he'd never be coming back again?'

His words were edged with anger, and an emotion it took her a moment or two to recognise. Pain. 'That's right,' she agreed slowly.

'So you think that you should have stopped him from driving that night?'

'Of course I should have stopped him!' she shot back bitterly, but Guy shook his dark head.

'Don't you know that we can't govern other people's lives?' he demanded quietly. 'Or decide their destiny. You could have stopped him from going, but how do you know that he wouldn't have been hit by a bus on his way to work the next day? Maybe,' he added, with slow deliberation, 'maybe it was just his time.'

Her lips froze. 'His time?'

'To die.' His mouth hardened.

'Fate,' she elaborated painfully. 'That's fate.'

'Yeah, fate.'

She stared straight into the burning silver gaze, dazzled by it. 'You honestly believe that?' she whispered, and he gave a hollow kind of laugh.

'Sometimes it's easier to think of it that way.' He shrugged. 'Easier for the living to let go and carry on. And you have to let go, Sabrina, you *have* to—you must realise that. Don't you?'

'But I feel so guilty!'

'Because he's dead and you're alive?'

His perception took her breath away. 'Yes.'

He gave a brittle smile. 'But nothing can change that,

Sabrina. Nothing can bring him back. You owe it to your-self to let go. And to Michael.'

'Yes.' She sighed with a kind of surrender made all the easier by that luminous look of understanding. 'Yes.'

He watched as the thready breath made her lips tremble, he saw her wide-eyed look of trust, and he knew what she wanted and needed more than anything else at the moment. Pure animal comfort. Even if doing it would half kill him.

He drew her into the circle of his arms and hugged her tightly against his chest, the wetness of her tears warming his skin through his shirt. Her breasts were soft and pointed and her hair was full of the scent of lilac, and it took every bit of his self-control to dampen down his instinctive desire as he smoothed the bright strands down with a distracted hand.

'It's going to be OK,' he muttered, and prayed for his body not to react to her proximity. 'I promise you.'

Through her tears it occurred to Sabrina that his kindness and understanding were just two more facets of a complex personality which perplexed and intrigued her more with each day that passed. And that simply wasn't on the agenda. Her stay here was only temporary, she reminded herself as more tears spilled onto his shirt.

Guy let her cry until her sobs became dry and shudder-ing, and then he went and made her some hot chocolate, sitting in front of her like a determined nurse while she drank it.

He thought how unselfconsciously provocative her movements were. Thought that she shouldn't look that sexy with eyes bright red from crying and hair which was matted by those tears. But sexy she looked. Extremely sexy.

'So.' He sat back on his heels. 'Are you going to let it go now, Sabrina?'

She couldn't have said no, even if she'd wanted to, not

with that silver gaze compelling her to start living her life again. 'Yes,' she said slowly. 'I am.'

'Good.' He smiled. 'And are you going to let me take you out for dinner next week?'

She forced herself to remember that the question wasn't as warmly intimate as it sounded. 'Sure,' she said lightly. 'Is this the client dinner?'

'That's right,' he agreed. 'I have a Middle-Eastern potentate I've just bought a picture for. How would you like to have dinner with Prince Khalim?'

'*Prince* Khalim?' She gulped. 'Just how many princes do you know, Guy?'

He smiled. 'Khalim is my oldest friend. I've known him since schooldays—it was through him I got most of my contacts.'

'But, Guy—'

'Don't worry about it,' he soothed. 'You'll like him—a little old-fashioned perhaps, but he's a nice guy.'

CHAPTER ELEVEN

FOR the next week, Sabrina was in a complete state of nerves. What on earth did you wear if you were going out for dinner with a *prince*?

She rang her mother and explained her predicament.

'Good heavens,' said her mother faintly. 'A *prince*? You'll never want to come home to Salisbury at this rate!'

Sabrina winced at how her mother had unerringly hit on the truth. She couldn't imagine wanting to either, but that had everything to do with Guy and nothing whatsoever to do with a Middle-Eastern potentate.

'What do I *wear*, Mum?' she repeated patiently.

'You've got lots of lovely clothes! Just be yourself,' said her mother. 'My goodness—wait until the neighbours hear about *this*!'

'Well, I don't want you to tell them,' said Sabrina stubbornly. Because however much she wished otherwise, one day soon she was going to have to go back and live at home, and she would do herself no favours whatsoever if she arrived with Guy Masters's magic dust still clinging to her skin.

She even tried to quiz Guy about the correct dress code one evening when he arrived home even later than usual and had been in a snarling temper. She produced a huge tureen of soup, and he stared down at the steaming bowlful and suddenly went very quiet.

'You don't like home-made soup?' she asked nervously.

Guy looked up. The soup looked perfect. Damn it—*she* looked perfect, standing there in a pair of white jeans and

128

a white T-shirt, with her bright hair caught back in a po-nytail.

'Haven't had a lot of experience of it,' he said shortly. 'My mother used to open a can.'

Sabrina pushed some cheese across the table towards him. 'Wasn't she keen on cooking, then?'

It was an such an artless question that Guy found himself uncharacteristically answering it. 'Not particularly. And we were always...moving,' he said slowly. 'So a lot of her time was taken up with settling into new places.'

'You make it sound quite nomadic, Guy.'

'Do I? I suppose it was when you compare it with living in one place all your life.'

'Like me, you mean?'

He shrugged. 'Well, you did, didn't you?'

'Yes,' she said carefully, as some warning light in his eyes told her to go back to the safer subject of cooking, rather than the potential minefield of childhood.

She sawed through a crusty loaf and handed him a huge chunk of it. 'My mother was so busy going out to work that she never had time to cook properly, except at week-ends.'

He nodded, seeing the sudden, defensive set of her face. Despite his reservations, he found himself asking, 'How old were you when your father left?'

'Eight.' She pulled a face. 'He fell in love with my mum's "best" friend.'

He winced. 'That must have been tough.'

'Yes.' She stared down at the soup without really seeing it. 'For a while it was dreadful.' She looked up and gave him a bright smile. 'But time heals, doesn't it? Corny, but true.'

'Yeah, but you always get left with a scar.' He shrugged, but he shook his head at the silent question in her eyes. 'Tell me more.'

'Just I always vowed that when I grew up I would learn how to cook properly.'

Unexpectedly, he found the thought of Sabrina as a little girl exquisitely touching. He sipped the soup. 'Well, you achieved it with honours,' he murmured.

She glowed with pleasure. 'Guy?'

'Mmm?'

'You know this dinner on Saturday night—'

He put his spoon down. 'Damn!'

'It's been cancelled?' she asked hopefully.

He shook his head. 'Nope—but I haven't organised anything and I'm in Paris all day tomorrow. You'll have to book the restaurant, Sabrina.'

'Like *Where*? I don't really know London at all!'

He reeled off a list of London's most famous eating places and Sabrina shook her head doubtfully.

'We'll never get a table at any of those places *this* late!'

He gave a small smile. 'Just try mentioning my name.'

From anyone else it would have sounded outrageously arrogant—from Guy it just sounded supremely confident.

'And what on earth can I *wear*?' she wailed.

'Wear what you want.' He shrugged. 'You always look pretty good to me.'

She had received better compliments in her life, but none had she embraced as warmly as Guy's careless words and she had to force herself to suppress the guilt. She *was* letting go, and starting to live again—and there was nothing unacceptable about enjoying a compliment.

It still didn't solve the problem of what to wear, of course.

Guy left at the crack of dawn the following morning. Sabrina heard him moving around the flat and for once came, yawning, out into the hall to say goodbye to him.

His hand tightened around the handle of his briefcase as he saw her hair in all its tousled disarray tumbling down over her shoulders. Was she trying to play the siren? he wondered distractedly. But that was just the thing—he honestly didn't think she *was*.

'Have you remembered your passport?'

'Sabrina!' he exploded. 'I've been flying to Paris at least once a month for the last I don't know how long! How the hell do you think I managed before you came into my life?' It had been a calm, ordered time which was slowly but surely fading from his memory, the end of which had seemed to coincide with him urging her to let her guilt and her sorrow go. He had only himself to blame, and yet he hadn't realised how familiar it could feel, living with a woman—even if you *weren't* having sex with her. He winced. Why remind himself of *that*?

'Send me a postcard.' Sabrina smiled.

'I won't have time,' he said tightly, because he was having to fight the terrible urge to kiss her goodbye—as if she were his *wife* or something. His smile tasted like acid on his mouth. 'And don't forget to book the damned restaurant!'

'I won't forget.' She stood at the front door until he'd disappeared out of sight, praying that he would turn round and give her that rare and brilliant smile. But he didn't.

Sabrina felt more than a little intimidated at the thought of booking a meal at a place she had only ever read about in magazines. Wouldn't even her best dress look out of place in a venue as upmarket as that? And, when she thought about it, wouldn't Prince Khalim be bored rigid with going to fancy restaurants, and Guy, too, for that matter? Wouldn't they rather try something a little *different*?

She spent her lunch-hour scouring the restaurant section of the capital's biggest glossy magazine, and eventually found what she'd half thought she'd been looking for. She picked up the phone and booked it.

But Guy was delayed in Paris. He phoned that night.

'This deal is taking longer than I thought,' he said, and she could hear the sounds of people in the background. 'I may even have to stay over for a few days.'

'A few *days*?'

'You'll be OK on your own, won't you?'

Sabrina pulled a face. She couldn't be missing him *already*, could she? 'Yes, of course I will.'

'Just lock up carefully.' There was a pause. 'Ring Tom Roberts if you need anything. Actually, I'll ring him—get him to keep an eye on you.'

'I don't need anyone to keep an eye on me! You make me sound helpless!' she objected, and could hear the smile in his response.

'Not helpless, Sabrina. Maybe just a little vulnerable at the moment.' And make damned sure you remember that, he thought grimly as he hung up before tapping out Tom's number.

Guy arrived back from Paris on Saturday morning, feeling all frazzled and frayed around the edges as he walked into the kitchen to a delicious smell of coffee. Sabrina was already dressed, busy buttering a slice of toast. He paused for a moment which felt dangerous. Because his kitchen had never felt more of a home than it did at that moment.

He'd missed her, he realised with a sudden sense of shock.

'Hi,' he said softly.

Sabrina turned round slowly, trying to compose her face, making sure that every trace of leaping excitement had been eradicated from her features. She smiled instead. 'Welcome home! How was your trip? Would you like some coffee?'

He wanted something a lot more fundamental than coffee, but he nodded his head, sat down at the table and took the mug of coffee she slid towards him.

'You're up early,' he commented.

'I'm working today, remember?'

He frowned. Had it really been three weeks since the last time she'd been in the shop on Saturday morning? 'Yeah.' He sighed. He'd been almost tempted to take the day off himself, and to ask her whether she wanted to go to a gallery with him, but if she was working... 'I guess I might as well go in myself.' He yawned.

Sabrina fixed him with a stern look. 'Oh, for goodness' sake, Guy! You've only just got back from Paris. Give yourself a break!'

He glared at her. 'I've managed to get along just fine for the last thirty-two years without anyone telling me how to live my life, if it's all the same to you, Sabrina.' He paused. 'Did you book the restaurant?'

'I did,' she said steadily, without missing a beat.

'Which one?'

Her bright smiled didn't falter. 'It's a surprise!'

'A surprise?'

She wondered what had caused that sudden hardening of his voice. 'You don't like surprises?'

'No,' he clipped out, and then saw her crestfallen face and relented. It was unpredictability he shied away from. She wasn't to know that surprises made him feel as though the control which was so fundamental to him could be in danger of slipping away. Loosen up, he told himself—just as he'd told her to. He smiled. 'It had better be a good one.'

'Oh, I think it will be.'

'We're picking Khalim up from his hotel at eight.'

She nodded, trying to be helpful. 'So shall I order us a car, too?'

'Yes,' he murmured, wondering why he got the distinct impression that the balance of power had somehow shifted in this relationship without him really noticing. He'd wanted her to try and let the past go, but he hadn't expected such an enchanting switch into sexy and sassy and bossy mode. It was much too irresistible a transformation. 'Thanks,' he added heavily.

Sabrina spent hours in the bathroom getting ready, comfortable in the knowledge that she wouldn't be holding Guy up. Thank heavens there were three, she thought, remembering her initial shock at discovering that one flat had three bathrooms all to itself. Back in Salisbury her mother would have been beating the door down by now.

In the spare room, she pulled out the hanger on which hung the dress she'd bought after work yesterday, and she looked at it with eager eyes. It was a dream—easily the most grown-up and sophisticated thing she had ever owned—but nothing less would do, not for a prince!

It was in deepest violet velvet and it fell to just above the knee, with long, fitted sleeves. In fact, the whole dress accentuated every curve of her body and the rich, vibrant colour contrasted deeply with her red-gold hair. It was a simple dress, possibly a little *too* simple, which was why she'd bought diamanté earrings and an ornate and glittering necklace to go with it.

She stepped back to look at herself in the mirror and gave a nod of satisfaction. The diamanté necklace and earrings sparkled and spangled in the light. She looked good! Maybe the best she had ever looked—and there was an added sparkle to her eyes and a soft flush to her cheeks.

Guy was standing by the window in the sitting room, doing up his cuff-links, and he looked up as she made her entrance, then froze.

Sabrina, who had been watching him expectantly, saw the sudden stiffening of his body, the swift hard gleam in his eyes, and her heart sank.

'You don't think it's suitable?'

A pulse hammered at his temple. 'Don't be so bloody naïve, Sabrina! Of course it's suitable—' He'd never seen anything more suitable in his life—and the thing it was most suitable for was being ripped off her body... He groaned and tried to pay a gracious compliment. 'It's lovely,' he finished lamely.

'Oh. Right.' She screwed her nose up. 'You don't think it's too over the top?'

'*No*, I don't!' He drew a deep breath. 'And I think we've just about exhausted the subject of what you're wearing. Now, where the hell is this bloody car?'

Sabrina hoped that he was going to moderate his language a little, especially in front of Prince Khalim, but now didn't seem a very good time to say so, especially since at that moment the doorbell rang, and the chauffeur was standing there, telling them that their car was ready. She picked up the same diaphanous silver wrap she'd worn in Venice and turned to Guy.

'Ready?' she asked, thinking that she'd never seen him in formal black tie regalia before, and just how darkly imposing and broad-shouldered it made him appear.

'And waiting,' he said, in a grim kind of voice.

Outside stood a long, gleaming, black car which made the limousine he'd hired in Salisbury look like an ancient old banger. Sabrina felt like a film star as she climbed inside.

But as they were whisked towards the West End Guy seemed to want to avoid all her attempts at conversation, and Sabrina forced herself to look out of the window, trying to appear interested in the sights as they sped by, wondering why he was sitting in such stony silence.

All he could think about was how much he wanted to kiss her, and it was driving him out of his mind. Since when had *kissing* been his number-one priority?

The car slid to a halt in front of the Granchester Hotel, which was situated right opposite Hyde Park and where a uniformed doorman immediately sprang to attention.

'I'd better go inside and tell him we're here,' said Guy, still in that same, heavy voice.

But at that moment there was some sort of commotion and several burly men in suits emerged from the hotel entrance and stood, looking this way and that.

'That's his security,' said Guy, seeing her expression of bemusement. 'They may want to check the restaurant out so your little "surprise" may have to be unmasked, Sabrina, dearest.'

In the dim light of the early evening, Sabrina blanched. Maybe she had misjudged the whole situation completely, but by then it was too late to do anything about it because the men in suits had all stood up straight to attention. And the most striking man she had ever seen in her life came gliding out of the hotel.

It wasn't just the fact that he was tall—although Guy was actually taller by about a head. Or that he was wearing a long, silky kind of robe which was a cross between white and gold and hinted at a hard body beneath. Or that his hair was darker than the night—much blacker than Guy's— and his skin the deep golden colour of some ancient and lovingly polished piece of wood. Or that his eyes were as black as onyx itself—curiously deep, all-seeing eyes which were as emotionless and as cold as any she had ever seen.

For he was all those things, and more, thought Sabrina. He was a prince—and not just by title. He oozed it from every autocratic pore of his body.

His nose was a cruel, hard curve, and so was his mouth, and something about his whole rather rich and haughty demeanour made Sabrina feel slightly panicky with nerves as she recalled the restaurant booking she'd made. What had she *done*?

As Guy opened the door he felt Sabrina shiver beside him, and he glanced down at her, his mouth tightening. So the old knockout Khalim effect was having its usual reaction, he thought cynically.

'Don't worry, he likes blondes,' he told her cryptically. 'So you should be on to a winner!'

'But I'm a strawberry-blonde!' she objected, stung by that critical note in his voice. 'That's different.'

'And strawberries are rich and luscious,' Guy answered softly. 'Be careful, Sabrina—he eats women like you for breakfast.'

Sabrina glared at his back as he stepped from the car and the two men greeted each other like the old friends they were.

'Guy!' said Khalim, the hard lips curving into a smile.

Guy jerked his head in the direction of the suits. 'Are you bringing this lot with you?'

Khalim glanced a flickering look at the back of the car, where Sabrina was sitting frozen with nerves. The black eyes narrowed.

'They will follow behind us,' he said, 'but they will sit outside in the car. They shall not bother us while we are eating.' His voice softened as another dark, enigmatic glance was directed at the car. 'And who do you have sitting and waiting so beautifully for us, Guy?'

Guy felt an unwelcome flicker of irritation. This was Khalim, Khalim whom he had known since school—when they'd forged an instant friendship after Guy had beaten him at chess. Khalim had never been beaten by anyone before—but, then, as Guy had coolly pointed out, he'd been brought up in an environment where letting Khalim win was paramount.

The two boys had fallen with fists on one another, and had had to be pulled apart—both snarling and glaring like young tiger cubs. And then one of them—they'd each taken the credit afterwards—had started laughing, and the laughter had been contagious and had created a bond which had never been broken down the years.

Khalim's father had given Guy his first big break, and Guy had never forgotten that.

So why did he now feel like the small boy who'd wanted to pulverise his schoolmate?

'This is Sabrina,' said Guy shortly.

He pulled open the car door and Khalim slid inside next to Sabrina, the silken fabric of his robe whispering and clinging to the lean definition of his muscular legs. 'Sabrina Cooper.'

'And Sabrina is your…?' Khalim paused delicately, as if searching for the right word.

'Friend,' said Guy instantly, because in that instant no other word seemed to do. 'She's staying in my flat for a few weeks.'

'Indeed?' murmured Khalim.

Sabrina felt the slow thudding of disappointment. Every word Guy had said was true—but, oh, if he'd wanted to emphasise that their love affair was dead, that her role in his life only transitory, then he couldn't have done it more succinctly. Or more cruelly.

'That's right,' she said staunchly, and attempted to echo his casual tone. 'I'm just passing through.'

'Indeed?' murmured Khalim again. Black eyes glinted as he raised her hand and lightly brushed his lips against the fingertips. 'Khalim,' he purred. 'And I am charmed.'

It was difficult not to be charmed herself by such quaintly old-fashioned manners. And the sight of Guy glowering from the other side of the car had her smiling back at the Prince.

'I've booked the restaurant for tonight,' she babbled. 'I do hope I've made the right choice.'

The curved smile edged upwards. 'Water and bread can

be sustenance enough,' said Khalim softly, 'when the company is this spectacular.'

Guy turned his head to look out of the window, thinking that he just might be sick. He'd heard Khalim's chat-up lines over the years—and as far as he knew—they had a one hundred per cent success rate. But this...this... *outrageous* flirting was really too much.

Sabrina had given the restaurant address to the driver when she'd made the phone booking for the car, but as it negotiated its way through Notting Hill and drew up outside a small, colourful café, her heart sank.

The signs, it had to be admitted, didn't look very promising. There was a garish awning outside, beneath which the sign read, THE PIE SHOP.

Guy's eyes narrowed incredulously. 'Just what *is* this place, Sabrina?'

'It got a very good review in the papers,' she defended, determined not to flinch beneath the quiet look of fury in his eyes. 'And I thought it would be...different.'

'It is certainly different,' said Khalim, his voice tilting with amusement. 'Come, let us go and see what delights The Pie Shop has to offer.

It was the kind of place which employed out-of-work actresses as waitresses—so at least the glamour quotient was high. But Khalim didn't seem at all interested in the nubile specimens who ushered them inside. In fact, his attention seemed to be all on Sabrina.

Almost worryingly so, she told herself as they were given a table in the corner.

There were no menus, just a huge blackboard with the dishes of the day printed on it in chalk.

'I'm surprised there isn't sawdust on the floor,' said Guy acidly, but Khalim was gazing around him with the air of a man who had stepped into a different world.

'No, but it is charming,' he murmured. 'Quite charming.

And the smell of the food delicious. Every summer my mother used to take me and my sisters into the mountains, and we would eat a meal with an old man who had spent his life caring for the goats and living in a simple dwelling. This place reminds me of that.'

Oh, *great*, thought Guy. He frosted a look at Sabrina across the table. 'Khalim hasn't eaten red meat for years.' He gave a pointed stare at the dish of the day—shepherd's pie. 'Any suggestions, Sabrina?'

She thought that she'd never seen him quite this grumpy before, but it occurred to her that if he hadn't wanted her to come along, then he shouldn't have asked her. 'How about fish pie?' she suggested brightly.

'Fish *pie*,' echoed Khalim, as if she'd just proposed a lavish banquet. 'Do you know—I haven't eaten fish pie since we were at school. Do you remember, Guy? Always on Fridays.' And he gave a wistful smile, which briefly softened his hard, proud face.

How did she *do* it, wondered Guy distractedly. How had she unerringly hit on the one dish which would produce a rare state of nostalgia in a man who'd very probably been offered every delicacy under the sun?

'Three fish pies,' he said to the waitress, and Sabrina, who'd been about to order the shepherd's pie, hastily shut her mouth. It might be considered bad manners to eat meat in front of the Prince.

It wasn't the easiest meal she had ever sat through, mainly because Guy would hardly meet her eye, just chatted to Khalim about the paintings he'd seen recently in Paris.

Khalim listened and ate his meal slowly and with evident pleasure. Occasionally he would turn to Sabrina and fix her with that hard, black stare as he asked her about her work in the bookshop as if it were the single most fascinating subject in the world.

And Sabrina smiled and tried to look attentive, while miserably ploughing her way through the fish pie.

After she'd pushed her plate away, Khalim leaned forward, his fingertips brushing against the bright glitter of her necklace.

'Who bought you these diamonds, my beauty?' he murmured.

Sabrina smiled. 'Oh, they're not real!'

'Really?' Khalim brushed one of the gems thoughtfully. 'Then it must be your skin which enhances them—for they look absolutely priceless.'

What Khalim didn't know about diamonds could be written on the back of a postage stamp, and Guy watched with increasing fury as the Prince's dark, elegant fingers contrasted against her milk-white skin.

'Shall we skip pudding?' he demanded.

They ordered coffee instead, and Guy was just paying the bill when Khalim lightly placed his hand on Sabrina's wrist.

'I'm in England for another couple of weeks,' he mused. 'Perhaps you would have dinner with me some night?'

Sabrina looked over at Guy, unsure of how you went about saying to a prince that it was a terribly sweet offer but that she was fast falling in love with someone else, thank you.

In love? Her cheeks grew hot, and the pounding in her heart increased. What in heaven's name was she thinking of? She couldn't be falling in love. She *couldn't*. It was too soon after Michael—much too soon.

She glanced over at the object of her affections, who was chatting to the waitress and giving her the benefit of the sunniest smile she'd seen all evening.

'Sabrina?' prompted Khalim softly.

Well, all *right*, she thought furiously, and smiled back at him. 'That would be wonderful,' she agreed shyly.

CHAPTER TWELVE

GUY maintained a simmering silence all the way home, even after they'd left Khalim back at his hotel and the chauffeur had dropped them back at the flat.

In fact, he waited until he'd slammed the front door behind them. He didn't have many neighbours, it was true, but the ones he did have had known him for years. And would probably have gone into extreme shock if they'd heard Guy Masters yelling at a woman, which was exactly what he felt like doing.

'Are you *mad*?' he demanded.

'And are *you* lacking in any social graces?' Sabrina returned hotly.

'You spent the whole night simpering up to Khalim!'

'Only because you could hardly bring yourself to say a civil word to me—and I was *not* simpering!'

He steadied his breath. Stay calm, he told himself. Stay calm. This wasn't like him at all. 'Do you have any idea of that man's reputation with women?'

Sabrina met his eyes with dignity. 'He seemed quite the gentleman—'

'*Quite the gentleman?*' he repeated faintly.

'Besides, I thought he was your friend.'

He heard the rebuke in her voice. 'He *is* my friend! He also has a legendary libido. Legendary. I can't believe that you'd be so naïve, Sabrina.' And he pictured the two of them together, and the black dagger of jealousy cut into him and sent the words spilling out before he could stop them. 'You weren't so naïve when...' But the words died as soon as he saw the look on her face.

142

'When what, Guy?' she asked coldly.

'Nothing.'

But she wasn't going to let this one rest. 'Oh, yes—*something*,' she contradicted furiously. 'Perhaps you think that if I go out with Khalim, I'll fall straight into bed with him. That he will be able to seduce me with the same ease as you did.'

He saw the hurt which clouded her ice-blue eyes and his mouth tightened. 'That's not what I said.'

'It's what you meant, though, isn't it? Well, *damn* you, Guy Masters, if that's your opinion of me, then there's no point me saying any more, is there? You obviously think I'm a tramp!' And she stalked off down to her bedroom, trembling with rage and distress.

He watched her go, fighting down the urge to run after her because he knew what the only outcome would be if he confronted her when emotions were running so high. God, he'd barely been able to watch Khalim coming on to her all night. And yet with his jealousy he'd offended her. Deeply.

But the time for reconciliation would be in the cold, clear light of logical thinking, not now—not when he was aching for her so badly that if he got within touching distance of her he would just want to haul her into his arms and crush his mouth down on hers and... Stifling a groan, he went off to take a much-needed shower.

Sabrina spent a restless night and woke up remembering the scene of the night before. And Guy's appalling insinuations. She turned onto her side and gazed sightlessly up at the wall, wondering if those heated words should change things.

She could leave and go back to Salisbury now. Today, if she really wanted to. Maybe that was what a sane, sensible person would do. The trouble was that she felt neither particularly sane nor particularly sensible. She wanted...

She turned onto her other side and stared at the exercise bike, which was now positioned underneath the window. What *did* she want?

Most of her wanted Guy, with a growing love she hardly dared to acknowledge—but what did Guy want?

Nothing, it would appear.

Oh, she suspected that he still felt desire for her—she wasn't *stupid*. She had seen that unmistakable darkening of his eyes, the sudden tension of his body when she'd been close to him sometimes. He certainly wasn't immune to her—but neither did he seem to want to do anything about it.

She sighed. Perhaps she should just be grateful that he was behaving like such a gentleman. Her mother *would* be pleased.

There was a rap on the door, and a voice called out softly, 'Sabrina? Are you awake?'

'I am now!' she replied acidly.

Behind the door, Guy smiled. 'I'm making breakfast.'

'What do you want—a medal?'

'Just your company.'

She pushed the duvet back and stepped out of bed. What was the point in sulking, and pretending she hated him? If she intended to stay—and she did—she couldn't behave like a petulant child simply because he'd lost his temper with her last night. 'You'll have to wait until I'm showered and dressed,' she said.

Guy gave another wry smile. The trouble was that he liked it when she started laying down the law. And it was novel enough to be very, very stimulating. 'Don't take too long.'

'Then go away and leave me to it.'

'Yes, Sabrina,' he murmured.

She appeared dressed and showered twenty minutes later, to find that he'd put a crisp white cloth on the dining-room table and there were freshly squeezed juice, warm croissants and different jams. And he was sitting, barefooted, in jeans and a T-shirt, reading a newspaper.

He looked up as she came in and their eyes met.

'I'm sorry,' he said, and forced himself to behave like a calm and rational human being instead of some kind of jealous monster. 'I had absolutely no right to talk to you like that. Whether or not you choose to go out with Khalim is entirely up to you.'

'You're absolutely right,' Sabrina agreed coolly as she sat down opposite him and picked up a napkin. 'It is.'

It was not the answer he'd been expecting. Or wanted. But he forced himself to smile. 'I'm going into the office for a couple of hours,' he said.

'But it's Sunday!' She pouted disapprovingly.

'Princess,' he said grimly, because much more of this and he really might lose his head. Or something even more dangerous. Like his heart. 'I just about know my days of the week!'

'You're going to burn out before you're forty,' she warned.

He drummed his fingers on the table. 'Lecture over now, is it, Sabrina?'

They spent the rest of that week being extremely polite to each other. And more than a little wary.

He was home earlier than usual on Thursday. Just as he'd been home earlier on Tuesday. Funny how the office suddenly seemed to have lost some of its old allure. He'd picked up a take-away on the way home, and they'd stood together, unpacking the foil containers, while Guy tried very hard not to be diverted by the sweet sheen of her hair.

'How about dinner tomorrow night?' he asked suddenly.

Sabrina looked up, surprised that he was keen to repeat

the experience after what had happened last time. Unless...
'You mean, with you?'

'Yeah, and another client.'

Her heart fell, but she was damned if she would show it. 'Not Khalim?' she posed, wondering guiltily whether she ought to tell him that an exquisite orchid from the Prince had arrived by post yesterday. And it was hidden in all its scented beauty in the one place that Guy would never find it.

Her bedroom.

'No, not Khalim.' He spooned some rice onto his plate. 'Actually, it's a businessman who wants to buy a painting which has just come onto the market.' He shrugged. 'Even though he doesn't particularly like it.'

'Then why on earth is he buying it?'

'As an investment. And as a coup.' The ice-blue eyes were narrowed at him perceptively. She had a strange and infuriating habit of looking at him in that questioning way, and when she did he just couldn't seem to resist telling her what she wanted to know. 'He's a bit of an idiot, actually.'

Sabrina put the spoon down. 'And you want to give up your Friday night to have dinner with an idiot—and mine, too?'

'It's business.'

'Oh, yes—*business*.' She couldn't keep the derision out of her voice. 'Better not miss out, then, Guy—you really need that extra million bucks, don't you?'

Guy froze. He hadn't been the recipient of undiluted criticism for more years than he cared to remember, and even if it had more than a kernel of truth in it, it wasn't *her* damned place to give it to him. 'I take it that's a refusal?' he snapped, thinking that there wasn't a single other woman of his acquaintance who would have turned him down.

'Too right it is! I'd rather stay in and read my book, if you must know.'

'Fine,' he said tightly. 'Then do that.'

'I will!'

They had just sat down in a frosty silence to eat their meal when the telephone began to ring.

'You'd better get that, Guy,' said Sabrina sweetly. 'You virtually bit my head off the last time I answered it when you were here!'

And no wonder. He stood up. Ever since that day his mother had taken to ringing him at work and bombarding him with all kinds of questions about Sabrina. Where had they met, and what was she like? And the more he seemed to protest that she was nothing more than a girl who happened to be staying for a while, the less his mother seemed to believe him.

'You've never had a woman living with you before,' she'd pointed out.

'She's not living *with* me,' he'd explained tersely. 'Just living in the same flat. It's no big deal, Ma—people do it all the time these days.'

'Not someone like you,' his mother had said serenely. 'I know how you like to be in control.'

'So?'

'Well, as every year passes you become more and more eligible—'

'Ma,' he'd objected on a note of drawling humour.

'It's true. And an attractive young woman invading your space would normally have you running screaming in the opposite direction.'

'Who says she's attractive?' Guy had asked suspiciously.

'Well, *is* she?'

'Mmm,' he'd agreed, without thinking. 'She is. Very.'

His mother had sounded oddly triumphant. 'So when are we going to meet her? Your brother and I are itching with curiosity.'

'Then itch away. You are *not* going to meet her,' he'd

said patiently. Then, having heard his mother's offended silence, he'd sighed. 'Not just yet, anyway…'

He picked the phone up. 'Guy Masters.'

'Guy? Khalim here.'

'Khalim!' He forced enthusiasm into his voice. 'What can I do for you?'

'May I speak with Sabrina, please?' came the honey-smooth response. 'I was going to ask her out to dinner on Saturday.'

Resisting the urge to slam the phone down, Guy marched back into the dining room. 'It's Khalim on the phone,' he said accusingly. 'For *you.*'

Infuriatingly, Sabrina found herself thinking about the orchid, and felt the blood rush hotly into her cheeks. 'I wonder what he wants.'

'To ask you out for dinner.' He stared at the pink cheeks and wondered what had caused her to blush. 'But we've been invited out to a party on Saturday.'

'We?' she asked disbelievingly.

'Well, I have,' he admitted. 'But I'm sure that Jenna won't mind if I bring someone.'

Oh, sure. Sabrina could just imagine how much Jenna would like *her* there. 'Jenna doesn't like me, Guy—on the only two occasions I've met her, she's looked at me as though I was an insect she found squashed onto the sole of her shoe.'

'She's better with men than with women,' he observed.

Understatement of the year. Sabrina paused by the door, thinking that she was fed up with only being good enough for client dinners with idiots or as the unwanted guest at the party of a predatory woman who obviously wanted Guy for herself.

'Actually, I just might go out with Khalim,' she said. 'It could be rather fun.'

Guy could hear her on the phone to his friend, and his

pulse began to hammer. He pushed his barely touched plate of food away, and scowled. She could do what she damned well liked.

Inexplicably, Guy found himself cancelling the client dinner on Friday, and then spent the next evening prowling the sitting room like an edgy jungle cat as he waited for Khalim to arrive. He seethed when Sabrina breezed into the sitting room and he saw that she was wearing that same silky silvery grey dress she'd worn in Venice. The night he'd taken her to his bed.

It was on the tip of his tongue to ask her whether she intended an action replay with his friend, but some last vestige of sanity made him bite back the jealous words that he instinctively knew she would never forgive. Words that deep down he knew he didn't mean—so why the hell did he keep imagining the whole scenario, as if someone were running a film reel through his mind?

Sabrina felt slightly on edge, wondering if she was equipped to cope with a man who, as Guy had already said, ate women like her for breakfast.

Suddenly she wished that she hadn't been so proud, or so stupid. Fancy letting Guy go alone to a party where Jenna would no doubt be waiting to get her hooks in him. 'Aren't you going to be late, Guy?' she asked tentatively, and then almost recoiled from the anger in his eyes.

'Want me to get out from under your feet?' he asked silkily.

'Don't be so insulting!'

He picked up his jacket with a careless finger. 'Just be careful, huh? You've got the number of my mobile, haven't you?'

'Why, do you think he's about to drag me off to his palace with him to make mad love to me all night?' she asked sarcastically.

'I wouldn't blame him if he did,' he drawled. He looked

at the silver-grey fabric, which clung so enticingly to the slender curves of her body, and swallowed. If Khalim attempted to do that then as one man to another he would completely be able to understand it. 'But just remember this, Sabrina—he'll never marry an Englishwoman. His destiny has been mapped out for him since birth.'

'I'm not looking for a husband!' she snapped.

'Good.' He gave the ghost of a smile. 'Have a good time.'

'What, after *that* little pep-talk?' she asked acidly.

After Guy had gone, she felt like ringing up Khalim to cancel—but, apart from the fact that she didn't have a number for him—even Sabrina realised that such a loss of face would be intolerable to a man like the Prince.

Even so, she felt as if the executioner's axe was about to fall while she waited for the doorbell to ring.

Guy walked into the party and wished he could walk straight out again. He narrowed his eyes against the mêlée. Too many people, too much noise, too much smoke, and the music was *hellish*.

'Hello, Guy,' came a low, husky voice by his side, and he turned round to see Jenna, an expression he didn't quite recognise making her lovely face look a little less lovely than usual.

'Hi,' he said, thinking how overly jovial he sounded. He handed her a slim, silver-wrapped present. 'Happy birthday!'

'For me?' she said coyly. 'What is it?'

The question irritated him far more than it had any right to. 'Why not open it and see?'

Jenna's perfectly painted fingernails greedily ripped open the paper. 'Oh,' she said slowly. 'A book.'

She said it, thought Guy wryly, as though he'd just given her a serpent.

'Apparently, if you only read one book for the rest of

your life, this is the one. It's up for a prize, and most people in the industry think it's just going to walk away with it.' He was, he realised, repeating Sabrina's enthusiastic praise almost word for word. She had recommended that he read it himself, and maybe he would. Maybe he would.

'Oh,' Jenna said.

The blinkers seemed to drop from his eyes as he surveyed Jenna's look of bemusement. It was going to be, he realised sadly, completely wasted on her. 'Hope you like it,' he finished lamely, and wondered just how long he could stay at this party without looking boorish.

'I'm sure I will!' Jenna's green eyes slanted from side to side. 'On your own?' she quizzed softly.

Something in her tone made his hackles rise. 'Obviously.'

Jenna shrugged. 'Nothing obvious about it at all—I'm suprised you haven't brought your new *flatmate* with you.'

Guy stared at her. Funny how you could know someone for years and years, and a remark which should have been completely inoffensive should suddenly sound like the most intolerable intrusion. His grey eyes gleamed. 'And why should that surprise you, Jenna?'

'Well…' Jenna drank some champagne and left some of the liquid to gleam provocatively on her lips. 'You know what people have been saying, don't you?'

'No, I don't. Why don't you tell me?' he suggested evenly.

Jenna shrugged. 'Oh, just that she's not your flatmate at all—but your lover.' She gave a shrill little laugh. 'As if!'

Some dark kind of explosion seemed to happen inside his head. 'You'd find that such a bizarre scenario, would you?' he asked quietly.

'Well…' Jenna shrugged, seemingly oblivious to the dangerous quality in his tone. 'I think that most people would, don't you? You're…' She gave a foolish, beaming smile, like someone who had decided to bet all their money on an outsider.

'Hmm? What am I?'

'You're…well, you're everything that most women would ever want, I suppose,' she stumbled. 'And she's…'

Guy froze. 'She's what?'

'Well, I'm sure she's very *nice*,' said Jenna insincerely. 'But she's just a small-town girl who works in a *bookshop*, isn't she?'

'As opposed to a small-minded girl who lives off her daddy's trust fund?'

Jenna stared at him. 'Guy!' she protested. 'That was completely uncalled for!'

His grey eyes were as cold as ice. 'What right do you think you have to criticise a sweet, beautiful woman who actually works hard for her living? Who has seen tragedy and looked it in the face, and managed to come to terms with it?'

'I didn't know anything about that!'

'You don't know anything about anything!' he snapped. 'Not about anything that really matters! Forgive me if I don't stay, Jenna, but I have something waiting for me at home!'

Or someone.

Except that he didn't—and why would he expect to? All he'd offered Sabrina had been some lousy dinner with a man he himself had admitted was a fool. And the only additional carrot he'd dangled in front of her had been a trip to the party of a woman who looked down her nose at her.

Was this what his life had become? Some kind of extravagant but superficial game? Going to all the right places but with all the wrong people—and for the wrong reasons, too?

And Sabrina was now out with Khalim—a man he liked and respected, but a man who was a veritable tiger where women were concerned. He had seen for himself that Khalim had been capitivated by Sabrina's easy, uncomplicated charm—just as he had been. He'd also said that Khalim would never marry an Englishwoman—but what if Sabrina's golden bright beauty was the exception to the rule? Khalim was used to getting whatever he wanted in life. Wouldn't he move heaven and earth to possess a woman if she'd touched his heart in a way that no one else had?

He drove like fury back to the flat, but it was, as he'd fully expected, empty.

He'd never spent a longer evening in his life—bar the one where he'd sat with his mother and waited for news which they'd both known in their hearts would be the worst possible news.

He tried reading, but that was useless, and he hated the television with a passion. He realised that he hadn't eaten, but couldn't face preparing any food. Or even eating some of Sabrina's carefully packed leftovers which sat at the back of the fridge. And the sight of her slavish economising made him want to hit something.

Or someone.

Guy forced himself to face the fact that she might not come home at all. That Khalim might now be making love to her with all the skill acquired from having had women offer themselves to him since he'd been barely out of his teens.

And if that *was* the case, then he must force himself to act like a rational man. He had no right to show temper or outrage. They weren't committing any crime. He didn't own her.

He glanced down at his watch. Where the hell *was* she?

He had just sprawled down on the sofa, a glass of wine in front of him, when he heard the sound of a key in the front door. He rose to his feet, but stood right where he was and waited. Because he knew that he might have to face the fact that Sabrina was not alone.

CHAPTER THIRTEEN

SABRINA walked into the sitting room to find Guy standing there, as motionless as if he'd been carved from some beautiful dark and golden stone. His eyes were the only animated part of his body, and they swept over her in a glittering and hectic question.

'Is Khalim with you?'

She shook her head. 'No. He's just driven off.'

Guy expelled a quiet breath of relief, but he didn't move. He had rushed in once before. This time it had to be different. He gestured towards the bottle of claret which stood on the table. 'Would you like some wine?'

It had been an emotional evening. She had drunk mineral water and jasmine tea, but right then she needed a drink. 'I'd love one.'

He poured her a glass and put it down on one of the small tables, keeping his voice deliberately casual. 'So. Good evening, was it?'

Sabrina dropped her shawl over the back of one of the chairs and went to sit down on one of the sofas. It hadn't been the evening she'd been expecting. But then she hadn't expected to find herself weeping quietly on Khalim's shoulder and telling him that she was in love with Guy—and that if he ever said anything to Guy about it, she would never forgive him.

And Khalim, still slightly shell-shocked from the first rejection he had ever encountered, had given a rueful smile and smoothed a tear-soaked strand of hair away from her cheek with a gentle finger.

'You think I would risk you not forgiving me?' he'd

mused. 'You know, Guy is a strong man, not a stupid man—and he is behaving like one if he ignores this most precious gift which is his for the taking.'

Sabrina had bitten nervously at her lip. How could she possibly tell Khalim the truth? That she'd fallen into his friend's arms in Venice with such indecent haste that he probably had no respect left for her.

'He's not interested in me that way,' she'd told him stolidly. 'Not any more. I know he's not.'

'Then for the first time in my life I must question his judgement,' Khalim had replied in a hard, cold voice.

'And anyway,' she'd said, in a small voice, 'even if he was, I don't think I could bear to make myself that vulnerable again. If you love someone, then losing them is just unbearable.'

His dark eyes had narrowed. 'Explain,' he'd ordered quietly. And she'd told him all about Michael and he'd listened thoughtfully.

'So you see,' she'd finished, 'it's much too soon for me to fall in love with someone else—it does a disservice to Michael's memory.'

The hard lips had curved briefly into a smile. 'But love has no respect for convention, Sabrina,' he had sighed.

And from that moment on he had behaved almost as though she was sick, and in a way maybe she was. For the pain in her heart was real enough, surely? As real as the sharp pierce of longing which ripped right through her whenever she thought of Guy.

Khalim had made her eat a little something, and told her something of his homeland. His voice had lulled her and soothed her, and his softly accented descriptions of his upbringing had transported her to another world.

Just as Guy had transported her to another world.

But it wasn't her world.

'It was certainly different,' she said to Guy, as she remembered.

He forced himself to keep the jealous monster at bay. 'Oh?'

She sat down, picked up her glass and sipped at it gratefully, acutely aware of the glittering grey gaze which held her fast in its dazzle. She thought that he looked almost strained tonight, with a strange kind of restlessness about him.

'How was Jenna's party?'

'Boring as hell.'

'Really?'

'Really. But I don't want to talk about Jenna's party. I'm much more interested in your evening.'

'Oh, Khalim had hired a private room in the most amazing restaurant you've ever seen,' she said, still slightly reeling from the experience. 'Imagine—a whole room to ourselves!'

Behind the hard line of his mouth Guy gritted his teeth. Just a taste of Khalim's average over-the-top seduction technique. 'How very impressive,' he said steadily.

He really *did* seem to be tense, as if he was hanging onto his self-control with difficulty, and Sabrina stared at him, willing her heart not to wrench, but it was hopeless. Every time she looked at him she felt nothing but an unbearable sense of longing.

'It was. Very,' she said simply. No need to tell him that she'd barely eaten a thing, or that the spectacular surroundings hadn't registered. She might as well have been sitting in some scruffy old café for all that she would have noticed—because Guy hadn't been there. And the world was just not the same place when Guy wasn't there.

'And are you going to see him again?'

Something in the harshness of the question made her go

very still, and she gazed up into the hard contours of his face. 'And if I am?'

There was a dangerous pause. 'I don't like it.'

'*You* don't like it?' Sabrina stared at him. She thought about his rage when she'd told him she was going to accept Khalim's offer of a date. If she thought about it rationally, all the facts added up to jealousy. So, was Guy jealous of Khalim and, if so, why, when he had shown no signs of wanting her for himself? 'Why not?'

'Why do you think?' he snapped. 'Because it's doing my head in to think that he wants you when I want you so badly for myself.'

Joy mingled with disbelief. '*You*...want me?' she repeated, her voice trembling.

'Of course I want you! Haven't I wanted you ever since I made the foolish suggestion that you come and live here?'

'Why was it foolish?' she breathed.

He knew that now was not the time for his habitual evasion. 'Maybe I was just fooling myself into thinking that what happened in Venice was a reckless one-off.' Hadn't part of him secretly hoped it had been? He shook his head. 'But my feelings for you haven't changed.'

Sabrina stared at him. He'd used the word 'feelings', but she suspected that he really meant desire. But, however he chose to phrase it, it didn't really matter—because nothing could change the way she felt about him. Nothing.

'Haven't they?' she whispered.

'Not a bit.'

Guy watched her eyes darken involuntarily as their eyes locked, and saw the soft tremble of her lips. And suddenly he knew that neither logic nor reason could stop what he was about to do.

With a hand that wasn't quite steady he put his glass down on the table, walked over to the sofa and stood looking down at her. He saw the sudden parting of her lips as she read the answering hunger in his eyes.

'Guy?' she said breathlessly.

'Sabrina?' came the soft mocking response. 'Do you think we've played the waiting game for long enough?'

She could barely get the single word out. 'Y-yes.'

He held his hand out to her and she took it. In an instant she was in his arms, and his eyes were hard and bright and hungry as he brought his lips down to kiss her.

And just that first heady contact set her on fire. Blazing. With a tiny moan, she coiled her arms around his neck like a snake and he pulled her hard into his body so that their hips melded, and she could feel the hard, powerful jut of him throught the fine linen of his trousers.

He kissed her with a frustration that went bone-deep, and Guy found himself lost in the sweetness of her mouth, as if he could never get enough of plundering its honeyed moistness. He pulled her even closer, feeling the tips of her nipples as they strained against the sheer, silky fabric of her dress.

With an effort he pulled his lips away from hers, and she made a murmured little protest as he looked down at her, his eyes glittering black, opaque with desire.

'Is this what you really want, princess?' he groaned. 'Because if you don't, we'd better stop this right now.'

Her arms were still around his neck, their hips still intimately meshed. She could feel the growing power of him and realised how much he wanted her. And how much of an effort it must have taken for him to say that.

'Yes, I do,' she said almost shyly—which was crazy when she considered that she hadn't been in the least shy with him before. But that night and that capitulation had been motivated by passion, pure and sweet and undiluted. While this…

This was love—more potent than any other emotion in

the world. But only for *her*, she reminded herself. Only for her. Guy wasn't making any declarations—he was just a man, with a man's libido.

And maybe, knowing that, she should have stopped him, but Sabrina knew that no force in the world could have stopped her. Not when she wanted Guy this badly. 'Yes,' she said again. 'Yes.'

He found the gleam of flesh on her pale shoulder utterly irresistible and trickled a slow finger over its satin curve, watching as she shivered in response.

'Mmm,' he murmured, as he slipped first one strap down and then the other, so that the material fell in soft folds to her waist. Her tiny breasts were thrusting furiously against the soft lavender lace of her bra, the tips rosy and hard, and he nudged the pad of his thumb against one, seeing her body jerk automatically in response.

Her eyelids fluttered to a close. 'Guy!' She uttered his name in choked response to that first touch, feeling the wet, wild warmth of response.

'Feels good, doesn't it?' he murmured, circling his thumb with feather-light torment.

Good? It felt as if she'd just been catapulted straight into a place where nothing existed but pure sensation. 'It feels fantastic,' she moaned.

'No, *you* feel fantastic.' His closed his hand possessively over one tiny breast and her nails immediately dug into his neck as she swayed against him, communicating her heated reaction as clearly as if she'd spoken it.

Guy frowned. She was so damned responsive! He always took his women to bed. Always. And yet suddenly he discovered that he didn't want to break the spell by moving from where they were and taking their clothes off. He wanted to do it to her right here. And right now. It was as simple and as elemental as that.

'I don't know if I can make it to the bedroom,' he groaned.

'Who cares?' she whispered back.

'You mean you don't?'

'No.' She would swing from the chandelier if he wanted her to.

He pushed her down onto the carpet and joined her there, pulling her into his arms and kissing her while his hand slid beneath her dress and smoothed it all the way up to her thighs. He gazed down at their milky pale curves and felt his resolve slipping away. 'I don't know if I can even bear the time to take your clothes off, princess. Or mine.' He grazed her a light stroking touch where she was most responsive, smiling as her body bucked against his hand.

Sabrina's head fell back against the Persian carpet as she felt the first honeyed flutter of his fingers, and her thighs parted for him of their own volition. 'Then don't,' she breathed hoarsely, feeling as wanton right then as she had ever felt. 'Don't. Let's just do it.'

She found herself fumbling at the button of his trousers, then rasping the zip down with difficulty, her hand straying agitatedly over his hard swell, and she heard him suck in a ragged breath.

'Make that a definite,' he moaned as he tugged her panties down right over her thighs, skimming them impatiently over her ankles and then tossing them over his shoulder. 'Now, my little temptress…'

Hearing the slumberous intent in his voice, Sabrina opened her eyes to see him kick off his trousers, exposing the true, daunting power of his arousal, and she shivered as he came to kneel over her.

He bent his head and touched his mouth against hers as he positioned himself close to her. Tantalisingly close. 'Want me?' he whispered.

She couldn't think of a time when she hadn't. Not if she

was being honest with herself. 'Oh, God, yes,' she moaned helplessly, as she writhed her hips impatiently beneath his.

'Well, then…' And he groaned as he entered her with one single, powerful thrust. 'You've got me.'

This time was different. This time she knew him—or at least as much of him as he was prepared to let her know. For there was always some sense that Guy was holding something of himself back. But who cared? Maybe she would never have all of him—but no person could ever totally possess another, could they?

But now—physically at least—he was as abandoned as she had only ever dreamed he could be.

In Venice he had been a skilful lover, but they had been strangers. This time his kisses were deeper, his caresses more tender. With each long, deep stroke, she felt enchained by his possession. It *felt* different. As if it really mattered.

No. That was simply an illusion, she forced herself to remember. Just the body's way of tricking the mind into thinking that this was something more than just a basic human need. She tried to keep a hold on her sanity, even as the first waves of orgasm began to shimmer her down into its sweet, shuddering waters. And only sanity prevented her from crying out how much she loved him.

Guy watched the arching of her back and the indolent splaying of her limbs, and only when he saw her body begin to judder and bloom did he allow himself to let go, to the most exquisite release.

Afterwards they lay together on the carpet, dipping in and out of a slumberous doze, their limbs still damp and tangled.

He heard her yawn and looked to where her tousled red-blonde hair lay ribboned across his chest. 'You do realise,' he murmured sleepily, 'that we're still half-dressed?'

She looked down at herself. Then at him.

Her dress lay rucked up to her waist, while Guy was wearing nothing but a T-shirt. She could see the beautifully pale curves of his buttocks and she felt a warm heat begin to suffuse her.

'Oh.'

He rolled on to her and captured her face as his hips crushed hers beneath him. 'Is that all you can say—"Oh"?' He saw her squirm and her agitated look and his eyes narrowed. *'Oh,'* he repeated softly, but he managed to fill the word with a sultry promise. 'Maybe we *had* better go to bed.'

Sabrina swallowed. 'What, right now?'

He smiled. 'Mmm. Right now.' And he pulled her to her feet, shaking his head as he saw her look around the room for her underwear. 'Leave that,' he instructed softly. 'You won't be needing any clothes tonight.' And saw her shivered response.

He took her by the hand and led her to his bedroom, in a section of the large flat she usually avoided, throwing the door open to reveal an airy room dominated by an enormous bed. Huge windows looked down onto the flower-filled square.

'I don't think you've ever been in here before, have you, princess?' he murmured. 'Do you like it?'

'Well, I have seen it,' admitted Sabrina, and saw the question in his eyes. 'I sneaked a look when I first moved in. I was...curious.' More than curious.

She had wanted to see whether the room could tell her more about the man, but it had thrown up few clues. The paintings were superb, the furniture modern and luxurious—but it was an oddly dispassionate room. As though he was wary about expressing too much of his personality through mere fixtures and fittings. Again, there was that distinctive air of containment.

Guy should have been riled at what could definitely have

been termed as an intrusion, but found himself smiling instead. He thought that few people would have admitted it. But then wasn't Sabrina's innate innocence one of her sweetest and most appealing features? Well, that and her stubborn insistence and the way she could make him mad and then make him smile an instant later. Even the way she nagged him about working too hard—which his mother had long given up on.

'Do you mind?' she asked. 'That I sneaked a look?'

He saw the uncertainty which had clouded the ice-blue eyes, and a wave of an emotion he didn't recognise washed over him. He forced himself instead to watch the pert thrust of her breasts.

'I'm rather turned on by the thought of you prowling around in here like a pussy-cat,' he said roughly. 'Come on, let's go to bed.'

CHAPTER FOURTEEN

SABRINA opened her eyes to the morning light and closed them again as images of the previous night came flickering back.

What had she *done*? Placed herself in the most precariously vulnerable position in the world—that was what she'd done. Given herself to Guy, heart, body and soul.

'Good morning, princess,' came a murmured greeting, and her eyes snapped open to see Guy standing, towering above her, already shaved and dressed for work in another exquisitely cut dark suit, and she felt a great wrench of longing.

'Hello,' she whispered, her heart thundering at the sight of him.

He smiled. 'You were sleeping so beautifully that I couldn't bear to wake you.'

She sat up and saw his eyes darken as her bare breasts were exposed, and some protective instinct made her gather the sheet around her.

'You're going already?' she asked him.

'Wish I didn't have to, but I have an early meeting,' he said softly, and sat down on the bed beside her.

Of course he did. Guy the workaholic. Guy the driven. He might have spent most of the night making exquisite love to her, but that didn't change his priorities, did it? And work came first. It always would.

Well, she might have been compliant in his arms last night, but that didn't mean that she had to exist in a passive state of insecurity now.

'This changes things, doesn't it?' she said slowly.

There was an imperceptible pause as the grey eyes narrowed. He'd hoped to avoid any kind of analysis. 'How come?'

'Oh, don't be obtuse, Guy, you're much too intelligent for that,' she told him crossly. 'If I'm living with you...' She saw the wariness on his face and wished she'd phrased it better. 'If I'm living here and we're having—'

'Sex?' he put in, with a wicked grin.

Thank goodness he'd interrupted her. She'd been about to say 'a relationship', but his drawled one-word question had brought what had just happened between them down to the lowest common denominator. And shown her more clearly than anything else could have done just how different their agendas were. She might love Guy—but that didn't mean he felt the same way about her. Men didn't need to be *in* love to make love the way he had done.

'Yes, sex.' She swallowed.

'Good sex.' He trickled a finger slowly from shoulder to breast, and she let the sheet fall. 'The very best,' he added slowly.

It should have been a compliment, so why did it sound little short of an insult? 'Thank you,' she said stiffly.

He flicked softly at one rosy nipple, feeling it surge into instant life beneath his finger. God, he felt like just getting back into bed with her and forgetting the damned meeting. His face hardened. He hadn't got where he was today by letting a woman trap him with her honeyed sweetness.

'Why should it change anything, except for the better?' he questioned softly. 'We carry on as we were, only now you share my bed at night. I can't think of anything I'd rather have.'

'No,' she said sadly. Of course he couldn't. He didn't want commitment, or even a relationship. He wanted sex, pure and simple—and obviously he thought that was all she wanted, too. And who could blame him? Hadn't she always demonstrated the sensual side of her nature around him?

He reluctantly moved his hand from her breast and cupped her face instead. 'What's the problem, Sabrina?' he asked gently. 'Why the long face? Let's just enjoy it, huh?'

And when she came to the end of her stay with him, what then? But consenting adults didn't make unnecessary emotional demands, did they? Guy didn't love *her*—and wouldn't he doubt *her* feelings if he had any idea what they were? Wouldn't he consider her fickle if she told him she'd fallen in love with him—only months after the death of the man she'd been due to spend the rest of her life with?

But love could strike without warning. It wasn't exclusive. Just because she'd been in love once before, that didn't mean it couldn't happen again. What she'd felt for Michael hadn't been what she felt for Guy. Her feelings were different, but that didn't make them any less valid. And they were all-consuming.

She wanted him, she realised, on whatever terms he was prepared to take her.

But he wouldn't know that. She would keep her dignity and play at being a modern woman, not a lovesick fool who would settle for anything—just as long as it included him.

'OK, let's just enjoy it,' she echoed, and slanted him a smile.

Her look was one of pure provocation, and just for one second Guy wavered, itching to undress and climb into bed with her and lose himself in her body.

But he'd broken so many rules where Sabrina was concerned—wouldn't one more be his downfall? Hadn't he controlled his life according to a rigid plan laid down by the circumstances of his youth? It would be nothing short of recklessness to go in deeper than he already was. Her fiancé wasn't long gone, he reminded himself. For Sabrina, this was a purely physical affair on the rebound. It had to be. Logic told him that.

He stood up quickly, not trusting himself to kiss her. Just being this close to her and knowing she was stark naked underneath that sheet was playing havoc with his senses. 'Time I was out of here,' he said abruptly, and then softened to give her a smile. 'I'll see you tonight, princess.'

She watched him go, heard the front door slam, shatteringly aware that he hadn't even kissed her. Maybe she should be grateful for that. At least he wasn't filling her head with false promises of happy-ever-after.

She sighed. They would carry on as before. Living together—only this time, as Guy had so unromantically put it, with sex as part of the equation.

The next three weeks ticked away like a time-bomb, with Sabrina alternating between giddy elation and wild despair but determined to show neither emotion.

Guy took her to the theatre, and to concerts. He even skipped work on the Saturdays when she was off and they explored London together, like tourists.

And at night...

At night he couldn't seem to keep his hands off her. And it was really quite disturbing how one dark, sensual look levelled mockingly at her across the sitting room was enough to send her running straight into his arms.

While sometimes she despised herself for her instant surrender whenever he touched her, at least she had the comfort of knowing that it didn't seem any different for him. She could reduce him to putty in her hands.

Why, she had even made him late for work this morning, and thrown his careful schedule into disarray. All because she had strolled into the bathroom one morning, wearing nothing but a pair of silver camiknickers while he'd been combing his hair.

Guy had stilled as he'd seen her reflection in the mirror, the pale swell of her breasts and the long curve of her legs beneath the frivolous lace trim. A pulse had begun to beat steadily at his temple.

'What are you doing?' he asked, in an odd kind of voice.

She batted him an innocent smile as she bent down to retrieve a book from where she'd been reading it in the bath the previous night while waiting for him to get back from Rome.

'I forgot this,' she said, and straightened up.

But the sight of the silver silk stretching tightly over her bottom had been enough to send his senses into overdrive. He put the comb down with a hand which wasn't quite steady.

'Kiss me goodbye,' he ordered throatily.

She went into his arms without a word, and pressed her lips to his, feeling them part on a sigh to greet her. 'Goodbye,' she whispered, but she couldn't resist moving her body closer and feeling the sudden responding tension in his.

His hand snaked around her waist, drawing her in closer still. He was painfully and erotically aware of her barely clothed state, even through the thickness of the suit he wore.

Trapped against his hard, virile body, Sabrina felt the warm pooling of a desire so strong that she couldn't have resisted it if she had tried. And she certainly wasn't trying.

'I don't want to be late,' he ground out, but once again he drove his mouth down onto hers in a sweet, crushing kiss.

'God forbid,' she murmured, and flicked her tongue inside his mouth, hearing him groan in response.

'Stop it, Sabrina,' he pleaded, but only half-heartedly.

Caught up with longing and compelled by a need to shatter that rigid control, she moulded her breasts brazenly against his torso. 'Stop what?' she murmured, and allowed her fingers to trickle down over the rocky shaft of his erection, feeling him jerk in distracted response. 'Do you want me to stop this?' She ran her hand expertly over him. 'Do you, Guy?'

A shudder ran through him as he felt her begin to unzip him. There would be no stopping now, he realised with a hot, heady rush of blood, and then his hands were on her breasts, feeling them spring into excited life beneath his hungry fingertips.

She struggled to free the zip and the trousers fell redundantly to his ankles. She heard him swear softly, and then, very deliberately, he moved the damp silk panel of her camiknickers aside and delved his fingers deep into the honeyed moistness. She gasped.

'Do you like that?' he murmured, feeling her thighs instantly parting for him. 'Do you?'

Her response was instant and overwhelming. Sabrina swayed as she clasped his dark head against her, murmuring a protest she didn't feel, her knees sagging weakly as she felt the swift heat of need. He lifted his head to glitter her a look of provocative assessment and swiftly turned her over so that she was bending over the bath.

He ripped her camiknickers off without compunction and let his silk boxer shorts fall to his ankles, and she realised that he was going to…going to…

'Oh, Guy!' she gasped ecstatically, as he entered her.

He groaned as he submerged himself in her hot, molten depths, thinking that it shouldn't be this simple—or this out of control. And then he wasn't doing any thinking at all. The world had shifted focus and then hardened, to a brighter focus, and now it splintered out of all recognition as they both cried out at the same time.

He pulled out of her and turned her around, thinking how shaken she looked. Well, hell, he was pretty shaken himself. When had he ever acted like *that* before? In Venice, he reminded himself grimly, that was when.

'You've made me late for work,' was all he said. Then he gave her a hard, crushing kiss before turning and swiftly walking out of the bathroom.

Flushed with orgasm, and a bitter kind of regret, Sabrina slammed the lock home behind him and then sank to her knees on the bathroom floor as dry, shuddering sobs began to tear at her throat. What on earth was happening to them?

As a demonstration of lust, that experience had been in a class of its own. Guy had used her for sex, but hadn't she gone ahead and *allowed* herself to be used? She loved him, yes, but he'd never given any indication that he felt even a *fraction* of love for her. And she didn't want to love again. Not like this. Bad enough that she'd loved and lost Michael—but at least Michael had felt the same way about *her*.

And she had known then with a sinking certainty that this one-sided love would bring her nothing but heartbreak. Far better to begin to distance herself. Starting from now.

It was late-night shopping this evening, and she'd make herself go browsing round after she'd finished work, deliberately make herself late home.

But Guy was even later. He'd had to juggle his day to include the missed meeting, and then had sat through it, bored and distracted, trying not to keep glancing down at his watch and thinking about Sabrina.

This was getting slightly ridiculous, he thought exasperatedly as he let himself into the flat. Going home at night had become the highlight of his day.

But tonight there was no meal cooking.

Just Sabrina sitting on the sofa, looking moody, an unopened book lying on her lap.

He dropped his briefcase and gave her a thoughtful look. 'Hi,' he said softly.

'Hi.'

He thought how wooden her voice sounded. And maybe he deserved it. 'Sabrina, listen—about this morning—'

'No, Guy, please.' She shook her head, her cheeks growing pink as shame vied with remembered pleasure. 'It happened—let's forget it.'

That was the trouble—he couldn't forget it. It had been on his mind all day. And so had she. 'I shouldn't have been so abrupt with you afterwards.'

'No, you shouldn't!' She threw him a furious look. 'And maybe *I* shouldn't have committed the terrible sin of wandering in looking like that when you were getting ready for work. How wicked of me to unwittingly throw temptation in your path, Guy! Heaven forbid that you should ever break your rigid routine and be *late*!'

'Sabrina,' he said softly, 'are we going to fight about this all night?'

'No, we aren't.' She drew a deep breath. They weren't going to fight about anything and she was going to be very calm and grown-up about what she had to say. 'We ought to talk about me going.'

He went very still, as though he hadn't heard her properly. '*Going?*' he echoed. 'What are you talking about?' His voice softened. 'Aren't you taking things a little too far, princess? I know what we did was pretty wham-bam-and-thank-you-ma'am, but there's no need to overreact.'

'This has nothing to do with this morning.' But she forced herself to remember that brutal and loveless kiss, and that somehow made what she had to say all the easier. 'I only came here on a temporary basis, remember? And the six weeks are nearly up.'

If she'd detonated a small bomb on the carpet in front of him he couldn't have been more shell-shocked. Her stay had merged into one pleasurable and sensual blur. Had she really been here for *that* long? Guy stared at her. 'But you aren't really going?'

It was a million miles away from the 'please, don't go' she'd been hopelessly praying for. She kept her face carefully composed. 'I have to, Guy—I won't have a job after next Friday, and they won't hold my job in Salisbury. Believe it or not, jobs in bookshops are highly sought-after.'

He could believe it quite easily—but then he'd seen her at work. A meeting had been cancelled and he'd called for her unexpectedly one lunchtime, dismissively waving away her protests that she'd brought a sandwich with her.

'We'll feed it to the pigeons,' he'd murmured, thinking that the books and the old polished wood of the shop only seemed to enhance her bright-haired beauty. One look at Sabrina sitting busy at her desk, and any sane person would have thought it the most perfect job in the world.

'So leave.' He shrugged.

Sabrina froze. 'Leave?'

Guy gave a slow smile. 'Sure. I can support you.'

'I don't want your support,' she said stiffly. 'Or your charity.'

'Sabrina.' His voice softened as he walked across the room and sat down beside her on the sofa, not missing the almost imperceptible shift of her body as she leaned away from him. 'It's not charity. I earn obscene amounts of money—'

'You said it, Guy.'

His eyes narrowed. 'You don't *need* to work,' he said quietly.

'*I don't need to work?*' she repeated in disbelief, before leaping to her feet to stare down at him in an angry blaze. 'Says who? Says *you*! Well, if that's the case, you don't know anything, Guy, not really!'

'Oh? This is fast becoming a real home-truth session,' he drawled. 'Do continue, Sabrina—I'm fascinated.'

'Don't you have any idea about my need for independence?' she stormed, ignoring the dangerous note in his voice. 'Or did you think I would just fall to the ground in a grateful heap because you've offered to ''support'' me?'

'Clearly not,' came the dry retort. A lot of women would have done. His mother, for example, had never forgotten what he'd done for her. But that had been different. That had been called survival.

Jenna, he realised, would have adored the idea. So would many of the other trust-fund babes. Not Sabrina, though, he realised slowly. Her principles were in a different class.

'It's *your* flat!' she stormed. '*You* have all the control here—so just imagine if you started paying for me, too. How unequal would *that* make things? At least buying groceries now and then makes me feel as though I'm doing my bit!'

He looked at her steadily. 'So what do you suggest we do?'

She looked at him sadly, realising that she'd talked herself into a corner. There was no solution—or at least not one that would make her happy. Only one thing could do that, and he wasn't offering her permanence.

Because if she accepted his offer to stay while he supported her, then where would that leave her? Busy clinging on to a relationship which would grow increasingly more one-sided.

Even if she found herself another job here in London, wouldn't that just be postponing the inevitable heartbreak when he tired of her?

'I'll leave at the end of next week,' she said impassively. 'As orginally planned.'

Guy's body quickened, even as his heart felt the unfamiliar pang of rejection. But if she was expecting him to *beg* her to change her mind, she had a lot to learn about him. Needing something enough to beg made you vulnerable, and he had once made a vow never to be vulnerable again. He paused. 'So, until you go, will we continue as…before, Sabrina?'

How very delicately phrased, she thought with a slight tinge of hysteria. 'You mean, will I be sharing your bed at night?'

He thought that there were a few more flattering ways she could have described it. 'That's exactly what I mean,' he answered coolly.

Her hunger for him warred with her self-respect, but it was never going to be much of a battle. She thought about how bleak her future would be without him, and knew that she wanted to savour every last, glorious moment. 'Ask me tonight,' she said flippantly.

He knew from the darkening of her eyes just what her answer would be, but any triumph was eclipsed by a slow, ticking anger. So she thought she could just play cat and mouse with him when it suited her, did she?

He rose to his feet with stealthy grace and pulled her into his arms without warning. 'Why don't I ask you now?' he drawled, before claiming her mouth in a kiss which had her reeling.

CHAPTER FIFTEEN

SABRINA let herself into the flat with a heavy heart and went to put the shopping in the kitchen.

Two more days. Just two.

It was inconceivable. Especially as Guy had spent the last few days seemingly hell-bent on showing her just what she would be missing. He didn't seem satisfied until he had her sobbing out her shuddering pleasure, night after night…but he'd never asked her to stay.

She made herself a coffee and then went to stand at the window, where the bright hues of early summer dazzled from the garden in the square. How on earth could she ever go back to being what she had been?

Or maybe that was the wrong way to look at it. She could never really go back to being the old Sabrina—there was a new one now, ready and willing to take her place. And rebirth, like birth, was always painful. Why else would she feel this terrible, tearing pain at the thought of never seeing Guy Masters again?

Would he miss her? she wondered achingly. Probably, just a little, yes. And certainly in bed. But the missing, like their relationship, would be unequal. Guy called the shots and Guy had all the control. He would miss her for a little while and then move on.

Sabrina glanced down at her watch. It was only just past six, so there was at least an hour and a half before he would grace the flat with his presence.

She had bought a load of cheap vegetables at the market, and she had just begun to chop them in order to make a soup when there was a sharp ring at the doorbell. Wiping

175

her hands down over the apron which she insisted on wearing, and which Guy always teased her about, Sabrina went to answer it, to find Tom Roberts standing on the doorstep.

'Hi, Tom.' She smiled affectionately.

She'd last seen Guy's cousin at a drinks party a couple of weeks ago, and then he'd been sipping at a Bloody Mary and laughing at something Sabrina had said. But today he looked wary.

'Hi, Sabrina—may I come in?'

'Oh, yes, of course, of course,' babbled Sabrina, and pulled the door open. 'Only I'm afraid that Guy isn't back from work yet.'

'I know that. It isn't Guy I've come to see. It's you.'

'Oh.' She smiled. 'That's nice. You'd better come in.'

'Thanks.' He followed her into the sitting room and sat down.

Sabrina looked at him expectantly. 'Can I get you a drink, Tom?'

'No, thanks—I'm out to dinner later and Trudi will kill me if I turn up with an inane grin on my face.' He suddenly grew serious. 'Is it really true? Guy says you're leaving.'

Hearing the words spoken aloud like that by a third person made Sabrina realise just how horribly true it was.

'That's right. I am.'

'But, Sabrina, *why*? I mean, I've never seen him looking so contented—happy, even! And you're the first woman he's ever lived with, even though women have been mounting campaigns to snare him for years. He says that he doesn't want you to go, but that you're going anyway. So why?'

She shook her head. 'I can't go into it, Tom. It's too complicated, and it isn't fair on Guy.'

'Fair on Guy?' Tom repeated slowly. 'Sabrina, look...' He seemed to be having difficulty choosing the right words.

'I've known Guy all my life, but, with him, what you see isn't automatically what you get.'

'You're talking in riddles, Tom.'

He pulled a face. 'Everyone looks at him and thinks that he's Mr Invulnerable—strong and rich and powerful—'

'Maybe that's because he *is*,' observed Sabrina drily.

'Yeah, I know all that. And that's what he likes to project. But that's only part of the package—he keeps a lot of himself hidden. That highly controlled and tough exterior he's cultivated—that's what he shows to the world.'

'You're telling me,' said Sabrina bitterly. 'The man for whom the term, ''workaholic'' was invented.'

'And have you never stopped to ask yourself why?'

'Tom, you know him better than almost anyone—so you must also know that he doesn't like to talk about himself.'

'Well, maybe it's about time you tried! I mean, like, *really* tried! Have you?'

'When a door is kept locked you give up trying to open it,' she said.

'You could always try kicking it down,' he suggested softly.

'Women don't kick doors down,' Sabrina objected, forgetting for a moment that they were talking metaphorically.

'But they can,' he objected. 'It just takes longer.'

She stared at Tom, taken aback by his vehemence, even though that wary look was still in place on his face. There was, she realised, something he wasn't telling her. And she knew that his loyalty to his cousin meant he wouldn't disclose it. 'Maybe I should,' she agreed slowly.

'Anyway…' Tom rose to his feet. 'Time I was going. And there's no need to mention to Guy that I was here.'

She shook her head. 'Don't worry. I won't.'

After he'd gone, Sabrina prowled the flat, the soup forgotten, and realised that she'd been guilty of some sort of emotional cowardice. She'd fought for her independence, and a kind of equality with Guy, and yet she'd allowed herself to be daunted by that enigmatic, don't-ask-me quality of his.

She had shared his life, and his bed, but had stood on the sidelines when it had come to exploring his feelings—mainly out of a selfish sense of self-preservation. She'd known that he hadn't wanted her to ask, and so she hadn't. She'd wanted Guy, but hadn't been prepared to risk being hurt by him—and you couldn't do that in a relationship. Loving someone automatically made you vulnerable to pain.

I've got to talk to him, she told herself. Whatever happens, I can't leave him without having done that.

Guy cut his meeting short, and it was clear from his secretary's expression that she clearly thought he had taken leave of his senses.

Well, maybe he had.

Or maybe he was just coming to his senses.

He found himself asking why he was prepared to let someone like Sabrina simply walk out of his life without argument. As if he had no control over the future. As though, because of one long-ago act, a pattern had been set in his life and he was powerless to change it. It was ironic, really, that he—the master of control—was allowing events to gather up speed by themselves.

He'd spent his life shielding himself from the prying questions of women on the make. Yet Sabrina was clearly *not* on the make—and neither did she ask him questions.

He was so caught up in his thoughts that he missed his stop on the tube. Another first, he thought wryly as he walked home in the golden summer sunshine. But the idea that Guy Masters—the cool and controlled Guy Masters—had misjudged a train journey he'd been making for the past who-knew-how-many years actually had him smiling ruefully.

He walked into the flat. 'Sabrina?' He watched while she drifted out of the sitting room, as graceful as that water nymph he'd first compared her to in Venice.

'Hello,' she said softly.

She'd used her waiting hour to shower, and to change and carefully apply her make-up. Because this was important, she realised. Very important. And, like a job interview she was determined to win, she just wanted to look her best. It was as simple as that.

Guy wanted to kiss her. Hell, he wanted to lose himself in the sweet torment of her body. But he didn't trust himself to touch her. Sometimes desire could cloud judgement, and right then he needed every bit of judgement he'd ever possessed.

'I need to talk to you, Sabrina.'

'And I need to talk to you.'

He nodded, but absently, as if he'd scarcely heard her. Like a man with a lot on his mind.

'Let's go into the sitting room,' he said abruptly.

Sabrina nodded as she followed him, vaguely disappointed at something in his tone but determined not to lose her nerve. She would chip, chip, chip away until she found out what she needed to know and what Tom hadn't been able to tell her.

In the sitting room neither of them sat, but instead stood looking at each other warily, like two fighters sizing each other up before a duel.

'Do you want to leave?' he demanded. 'I mean, really?'

Truth? Or lie? Communication? Or hiding behind social niceties? What did she have to lose? 'Of course I don't!'

Relief flooded his veins like a drug, and Guy drew in a deep breath. 'Well, that's good—because I don't want you to either. I want you to stay here. With me.'

Sabrina stared at him steadily. She had played her part—now she needed to know the truth from *him*. 'Why?'

How else to say this without shooting straight from the hip? But Guy used words carefully—he recognised their power and their significance—and there were certain words that he would not use lightly. Or recklessly. Unless he was certain that he meant them. And he didn't want to frighten her either. Or push her into something before she was ready. 'I…care for you, Sabrina,' he said slowly. 'That's why.'

So he cared for her. It was a curiously colourless way to phrase it, but Sabrina nodded her head slowly, less disappointed than she'd imagined she would be. He wasn't offering her the moon, no, but it was a start. For Guy to even *admit* caring for her was something. Because he was not, she knew, a man who would make a declaration without thinking it through first, or without meaning it.

But if she stayed then there had to be a new honesty between them. 'Why leave it until the day before I was going?' she demanded. 'Why on earth didn't you say something before?'

'Because I was burying my head in the sand and believing in the impossible.' He sighed. 'I imagined that my life would continue in its calm and uncluttered way once you'd gone. I didn't realise that the thought of you not being here was going to drive me out of my mind!'

Well, that was a bit better. A lot better. She actually smiled, but the smile had a hint of reproof about it. 'Hell, Guy, I've virtually packed all my suitcases!'

'Then unpack them,' he drawled silkily, but something in her face made him backtrack. He owed her more than that rather dispassionate request that she stay with him. 'Listen to me, Sabrina. I'm no good at trust—you'll have to help me. I'm used to women who are…' he paused '…*different* from you.'

Women who wouldn't want to know him if he was just an average guy. Not like Sabrina. She'd fallen under his spell without knowing *who* he was. His gaze was unflickering. 'And I guess my childhood sowed the seeds of distrust almost from the start.'

She held her breath. Here, she was certain, lay the key to the barrier he'd erected around himself. This was what Tom had been hinting at. 'Do you want to tell me about it?' she asked him softly.

He paused only for as long as it took to be mesmerised by the ice-blue dazzle of her eyes. 'Yes,' he said simply, and gave a long sigh. 'You're always complaining that I work too hard...'

Her persistence had, in fact, sown the first seeds of doubt in his mind. Had made him look closely at her accusations. 'And you've made me see how right you are. When you live alone, there's no one to question you—no one to compare yourself with. It's become a habit that's hard to break, a habit that started a long time ago...'

'Tell me, Guy,' she urged quietly, remembering how he'd let her unburden herself over Michael. And suspecting that he now needed to do the same for himself.

His mouth flattened. 'My father was the opposite to the way I am—his whole life was a reckless gamble. He would hear about some sure-fire scheme to make money and he would invest everything he had. Our life became a lottery. My mother and my brother and I used to find ourselves living in mansions. Or hovels, more often than not,' he went on, with a disparaging shrug. 'With my mother trying to feed two growing boys—and next to nothing in the cupboard. I guess it was just fortunate that a family trust paid for our education, or things would have come to a head much sooner.'

'But something happened?' prompted Sabrina, hurting

herself at the look of pain which had frozen his features. 'Something really bad?'

Was it that obvious? he wondered. He'd thought that he'd trained his face to hide all emotion—but Sabrina seemed to have the ability to make it come creeping back again. The words he'd locked away for so long came tumbling out as if they couldn't wait to be spoken.

'His schemes became more and more bizarre and my mother grew concerned. She tried to get all our assets put in her name, but he was far cleverer than she was. I guess these days she wouldn't have stayed with him—but things were different then. And she was loyal, too.' Just as you would be, he thought suddenly.

He saw her look of horror and heard himself defending his father. And that was something else he'd only just realised. That, whatever wrong he had done, his father was still his father.

'Oh, it wasn't a malicious action on his part—more a lack of judgement and a sense of misplaced pride. But one day he went too far and lost everything.' Guy shrugged. 'The business, the house, the car. Everything. With debts galore thrown in for good measure. Only this time his spirit was broken, too. I was fifteen, and my brother was twelve.'

There was a grim silence. Sabrina didn't say a word.

'My mother's parents took us in—they had a beautiful big house close to the cliffs in Cornwall.' His eyes grew distant as he thought back to a time he'd buried away deep in the recesses of his mind. 'But accepting charity—even family charity—was anathema to my father. He tried working in paid employment, but he could never cope with working for other people. His mood went down and there seemed to be no way that anyone could reach out and help him. And he and my mother never communicated particularly well.'

Sabrina nodded. That explained a lot, too. Guy's fear of

relationships, his wariness of commitment and sharing. A bad role-model could put you off for life.

His face grew dark as he forced himself to say the words. 'One night he went out and never came back again.'

'What happened?' whispered Sabrina hoarsely.

He didn't coat it with any sugar. 'He went out walking on the cliff-top. It was a wild night and the wind was blowing up a storm. He fell… We'll never know what really happened—whether he lost his footing, or if the wind caught him off balance. Or whether he jumped.'

He met her eyes with such a bleak expression that Sabrina couldn't help herself. In fact, even if he'd been just about to kick her out she still would have gone straight over and put her arms around him and hugged him as tightly as she knew how. Trying, however futilely, to take some of his pain away.

'Oh, Guy,' she whispered brokenly. 'Guy.'

He dropped a kiss onto her beautiful head, but forced himself to continue, feeling the burden lifting even as he shared it with her.

'I determined then that I would never be placed in such a vulnerable position again—and neither would my mother or brother.'

'So how did you manage?'

'Against everyone's advice, I left school at sixteen and started working, and I never really stopped. Khalim's father gave me a break, and I was off.' Off on a merry-go-round of hard work which had continued until this bright-haired temptress had walked into his life.

Sabrina rubbed her cheek against his shirt. He'd told her everything she'd wanted to know, without her having to ask him. He'd trusted her enough to open up to her. Would his trust now spread out and out, like ripples on a pond, so that their relationship got bigger and bigger?

'I didn't plan to feel this way about you, Sabrina,' he

admitted huskily as he caught her by the shoulders and forced her to look up at him, his own eyes soft with promise.

She felt the glimmer of tears. 'As if anyone has any control over their feelings.' She gulped. 'I wasn't planning on…' Her words tailed off. To talk of love would frighten him almost as much as it frightened her.

'On what?'

'Needing you like this,' she compromised.

'Need can be a powerful emotion, princess.' He tipped her chin upwards with the tip of his finger and gave a slightly shell-shocked smile. 'I find I need *you* pretty badly myself.'

She recognised what it had cost him to admit that. She stood on tiptoe to plant a soft kiss on his lips, and he sighed.

'So you'll stay?' he asked.

She drew her mouth away, her dreamy expression replaced by one of caution. Should she stay? But did she really have any alternative, when the thought of leaving filled her with a kind of mad despair?

All he'd told her was that he cared for her. He'd made no promise other than an unspoken one, which was that he trusted her enough to open up his heart. And surely trust— coming from a man like Guy—was worth all the most passionate declarations in the world.

'Sabrina?' he prompted softly.

'You know I will.'

'What's the date?' he asked suddenly, stroking a red-gold lock of hair off her cheek.

She thought back to all the order forms she'd filled in at the bookshop that morning. 'June the tenth. Why?'

He kissed the tip of her nose. 'Just remember it,' he urged softly.

EPILOGUE

GUY closed the front door and turned to look at Sabrina, a slow smile lighting up his face as he thought how beautiful she looked in her mint-green dress with her glorious bright hair tied back with a matching green ribbon.

'So, how did that go, do you think?' he asked her.

'I think they enjoyed it.' Her eyes glinted with mischief. 'Your mother kept asking me whether we'd arranged a wedding date.'

'And what did you say?'

'I said no, of course. Because we haven't.' But there was no resentment in her voice. 'And your sister-in-law kept telling me how much she had enjoyed her two pregnancies.'

'I'll bet she did!' He grinned. 'Like some more champagne?'

She'd barely touched a drop all afternoon. She'd been so nervous about meeting Guy's mother and stepfather and his brother and wife and their two children. But the lunch had gone like a dream, and now relief began to seep into her veins. 'Love some.'

He opened up the French doors leading onto the balcony and brought out two fizzing flutes. He handed her one as they sat side by side on the small bench, turning their faces towards the sun.

'Do you know what the date is, princess?' he asked quietly.

The glass was halfway to her mouth, but she quickly put it down on the decking and turned to look at him as a distant memory stirred in her mind. 'But you know the

date!' she exclaimed. 'We've had this lunch in the diary
for ages. It's June the tenth. Why?'

He put his own glass down to join hers—champagne was
the very last thing on his mind. 'It's exactly a year since I
persuaded you to stay,' he said softly. 'Remember?'

She nodded, mesmerised by the dawning tenderness on
his face. 'I didn't take a lot of persuading,' she said drily.

He smiled. 'It didn't seem like that at the time. I knew
then that I loved you, princess.' He lifted her hand to his
mouth and kissed one fingertip after another. 'But I didn't
want to rush you, or push you into something you weren't
ready for. You needed time to recover from Michael's
death and time to decide whether you could ever trust yourself to love again.'

'Oh, Guy,' she whispered, shaken by the depth of his
understanding. 'Darling, darling Guy.'

'I love you,' he said in a wondering kind of tone, as
though he had just discovered a foreign language in which
he was fluent.

And Sabrina realised that deep in her heart she'd known
that he loved her. Loving wasn't just about saying three
little words—Guy had shown her in every way that counted
that he cared. His consideration, his softness, his intelligent
regard and respect for her and the beautiful power of his
lovemaking had left her in no doubt of that whatsoever.

'I love you,' she said softly.

He leaned forward to gently kiss her. He had known that,
too. Her love for him was as bright as the June sunshine
which was beating down so warmly on their faces.

Their lives together had merged and harmonised. Guy
had stopped working on Saturdays, too. And now he came
home at a decent hour in the evenings—sometimes even
before her—which was a good thing. Unwilling to lose her,
Wells had created a new job for her—enlarging the children's section of the bookshop. Sabrina had organised au-

thor signings and related talks, which had been avidly and ecstatically received, and now she had groups of school-children from all over London to enjoy them.

'So will you marry me?' he asked, very, very softly. 'Now that you've had time to heal properly?

'Oh, yes, I'll marry you,' she responded huskily. 'You know I will.'

Sabrina looked at his dear, sweet face and her heart turned over with love for him. It was true that time was a great healer, but in a way Guy had been helping to heal her from the moment she'd met him. Some people didn't believe in love at first sight, but Sabrina did. Something primitive had shimmered down on them from the first moment they'd set eyes on each other, and since then the feeling had just grown and grown.

Some things happened because they were meant to, and she and Guy were meant to. You could call it fate or you could call it destiny, but Sabrina called it pure and perfect love.

Surrender to
the Sheikh

CHAPTER ONE

THERE was something about a wedding. Something magical which made everyday cynicism evaporate into thin air. Rose twisted the stem of her champagne glass thoughtfully as they waited for the best man to begin speaking.

She'd noticed it in the church, where even the most hardened pessimists in the congregation had been busy dabbing away at the corners of their eyes—well, the women, certainly. Women who would normally congregate in wine bars, denouncing the entire male sex as unthinking and uncaring, had been sitting through the entire service with wistful smiles softening their faces beneath the wide-brimmed hats.

Why Rose had even shed a tear herself, and *she* was not a woman given to a public display of emotion!

'In my country,' announced the best man, and his jet-black eyes glittered like ebony as they fixed themselves on the bride and groom, 'we always *begin* the wedding feast with a toast. That their mutual joy shall never be diminished. And so I ask you to raise your glasses and drink to Sabrina and Guy.'

'Sabrina and Guy,' echoed the glittering crowd, and obediently raised their glasses.

Not for the first time, Rose found herself surveying the best man over the top of her glass, along with just about every other female in the room, but then it was hard not to.

He was certainly spectacular—and spectacular in the true sense of the word. But, there again, not many men were fortunate enough to have a real live *prince* acting as their steward!

His name was Prince Khalim, as Sabrina had informed her excitedly when she'd begun to plan the wedding. A real-life

5

prince with a real-life country of his own—the beautiful
Maraban—over which he would one day rule, as his fore-
bears had ruled for centuries. He was an old schoolfriend of
Guy's, Sabrina had shyly confided to Rose—the two men
being as close as two men who'd known each other since
childhood could be.

Rose had been expecting the prince to be short and squat
and rather ugly—but, for once, her expectations had been
way off mark. Because Prince Khalim was quite the most
perfect man she had ever set eyes on.

He was tall—though perhaps not quite as tall as the
groom—and he wore the most amazing clothes that Rose had
ever seen. Exotic clothes in sensual fabrics. An exquisite
silken tunic coloured in a soft and creamy gold, with loose
trousers worn beneath.

Such an outfit could, Rose reasoned, have made some men
look as though they were on their way to a fancy-dress
party—maybe even a little bit feminine. But the silk whispered tantalisingly against his flesh, and there was no disguising the lean, hard contours of the body which lay beneath. A body which seemed to exude a raw and vibrant
masculinity from every pore.

Rose swallowed, the champagne tasting suddenly bitter in
her throat. And then swallowed again as those onyx eyes
were levelled in her direction and then narrowed, so that only
a night-dark gleam could be seen through the thick, black
lashes.

And with a slow and predatory smile, he began to move.

He's coming over, Rose thought, her hands beginning to
shake with unfamiliar nerves. He's coming over *here!*

The gloriously dressed women and the morning-suited
men parted like waves before him as he made an unhurried
approach across the ballroom of the Granchester Hotel, his
regal bearing evident with every fluid step that he took. There
was a dangerous imperiousness about him which made him
the focal point of every eye in the ballroom.

Rose felt her throat constrict with a sudden sense of fear coupled with an even more debilitating desire, and for one mad moment she was tempted to turn around and run from the room. An escape to the powder room! But her legs didn't feel strong enough to carry her, and what would she be running from? she wondered ruefully. Or whom?

And then there was time to think of nothing more, because he had come to a halt in front of her and stood looking down at her, his proud, dark face concealing every emotion other than the one he made no attempt whatsoever to conceal.

Attraction.

Sexual attraction, Rose reminded herself, with a fast-beating heart.

It seemed to emanate from him in almost tangible waves of dark, erotic heat. He wanted to take her to his bed, she recognised faintly, the cruel curve of his mouth and the glint in his black eyes telling her so in no uncertain terms.

'So,' he said softly, in a rich, deep voice. 'Are you aware that you are quite the most beautiful woman at the wedding?'

He sounded so English and it made such an unexpected contrast to those dark, exotic looks, thought Rose. She forced herself to remain steady beneath the dark fire of his stare and shook her head. 'I disagree,' she answered coolly—unbelievably coolly, considering that her heart was racing like a speed-train. 'Don't you know that the bride is always the most beautiful woman at any wedding?'

He turned his head slightly to look at Sabrina in all her wedding finery, so that Rose was given an unrestricted view of the magnificent jut of his jaw and the aquiline curve of his nose.

The voice softened unexpectedly. 'Sabrina?' he murmured. 'Yes, she *is* very beautiful.'

And Rose was unprepared for the sudden vicious wave of jealousy which washed over her. Jealous of *Sabrina*? One of her very best friends? She sucked in a shocked breath.

He turned his head again and once again Rose was caught

full-on in the ebony blaze from his eyes. 'But then so are you—very, very beautiful.' The mouth quirked very slightly as he registered her unsmiling reaction. 'What is the matter? Do you not like compliments?'

'Not from people I barely know!' Rose heard herself saying, with uncharacteristic abruptness.

Only the merest elevation of a jet eyebrow which matched the thick abundance of his black hair gave any indication that he considered her reply offhand. It was clear that people did not speak to him in this way, as a rule.

He gave an almost regretful smile. 'Then you should not dress so fetchingly, should you? You should have covered yourself in something which concealed you from head to foot,' he told her softly, jet eyes moving slowly from the top of her head to the tip of her pink-painted toenails. 'It is all your own fault.'

Even more uncharacteristically, Rose felt colour begin to seep heatedly into her cheeks. She rarely blushed! In her job she dealt with high-powered strangers every single day of her working life, and none of them had had the power to have her standing like this. Like some starstruck adolescent.

'Isn't it?' he prompted, on a sultry murmur.

Rose blinked. She *had* dressed up, yes—but it was a wedding, wasn't it? And every single other woman in the room had gone to town today, just as she had.

A floaty little slip-dress made of sapphire silk-chiffon. The same colour as her eyes, or so the cooing sales assistant had told her. And flirty little sandals with tiny kitten heels. She'd bought those in a stinging pink colour, deliberately *not* matching her dress. But then matching accessories were so passé—even the saleswoman had agreed with that. No hat. She hated confining her thick blonde hair beneath a hat—particularly on a day as hot as this one. Instead, she had ordered a dewy and flamboyant orchid from the nearby florists, in a paler-colour version of the shoes she wore. She'd pinned it into her hair, but she suspected that very soon it would start wilting.

Just as *she* would, if this exotic man continued to subject her to such a calculating, yet lazy look of appraisal.

She decided to put a stop to it right then and there, extending her hand and giving him a friendly-but-slightly-distant smile. 'Rose Thomas,' she said.

He took the hand in his and then looked down at it, and Rose found her eyes hypnotically drawn in the same direction, shocked by her reaction to what she saw. Her skin looked so very white against the dark olive of his and there seemed to be something compellingly erotic about such a distinctive contrast of flesh.

She tried to pull her hand away, but he held tight onto it, and as she drew her indignant gaze upwards it was to find the black eyes fixed on her mockingly.

'And do you know who I am, Rose Thomas?' he questioned silkily.

It was a moment of truth. She could feign ignorance, it was true. But wouldn't a man like this have been up against pretence and insincerity for most of his life?

'Of course I know who you are!' she told him crisply. 'This is the only wedding I've ever been to where a real-life prince has been acting as best man—and I imagine it's the same for most of the other people here, too!'

He smiled, and as she saw the slight relaxation of his body Rose took the opportunity to remove her hand from his.

Khalim felt the stealthy beat of desire as she resisted him. 'What's the matter?' He gave her an expression of mock-reproach. 'Don't you like me touching you, Rose Thomas?'

'Do you *normally* go around touching women you've only just met?' she demanded incredulously. 'Is that a favour which your title confers on you?'

The beat increased as he acknowledged her fire. Resistance was so rarely put in the way of his wishes that it had the effect of increasing them tenfold. He saw the clear blue brilliance of her eyes. No, a hundredfold, he thought and felt his throat thicken.

He gave a shrug. A little-boy look—the black eyes briefly appealing. It was a look that had always worked very well at his English boarding-school, especially with women. 'You took my hand,' he protested. 'You know you did!'

Rose forced a laugh. This was ridiculous! They were sparring over nothing more than a handshake! And Khalim was Guy's friend. Sabrina's friend. She owed it to them to show him a little more courtesy than this. 'Sorry.' She smiled. 'I'm a little overwrought.'

'Is it a man?' he shot out, and before she had time to think about the implications she shook her head.

'What an extraordinary conclusion to jump to!' she protested, but the admonishment made no difference.

'What, then?' he persisted.

'Work, actually,' she said.

'Work?' he demanded, as though she had just said a foreign word.

But then maybe to him it *was* a foreign word. A man like Prince Khalim had probably never had to lift his hand in work. 'Just a busy week.' She shrugged. 'A busy month—a busy year!' She sipped the last of her champagne and gave him a look of question. 'I'm getting myself another one of these—how about you?'

Khalim sucked in a breath of disapproval. How he hated the liberated way of women sometimes! It was not a woman's place to offer a man drinks, and he very nearly told her so, but the fire in her eyes told him that she would simply stalk off if he dared to. And he wanted her far too much to risk that...

'I rarely drink,' he said coolly.

'Good heavens!' said Rose flippantly. 'How does your body get hydrated, then? By intravenous infusion?'

The black eyes narrowed. People didn't make fun of *him*. Women never teased him unless invited to, by him. And never outside the setting of the bedroom. For a moment, he considered stalking away from *her*. But only for a moment. The bright lure of her flaxen hair made him waver as he imagined unpicking it, having it tumble down over his chest—its contrast as marked as when he had pressed his fingers against her soft white skin, just minutes ago.

'Alcohol,' he elaborated tersely.

'Well, I'm sure they run to a few soft drinks,' said Rose. 'But it doesn't matter. I'm going to, anyway. It was nice talking to you, Pr—'

'No!' He caught hold of her wrist, enjoying the purely instinctive dilating of her blue eyes in response to his action, the way her lips fell open into an inviting little 'O'. He imagined the sweet pleasures a mouth like that could work on a man, and had to suppress a shudder of desire. 'Not Prince anything,' he corrected softly. 'I am Khalim. To you.'

She opened her mouth to say something sarcastic, like, Am I supposed to be flattered?—but the ridiculous thing was that she *was* flattered. Absurdly flattered to be told to use his first name. She told herself not to be so stupid, but it didn't seem to work.

'Let me go,' she said breathlessly, but she thrilled at the touch of his skin once more.

'Very well.' He smiled, but this time it was the smile of a man who knew that he had the ability to enslave a woman. 'But only if you agree to come and find me once the music starts, and then we shall dance.'

'Sorry. I never run after a man.'

He could feel the rapid thundering of her pulse beneath his fingertips. 'So you won't?'

The silky voice was nearly as mesmeric as the silky question. 'You'll have to come and find *me*!' she told him recklessly.

He let her go, taking care to conceal his giddy sense of elation. 'Oh, I will,' he said quietly. 'Be very sure of that.' And he watched her go, an idea forming in his mind.

He would make her wait. Make her think that he had
changed his mind about dancing. For he knew enough of
women to know that his supposed indifference would fan the
desire she undoubtedly felt for him. He would tease her with
it. Play with her. He knew only too well that anticipation
increased the appetite, and thus satisfied the hunger all the
more. And Rose Thomas would sigh with thankful pleasure
in his arms afterwards.

On still-shaking legs, Rose headed for the bar, hoping that
the bewilderment she felt did not show on her face. She did
not fall for men like Khalim. She liked subtle, sophisticated
and complex men. And while she recognised that he had a
keen intelligence—there was also something fundamentally
dangerous about this black-eyed stranger in his exotic robes.

Inside, she was jelly. *Jelly.* Her hands were trembling by
the time she reached the corner of the ballroom where a
white-jacketed man tended an assortment of cocktails and
champagne.

She could see Sabrina at the far end of the room, a vision
in white as she giggled with one of her bridesmaids—Guy's
youngest niece.

'Champagne, madam?' smiled the bartender. 'Or a Sea
Breeze, perhaps?'

Rose opened her mouth to agree to the former, but changed
her mind at the last minute. Because something told her she
would need her all her wits about her. And alcohol might
just weaken an already weakened guard.

'Just a fizzy water, please,' she said softly.

'Too much of a good thing?' came a voice of dry amusement, and she looked up to find Guy Masters smiling down
at her.

Rose liked Sabrina's new husband enormously. He was
outrageously handsome, outrageously rich and he loved
Sabrina with an intensity which made Rose wistful, and determined that she would never settle for second-best.

Rose had met Sabrina when she had gone in search of a

rare book, and Sabrina had helpfully scoured all the index-files until Rose had found what she'd been looking for. It had been the day after Sabrina had become engaged to Guy, and she had excitedly shown off her ring to Rose—a plain and simple but utterly magnificent diamond.

Sabrina hadn't really known anyone in London, other than Guy's friends, and the two women had been of similar age and similar interests.

'Or are you driving?' questioned Guy, still looking at her glass of mineral water.

'Er, no,' she said, in a faint voice. 'I just want to keep a clear head about me.'

'Quite wise,' remarked Guy, and he lowered his voice by a fraction. 'Since my old friend Khalim seems to have set his sights on you.'

'He...he does?' And then thought how obscenely *star-struck* that sounded. She cleared her throat and fixed a smile onto her lips. 'Not really. We just had a chat, that's all.'

'A *chat*?' asked Guy, now sounding even more amused. 'Khalim exchanging small talk? Now, that'll be a first!'

'Wonderful wedding!' said Rose valiantly, with an urgent need to change the subject. 'Sabrina looks absolutely stunning.

At the mention of his new wife's name, Guy's face softened into a look of tenderness, the intentions of his school-friend instantly forgotten. 'Doesn't she?' he asked indulgently, and then a slight note of impatience entered his voice. 'Between you and me, I just wish we could forget the damned dancing and just *leave*!'

Rose smiled. 'And deny your wife her wedding day! I think you can wait a little longer, don't you, Guy? After all, you've been living together for well over a year now!'

'Yeah,' sighed Guy. 'But this is the first time it will have been, well, legal...' He looked down into Rose's face. 'Why, you're *blushing*!' he observed incredulously. 'I'm sorry, Rose—I certainly didn't mean to embarrass you—'

'No, you weren't. Honestly,' Rose assured him hastily. She wasn't going to point out that it was a pair of glittering jet eyes being lanced provocatively in her direction which had the heat singing remorselessly in her veins. In a way, she wished that maybe Guy and Sabrina *would* leave. And then she could leave, too. And she wouldn't have to dance with Khalim and put herself in what was clearly becoming apparent would be a very vulnerable position indeed.

You don't *have* to dance with him, she reminded herself sternly. It wasn't a royal command. Well, of course it *was*, she realised with a slight edge of disbelief. But even if it was, she was not one of Khalim's subjects and London was not part of his kingdom! She could just give him a small, tight smile and tell him that she wasn't really in the mood for dancing.

Couldn't she?

But in the event she didn't have to. Because Khalim came nowhere near her. She found herself observing him obsessively, while doing her level best not to appear to be doing so.

He stood out from the crowd of fabulously dressed guests, and not by virtue of his own glorious and unconventional attire. No, it went much deeper than that. Rose had never met anyone of royal blood before, and of course she had heard the expression of regal bearing—but up until now she realised that she hadn't really known what it had meant.

There was some innate grace about the way he carried himself. Some fundamental and rare elegance in the way he moved. She had never seen anything like it. People noiselessly slipped from his path. Women stared at him with looks of undisguised and rapacious hunger on their faces.

Did he notice? Rose wondered. His proud, handsome face did not seem to register any emotion at all. But maybe he was used to it. Why, he had only had to lay his hand autocratically on *her* wrist to have her virtually melting at his feet.

The meal was served and Rose found herself seated with a banker on one side of her, and an oceanographer on the other. Both men seemed amusing and intelligent and the oceanographer was handsome in the rugged kind of way which denoted a healthy, outdoor lifestyle. He flirted outrageously with Rose, and even an hour ago she might have been receptive enough to respond.

But the only man who burnt a searing image on her subconscious sat at the top table, picking at his food with the kind of indifference which suggested that conventional hunger was not uppermost in his mind.

At that moment, Khalim looked up and glittered a black look in her direction—a look which sent a shiver tiptoeing down her spine. Quickly, she put her fork down and pushed the plate away.

'So what do you do, Rose?' asked the oceanographer.

She turned to look at him with a smile. 'I'm a head-hunter.'

'Really?' He grinned. 'I guess you earn lots of money, then!'

Which was what people *always* said! 'I wish I did!'

The waitress leaned over, a look of concern on her face. 'Is everything all right with the salmon, miss?'

Rose nodded, looking guiltily at the untouched plate. 'It's fine! I'm just not very hungry, that's all!'

The waitress had the kind of build which suggested that no plate of hers was ever returned unless completely clean. 'Someone in the kitchen just said that we shouldn't bother offering the top table any pudding—so much food has come back from there as well! Maybe you should be sitting with *them*!' she joked.

'Maybe!' laughed Rose politely, half of her thankful that she was nowhere near Khalim, while the other part of her wished desperately to be within his exciting and yet dangerous proximity. She risked another look, seeing how the diamond lights of the chandeliers emphasised the creamy-gold silk of the robes he wore and the raven gleam of his black hair.

Valiantly she forced a few raspberries down her throat, but even the plump and succulent fruit failed to tempt her. And then at last it was time for the cutting of the cake, and the speeches.

Rose could barely take in a word of the best man's speech—she was so mesmerised by his dark, proud face. Her eyes feasted on his features—the hard, bright eyes and the stern expression which made her feel she'd won the lottery when it softened into affection. His mouth was a contrast of lush, sensual curves, but the upper lip had a hard, almost cruel streak. She shivered. Be warned, she thought.

Guy's speech had every woman in the room all misty-eyed with emotion as he gazed down in open adoration at Sabrina and spoke of his love for her.

And then the band struck up and people drifted onto the dance-floor and Rose's heart was in her mouth as she remembered Khalim's intention to dance with her.

But he did not come near her, just returned to his seat and sat there imperiously, his gaze drifting over her from time to time, the black eyes luminous with sensual promise.

Rose allowed herself to dance with whoever asked her, but her heart wasn't in it. She moved mechanically as the oceanographer took her in his arms, stiffening with rejection when he tried to pull her a little closer.

She sat down and was just beginning to seriously hope that Guy and Sabrina would depart for their honeymoon, so that she could leave as well, when Khalim appeared in front of her, the black eyes narrowed in mocking question.

'So,' he said softly. 'I have taken you at your word and come to find you.' The black eyes glittered. 'Though you made yourself very easy to find, Rose—you sweet, blushing flower. Now—' his voice dipped in sultry question '—shall we dance?'

Her cheeks *were* stinging at the implication that she had just been sitting there, waiting for him—but then, *hadn't* she?

'Is that supposed to be an invitation I can't resist?' she shot back at him.

A smile hovered at the edges of his mouth. 'No, Rose,' he purred. 'It is a royal command.'

She opened her mouth to object, but by then it was too late, because he had taken her hand with arrogant assurance and was leading her onto the dance-floor.

'Come,' he said quietly.

She moved into his arms as though her whole life had been a dress rehearsal for that moment. He placed his hands at the slim indentation of her waist, and Rose's fingers drifted with a kind of irresistible inevitability to his shoulders. She breathed in the faint scent of sandalwood about him, its soft muskiness invading her senses with its sweet perfume.

Rose considered herself a modern, independent woman, but a minute in Khalim's embrace was enough to transform her into a woman who felt as helpless as a kitten.

Khalim felt the slow unfurling of desire as he moved his hands down to rest on the slender swell of her hips. 'You dance beautifully, Rose,' he murmured.

'S-so do you,' she managed breathlessly, gloriously aware of the hard, lean body which moved with such innate grace beneath the silken robes. 'L-lovely wedding, wasn't it?' she commented, and said a silent prayer that her sanity would return. And soon!

He didn't reply for a moment. 'All women like weddings,' he mused eventually.

She thought she heard deliberate provocation and lifted her head to stare him straight in the eyes, the bright sapphire of her gaze clashing irrevocably with glittering jet. 'Meaning that men don't, I suppose?'

He raised a mocking brow and thought how bright her hair, and how white her soft skin, against which the soft curves of her lips were a deep, rich pink. Like the roses which bloomed in the gardens of his father's palace and scented the night air with their perfume. His pulse quickened. 'Do you always jump to conclusions, I wonder?'

'But you meant me to,' she parried. 'It was a remark designed to inflame, wasn't it?'

He shook his head, his desire increased by her feisty opposition. 'It was simply an observation,' he demurred. 'Not a…how-do-you-say?' He frowned, as if in deep concentration. 'Ah, yes—a sexist comment!'

Rose leaned away from him a little, and felt the almost imperceptible tightening of his hands on her hips, as though he couldn't bear to let her go. 'You can't pretend to be stumbling over the language with *me*, Khalim!' she said crisply, trying to ignore the thundering of her heart beneath her breast, 'when I happen to know that you went to school in England and are as fluent as I am!'

She was *very* fiery, he thought with a sudden longing. 'And what else do you know about me, Rose Thomas?' he mused.

Briefly she considered affecting total ignorance. This was a man with an ego, that was for sure! Yet how often did people speak their minds to a man with his power and his presence?

'I know that you are the heir to a mountain kingdom—'

'Maraban,' he elaborated softly, and his voice deepened with affectionate pride.

Something imprecise shimmered over her skin at the way he said that single word and a sense of hazy recognition made her shiver. 'Maraban,' she repeated wonderingly, until she realised that she was in danger of sounding starstruck again.

'What else?' he prompted, intrigued by that dreamy look which had softened her features when she had said the name of the land of his birth. And then his mouth hardened. Maraban was an oil-rich country—and didn't fabulous wealth always produce enthusiasm in the greedy hearts of most Westerners?

She wondered what had caused the fleetingly judgemental

look which had hardened his face into a stern mask. She snapped out of her reverie to deliver a few home truths.

'I've heard that you have something of a reputation where women are concerned,' she told him crisply.

'A reputation?' It sounded too close to unaccustomed criticism for Khalim not to experience a sudden flicker of irritation. 'Do elaborate, Rose.'

'Do I need to? You like women, don't you?'

His smile grew cynical. 'And is it wrong to enjoy the many pleasures which the opposite sex can offer?'

His words were accompanied by the splaying of his fingers over her back, and Rose found herself wondering what it would be like if her skin were bare. And his... She swallowed. 'You make women sound like an amusement arcade!'

He smiled. 'It is an interesting analogy,' he remarked, and resisted the urge to move his fingertips to lie just below the jut of her breasts. He wanted her, and he never had to try very hard, not where women were concerned. There had only ever been one woman who had turned him down, and that had been Sabrina.

He moved his head slightly as the bride and groom passed by, and saw Sabrina gazing up into the face of her new husband. Khalim had instantly forgiven and understood her rejection, because she had been in love with his best friend.

Resisting the urge to explore Rose's breasts, he kept his hands right where they were. For while his seduction of Rose Thomas was a certainty, he suspected that he would have to take things slowly...

'So,' he said huskily. 'You are at an advantage, are you not? Since you know something of me, while I know nothing of you, Rose—other than the fact that you are the most beautiful woman in the room.'

'So you said earlier,' answered Rose sweetly, pleased to see the fleeting look of irritation which hardened the dark face. She teased him a little more—just for the hell of it. 'I can't see why women fall for your charms if you keep coming out with the same old compliment!'

'Oh, can't you?' he questioned silkily, and with a fluid movement of grace caught her closer still, so that their bodies melded together with shocking intimacy. He noted with satisfaction the instant darkening of her eyes, the two high spots of colour to her cheeks. Through the thin layers of silk which covered him, and her, he could feel the tiny tight buds of her breasts as they flowered against his chest and he felt another sharp pull of desire.

'D-don't,' protested Rose weakly, shaken by a sweet flood of need, stronger and more powerful than anything she had ever experienced before.

Triumphantly, Khalim felt her tremble against him and pressed his lips close to where the bright, flaxen hair gleamed against her ear. 'Don't what?' he whispered.

'Don't.' But her voice shook so that the word was unrecognisable and she had to try again. 'Don't stand so close to me.'

With the instinctive mastery of the conqueror, he did exactly as she asked, moving a little away from her, and he heard her unmistakable little of gasp of protest. 'Is that better?' he questioned silkily.

Better? Rose felt as bereft as if someone had just shorn off her long hair and left her neck bare and cold. She found herself wanting to beg him to pull her back into that warm, enticing circle, until common sense began to reassert itself. She was not the kind of woman to beg a man to do *anything.* 'Much better,' she agreed levelly.

He didn't believe her for a moment. Khalim smiled, acknowledging what he knew to be a universal truth—that the chase was often the most exciting part of the conquest. 'So why don't you tell me something about yourself?' he murmured.

She turned her face upwards, her eyes sparking a challenge. 'What would you like to know?'

'Everything. Absolutely everything.'

Rose's mouth curved into a smile. 'You'll have to be a *little* more specific than that, I'm afraid!'

He wondered what she would say if he told her the only thing he really wanted to know was what her naked body would look like. Stretched out in rapturous abandon on the slippery-soft sheets of his enormous bed. 'So tell me what you do,' he murmured.

'You mean, work-wise?'

He nodded, thinking that she had no need at all to work. She could easily be a rich man's mistress, he thought. His. Why had he never met her before? 'Or shall I guess what kind of work you do, Rose?'

'You can try!'

'Simple. A model?' he mused.

'I'm not tall enough,' she objected, hating herself for the warm glow which his compliment produced. 'Or thin enough.'

Irresistibly, his eyes were drawn to the luscious swell of breast and hip. 'You are perfect,' he said huskily. 'Quite perfect.'

Within the circle of his arms, Rose shivered. She wasn't *used* to men saying things like that, and certainly not within minutes of meeting her! Mostly, she mixed with lofty intellectuals who might occasionally pay her a clever-clever compliment. Not men who made no attempt to hide a primitive and compelling kind of desire. 'That's outrageous flattery!' she protested.

'Flattery, yes. Outrageous, no!' He turned her round in time with the music, admiring her natural and subtle grace.

He really was the most wonderful dancer, thought Rose. She rarely danced properly like this—and never with a prince! It was heavenly to glide around the dance-floor in the arms of a man. Instead of everyone jigging about doing their own thing and usually managing to connect with her on the way!

He was staring down at her in a thoughtful way, and she immediately wiped the look of dreamy bliss off her face. 'So you've given up, have you? You're not very good at guessing, are you?' she challenged.

'Maybe not, but there are many things I am *extremely* good at, Rose,' he boasted silkily, and chose just that moment to move a silken thigh between hers, immediately losing himself in an erotic dream of making love to her.

In time with the sexual boast, Rose felt the pressure of his leg, and the unmistakable iron of the steely muscle which lay beneath the delicate fabric. An unfamiliar hunger shot through her as she felt her heart-rate soar and something deep inside her began to slowly dissolve. She had to stop this. Now.

'I'm a head-hunter,' she said quickly.

Khalim's dream was shattered by her words. 'Head-hunter?' he questioned, and frowned, his mind firing up with savage imagery.

'Yes, you know—I find people for jobs!'

'I know what a head-hunter is! And you are successful in your line of work?'

'Yes, I am.'

'Then, you must be a very intuitive woman, Rose.' The tip of his finger rippled slowly over the curve of her waist and he felt her shiver in response. 'Ve-ry intuitive.'

Warning bells began ringing in her mind. 'I-I think I've had enough dancing,' she said breathlessly, feeling ridiculously disappointed when he took her at her word and let her go.

'I agree.' The tug of desire had become persistent and uncomfortable. It made him want to take her. To… Khalim found himself having to fight for the rigid self-control which had been a fundamental part of his upbringing. And it was many years since he had had to fight for anything. He took a step backwards, steadying his suddenly shallow breathing.

Missing the feel of silk and the scent of sandalwood, Rose

placed her hands over her flushed cheeks and could feel pulses fluttering absolutely everywhere. And it was only then she noticed that the floor was completely empty and that everyone was standing watching them.

'Oh, my God!' she moaned. 'Look!'

'It seems that we have inadvertently been providing the floor show,' said Khalim, in some amusement, as he followed the direction of her gaze.

Rose's distress grew even more intense, especially as Guy had chosen that moment to approach them and had clearly overheard Khalim's remark.

'A very *erotic* floor show,' he teased.

Rose suppressed a groan. They had been acting like a couple of irresponsible teenagers!

'We were simply dancing.' Khalim shrugged, his black eyes sending out a conspiratorial gleam to Rose.

'Is that what you call it?' joked Guy. 'Anyway, Sabrina and I are planning to leave now.' His grey eyes crinkled as he looked at his best man. 'And thanks for the honeymoon, Khalim.'

Silken shoulders were raised in a careless shrug. 'It is nothing other than my pleasure to give,' he drawled.

'Sabrina told me the destination was a secret,' said Rose.

The two men exchanged glances.

'And so it is. Traditionally, a secret shared between the groom and best man. But do not fear, I will tell you later, beautiful Rose,' promised Khalim softly.

'Later?' she asked, with a quick glance at her wrist-watch. Who had said anything about later?

'But of course. You and I are going for a drink together afterwards.'

Guy smiled. 'Are you?'

Rose saw the black eyes being levelled at her consideringly, saw the arrogant expectation that she would simply fall in with his regal wishes! And who really could blame him, after her shameless display on the dance-floor?

'But you told me you rarely drink, Khalim,' she reminded him innocently. 'So wouldn't that be an awful waste of your time?'

He opened his mouth to object, and then shut it again. Somewhere deep in his groin, Khalim felt a pulse begin to beat with slow insistence. He felt the sweet, sharp tang of desire and yet he instantly recognised her determination to oppose him. It flashed in sapphire sparks from her beautiful blue eyes. No matter what he said, Rose Thomas was not planning on going anywhere with him tonight. 'You don't want to?'

The note of incredulity in his voice was unmistakable, and Rose was very tempted to smile. But something in the cold glitter of his gaze made her decide that smiling maybe wasn't the best idea. 'It's been a long day,' she told him apologetically. 'And I'm bushed! Some other time, perhaps?'

Khalim's face grew distant; indeed, he barely noticed Guy slipping away to find Sabrina. 'I never issue an invitation more than once,' he told her coldly.

Rose was aware of a lurching sense of regret. You've missed your chance, girl, she thought—even while the sane part of her rejoiced. This man was different, she recognised. Different and dangerous. He had the power to make her vulnerable, and he was the last person she wanted to be vulnerable around. Why, a man like that would chew her up and spit her out in little pieces!

'What a pity,' she said lightly.

His black eyes lingered on the lushness of her lips, the creaminess of her skin. 'A pity indeed,' he agreed, briefly bowing his dark head before sweeping away from her across the ballroom.

And she watched him go with a thundering heart.

'They're leaving!' called someone, and Rose looked across the room to see that Sabrina had changed out of her bridal gown into a silvery-blue suit and was carrying her bouquet, Guy in an impressive dark suit at her side.

Everyone began to surge out of the ballroom to wave them off, but Rose hung back. She could see Khalim talking to Guy and she found herself unwilling to face him, aware of a dull sense of an opportunity lost, an opportunity never to be repeated.

She saw Sabrina turn and teasingly hold her bouquet of lilies above her head while every female present lifted their arms in hope of catching it. Even Rose eagerly raised her arms to catch the waxy blooms as they came flying in her direction, but the redhead beside her was more eager still.

'Gotcha!' she shouted as she leapt into the air and pounced triumphantly on the bouquet.

It's only a tradition, Rose told herself dully as she watched the girl ecstatically smelling the flowers. Why would catching a bunch of flowers guarantee that you would be the next to be married? And it wasn't as if she even *wanted* to get married, was it? These days lots and lots of women in their late twenties were electing to stay single.

But when she looked up again, it was to find herself caught in the lancing gaze of a pair of glittering black eyes.

I have to get out of here, she thought, with a sudden sense of panic.

CHAPTER TWO

In a daze, Rose left the Granchester and found herself a taxi, but afterwards she couldn't recollect a single moment of the journey. Not until the cab drew up outside the flat she shared in Notting Hill did reality begin to seep back into her consciousness as she tried to rid herself of the memory of the dark prince, with his proud, sensual face.

She let herself in through the front door and put her handbag on the hall table, relieved to be home. And safe.

She loved her flat—it was her very first property and occupied the first floor of a grand old high-ceilinged house. But it was an ambitious project for a first-time buyer and the repayments on her loan were high, which was why she had taken on a flatmate—Lara.

Lara was a struggling actress who described herself as Rose's lodger, but Rose never did. Equality was something she strove for in every area of her life. 'No, we're flatmates,' she always insisted.

It was a typical bachelor girls' home—full of colour in the shared areas and rather a lot of chaos in Lara's bedroom—because, much as she nagged, there didn't seem to be anything Rose could do to change Lara's chronic untidiness. So now she had given up trying.

There were brightly coloured scarves floating from a coatstand in the hall, and vases of cheap flowers from the market dotted around the sitting room. And the bathroom was so well stocked with various lotions and potions that it resembled the cosmetics counter of a large department store!

'Anyone at home?' she called.

'I'm in the kitchen!' came the muffled reply, and Rose walked into the kitchen to find Lara busy crunching a choc-

26

olate biscuit and pouring coffee into a mug. Her staple diet and *my* coffee, thought Rose ruefully as Lara looked up with a smile and held a second mug up. 'Coffee?'

Rose shook her head. 'No, thanks. I think I need a drink.'

Lara raised her eyebrows in surprise. 'But you've just been to a wedding!'

'And I barely touched a drop all day,' said Rose grimly. She had deliberately avoided liquor so that she would have all her wits about her, and then just look at the way she had behaved on the dance-floor! She sighed as she poured herself a glass of wine from the cask in the fridge.

'Are you okay?' asked Lara curiously.

'Why shouldn't I be?'

'You just seem a little…I don't know…tense.'

Tense? Rose sipped at her wine without enjoyment. She could see her reflection in the pig-shaped mirror which hung on the kitchen wall. Her face was *unbelievably* pale. She looked as if she'd seen a ghost. Or a vision maybe… 'I guess I am,' she said slowly.

'So why? What was the wedding like? Awful?'

'No, beautiful,' said Rose reflectively. 'The most beautiful wedding I've ever been to.'

'Then why the long face?'

Rose sat down at the kitchen table and put her wineglass down heavily. 'It's stupid, really—' She looked up into Lara's frankly interested brown eyes. 'Did I ever tell you that Sabrina's new husband is best friends with a prince?'

Lara's eyes grew larger. 'You're winding me up, right?'

Rose shook her head and bit back a half-smile. It did sound a bit far-fetched. 'No, I'm not. It's the truth. He's prince of a country—more a principality, really—called Maraban—it's in the Middle East.'

'And next, I suppose you'll be telling me that he's outrageously good-looking and rich, to boot!'

Rose sighed. 'Yes! He's exactly that. Just about the most

perfect man you've ever seen. Tall, and dark and hand-some—'

'Oh, ha, ha, ha!'

'No, he *is*! Honestly. He's divine. I danced with him…'
Her voice tailed off as she remembered how it felt to have
his body so tantalisingly close to hers. 'Danced with him,
and—'

'And what?'

'And—' No need to point out that she had got a little
carried away on the dance-floor. She squirmed with remembered pleasure and glanced up to see Lara's open-mouthed
expression.

'Oh, Rose, you *didn't*?'

Rose blinked as the implication behind Lara's question
squeaked its way home. 'No, of course I didn't! You surely
don't imagine that I'd meet a man at a wedding and hours
later leap into bed with him, do you?' she questioned indignantly.

But you did it in thought if not in deed, didn't you?
mocked the guilty voice of her conscience.

Lara was looking at her patiently. 'So what happened?'

'He, well, he asked me to go for a drink with him once
the bride and groom had left,' explained Rose.

'What's the problem with that? You said yes, of course?'

'Actually,' said Rose, in a high, forced voice, not quite
believing that she had had the strength of will to go through
with it, 'I said no.'

Lara was blinking at her in bemusement. 'You've lost me!
He's gorgeous, he's royal and you *turned him down*! *Why*,
for heaven's sake?'

'I don't know.' Rose sighed again. 'Well, maybe that's not
true, I suppose I do, really. He's so utterly irresistible—'

'That's usually considered a plus where men are concerned, isn't it?'

'But he would never commit, I know he wouldn't—it's
written all over his face!'

Lara stared at her incredulously. 'Never *commit*?' she echoed. 'I can't believe I'm hearing this! Rose, you've danced with the guy once and already you're talking commitment? And this from the woman who has always vowed never to get married—'

'Until I'm at least thirty-five,' said Rose with a look of fierce determination. 'I'll have achieved something by then, so I'll be ready! And people live longer these days—it makes sense to put off getting married for as long as possible.'

'Very romantic,' said Lara.

'Very realistic,' commented Rose drily.

'So why the talk of commitment—or, rather, the lack of it?'

Rose took a thoughtful sip of wine. She wasn't really sure herself. Maybe because she didn't want to be just another woman in a long line of discarded women.

But wouldn't it just sound fanciful if she told Lara that Khalim had a dangerous power about him which both attracted and yet repelled her? And wouldn't it sound weak if she expressed the very real fear that he could break her heart into smithereens? Lara would quite rightly say that she didn't know him—but Rose was intuitive, more so than usual where Khalim was concerned. She knew that with a bone-deep certainty—she just didn't know why.

She had been 'in love' just twice in her life. A university affair which had occupied her middle year there and then, in her early days in advertising recruitment—she'd dated an account executive for nine fairly blissful months. Until she had discovered one evening that he wasn't really into monogamy.

She wasn't sure whether it was her pride which had been hurt more than anything else, but from that day on she had been sensible and circumspect where men were concerned. She could take them or leave them. And mostly she could leave them...

'Do you fancy going to see a film?' asked Lara, with a glance at the kitchen clock. 'There's still time.'

Rose shook her head. What would be the point of going to a film if you knew for a fact that you wouldn't be able to concentrate on anything other than the most enigmatic face you had ever set eyes on? 'No, thanks. I think I'll take a shower,' she said with a yawn.

Aware that he was being closely watched by his emissary, Khalim paced up and down the penthouse suite with all the stealth and power of a sleek jungle cat. Outside the lights of the city glittered like some fabulous galaxy, but Khalim was impervious to its beauty.

Whenever he was in London on business, which he usually arranged to coincide with Maraban's most inhospitable weather—Khalim always stayed at the Granchester Hotel. He kept the luxurious rooms permanently booked in his name, though for much of the year they lay empty. They had been decorated according to his taste in a way which was as unlike his home in Maraban as it was possible to imagine. Lots of pale, wooden furniture and abstract modern paintings. But that was how he liked to live his life—the contrast between the East and the West each feeding two very different sides of his nature.

Once again, black eyes stared unseeingly out at the blaze of lights which pierced the night sky of London.

Eventually, he turned to Philip Caprice and held the palms of his hands out in a gesture which was a mixture of frustration and disbelief. He'd been bewitched by a pair of dazzling eyes so blue and hair so pale and blonde that he couldn't shake her image from his mind. He had wanted her here with him tonight—on his bed and beneath his body. And he would fill her. Fill her and fill her and…he gave a groan and Philip Caprice looked at him in concern.

'Sir?' he murmured. 'Is something the matter?'

'I cannot believe it!' Khalim stated bluntly and gave a low laugh. 'I must be losing my touch!'

Philip smiled, but said nothing. It was not his place to offer an opinion. His role was to act as a sounding-board for the prince—unless specifically invited to do otherwise.

Khalim turned hectic black eyes towards his emissary, trying to forget her pale enchantment. He could feel the fever of desire heating his blood, making it sing like a siren as it coursed its way around his veins. 'You are not saying anything, Philip!'

'You wish me to?'

Khalim drew a deep breath, swamping down the unfamiliar feeling of having been thwarted. 'Of course,' he said coolly, and then saw Philip's look of indecision. 'By the mane of Akhal-Teke, Philip!' he swore softly. 'Do you think my arrogance so great, my ego so mighty, that I cannot bear to hear the truth from you?'

Philip raised his dark eyebrows. 'Or my interpretation of the truth, sir? Every man's truth is different.'

Khalim smiled. 'Indeed it is. You sound like a true Marabanesh, when you speak like that! Give me your interpretation, Philip. Why have I failed with this woman, where never I have failed before?'

Philip intertwined his long fingers and spoke thoughtfully. 'All your life you have had your every wish pandered to, sir.'

'Not all.' Khalim's eyes narrowed dangerously as he mouthed the soft denial. 'I learnt the rigours of life through an English boarding-school!'

'Yes,' said Philip patiently. 'But ever since you reached manhood, little has been denied to you, sir, you know that very well.' He paused. 'Particularly where women are concerned.'

Khalim expelled a long, slow breath. Was he simply tantalised because for once something had eluded him? Why, some of the most beautiful women in the world had offered themselves to him, but his appetite had always been jaded by what came too easily. 'Only one other woman has ever turned me down before,' he mused.

'Sabrina?' said Philip softly.

Khalim nodded, remembering his easy acceptance of *that*. He tried to work out what was different this time. 'But that was understandable—because she was in love with Guy, and Guy is my friend whom I respect. But this woman...this woman...'

And the attraction had been mutual. She had been fighting her own needs and her own desires, he knew that without a doubt. When he'd taken her in his arms, she'd wanted him with a fire which had matched his own. He'd been certain that he would make love to her tonight, and the unfamiliar taste of disappointment made his mouth taste bitter.

'What is her name?' asked Philip.

'Rose.' The word came out as if it were an integral line of the poetry he had learnt as a child. It sounded as scented-sweet and as petal-soft as the flower itself. But the rose also had a thorn which could draw blood, Khalim reminded himself on a shudder.

'Maybe *she's* in love with someone else?' suggested Philip.

'No.' Khalim shook his head. 'There is no man in her life.'

'She told you that?'

Khalim nodded.

'Maybe she just didn't...' Philip hesitated before saying '...find you attractive?'

Khalim gave an arrogant smile. 'Oh, she did.' He placed his hand over his fast-beating heart. 'She most certainly did,' he murmured, remembering the way she had melted so responsively against his body. And her reaction had not just been about chemistry—undeniable though that had been. No, hers had been a hunger sharpened and defined by the exquisite torture of abstinence.

As his had been. How long since a woman had excited him in this way? Since his father's illness when much of the burden of responsibility for running the country had fallen onto his shoulders, there had been little time to pursue pleasure. And no woman, he realised, had ever excited him in *quite* this way.

Khalim swallowed. Her scent was still clinging to the silk of his robes. Unendurable.

'I must take a bath,' he ground out.

He had a servant draw him up a bath scented with oil of bergamot, and, once alone, he slipped off the silken robes, totally at ease in his nakedness. His body was the colour of deeply polished wood—the muscles honed so that they rippled with true power and strength.

It was a taut and lean body, though he had never stepped inside a gym in his life—that would have been far too narcissistic an occupation for a man like Khalim. But the long, muscular shaft of his thighs bore testimony to hard physical exercise.

Horse-riding was his particular passion, and one of his greatest sources of relaxation. He felt at his most free when riding his beloved Akhal-Teke horse across the salt flats of Maraban with the warm air rushing through his dark hair and the powerful haunches of the stallion clasped tightly between his thighs.

He lay back among the bubbles and let some of the tension soak from his skin, but not all—not by a long way. Rose Thomas and her pale blonde beauty were uppermost in his mind, and thoughts of her brought their own, different kind of tension. He felt the hardening of his body in response to his thoughts, and only through sheer determination of will did he suppress his carnal longing. But then, he had never once lost control over his body…

Should he woo her? he thought carelessly. Besiege her with flowers? Or with jewels perhaps? He rubbed thoughtfully at the darkened shadow of his chin. There wasn't a woman alive who could resist the glittering lure of gems.

He smiled as he stepped from the circular bath and tiny droplets of water gleamed like diamonds on the burnished perfection of his skin.

He had no appetite. Tonight he would work on some of the outstanding government papers he had brought back with him from Maraban.

He slipped on a silken robe in deepest, richest claret and walked barefoot back through the vast sitting room and into the adjoining study, where Philip was busy tapping away at the word processor.

He looked up as Khalim came in.

'Sir?'

'Leave that, now,' ordered Khalim pleasantly. 'I have something else for you.'

'Sir?'

'Find out where Rose Thomas lives. And where she works.'

CHAPTER THREE

EVEN after an hour-long bath and drinking chamomile tea, Rose slept surprisingly little that night. Especially considering that she had had a long and heavy week at work the previous week and then gone out with Sabrina on her 'hen-night' a couple of nights before the wedding.

She tossed and turned for most of the night as an aching sense of regret kept sleep at bay.

And a pair of black eyes kept swimming into her troubled thoughts. Eyes which glittered untold promise, and a body which promised untold pleasure.

She rose late, and was just getting dressed when she heard Lara's voice calling her name excitedly.

'Rose! Quickly!'

'I'll be there in a minute!'

She pulled on an old pair of jeans and a simple pale blue T-shirt and walked into the sitting room, where Lara was clutching excitedly at the most enormous bouquet of flowers she had ever seen.

There were massed blooms of yellow roses, studded with tiny blue cornflowers, and the heady fragrance hit her as soon as she entered the room.

'Wow!' said Rose admiringly. 'Lucky girl! Who's the secret admirer?'

'They aren't for *me*, silly!' choked Lara jealously. 'It's your name on the card—see.'

Her fingers trembling, Rose took the proffered card with a dawning sense of inevitability. She stared down at the envelope, and the distinctive handwriting which spelt out her name.

35

'Well, aren't you going to open it?' demanded Lara. 'Don't you want to know who they're from?'

'I know exactly who they're from,' said Rose slowly. 'Khalim sent them.'

'You can't know that!'

'Oh, yes, I can.' She gave a wry smile. 'I may have had a few sweet and charming boyfriends, but not one who would spend this much on a bunch of flowers.' But curiosity got the better of her, and she ripped the envelope open to find her hopes and her fears confirmed.

The message was beautifully and arrogantly stark.

'The yellow is for your hair; the blue for the sapphire of your eyes. I will collect you at noon. Khalim.'

'Oh, my *goodness*! How utterly, utterly romantic!' squeaked Lara, who was busy looking over her shoulder.

'You think so?' asked Rose tonelessly.

'Well, I'd be in absolute heaven if I got flowers like these from a man! And what a masterful message! You'd better get a move on!'

But Rose wasn't listening. 'What a *cheek*!' she exploded as her eyes roved over the message again. 'How dare he just *assume* that he can tell me a time and I'll be meekly sitting here waiting, like a lamb to the slaughter?'

'But you aren't going out anywhere else today, are you?' asked Lara in a puzzled voice.

'That isn't the point!'

'Well, what *is* the point?'

'The point is that I don't *want* to go out with him!'

'Don't you? Honestly?'

Honesty was a bit more difficult. Rose had worked hard on her independence and her sense of self-possession—both qualities which she suspected Khalim could vanquish with the ease of a man who had sensual power untold at his fingertips.

'A tiny bit of me does,' she admitted, and saw Lara's face

go all mushy. 'But the rest of me is quite adamant that he would be nothing but bad news!'

Lara sighed. 'So what are you going to do? Tell him that to his face? Or just pretend to be out when he calls?' She brightened a little. '*I* could go instead, if you like!'

Rose was unprepared for the shaft of jealousy which whipped through her with lightning speed. She shook her head. 'I'm a realist,' she said proudly. 'Not a coward. If I turn Khalim down again, then he'll just up the ante—and I am not prepared to be bombarded with charm and expensive trinkets.'

And wouldn't he just wear her down anyway?

'He's the kind of man who thrives on the chase,' she said slowly. 'The kind of man who isn't used to being rejected— it's probably a first for him!'

'So what, then?'

Little shivers of excitement rippled down Rose's spine as a decision formed in her mind. 'I'll go,' she said, in a voice which wasn't quite steady. 'And I'll convince him that I'm not the sort of woman he wants.'

'What sort of woman is that?' asked Lara, mystified.

'A temporary concubine!' said Rose, and then, seeing Lara's expression of mystification grow even deeper, added, 'Someone who will live with him as his wife, until he tires of her, and then on to the next!'

'You don't sound as though you like him very much,' said Lara thoughtfully.

And that was just the trouble. She didn't. And yet she did. Though how could she form *any* kind of opinion about the man, when she didn't really know him at all? She was simply sexually captivated by a man who exuded an animal magnetism which was completely foreign to her.

'I'm going to go and get ready,' she said, looking down at her faded jeans.

'What shall I do with the flowers?'

At the door, Rose turned and smiled. 'I'll forgo the obvious suggestion! You keep them, Lara,' she added kindly, and went back into her bedroom to change.

At least her wardrobe was adequate enough to cope with most things—even something like this. Her job meant that she had to look smart or glamorous whenever the occasion beckoned. Though an outing with a prince was so far outside her experience!

Still, a midday assignation was unlikely to call for much in the way of glitter, and she deliberately chose her most expensive and understated outfit. A demure shirt-dress in chalky-blue linen. It looked very English, she decided, and not in the least bit exotic. As she slid the final button into its hole she wondered whether that was why she had chosen it. To emphasise the differences between her pale restraint and his dark, striking beauty.

She swept her hair back and deftly knotted it into a French plait, and had put on only the barest touch of make-up before she heard the pealing of the front door bell. Drawing in a deep breath for courage and hoping that it might calm the frantic beat of her heart, Rose went out into the hall to answer it.

She pulled open the front door and saw that it was not Khalim who stood there, but a very tall dark-haired man dressed in an immaculate suit, his green eyes glittering with something akin to amusement as he looked down at her belligerent expression.

'Miss Thomas?' he asked smoothly.

He had a cool and rather beautiful face and was the kind of man who might, under normal circumstances, have made her heart beat a little faster. But these were not normal circumstances, Rose reminded herself.

'That's me,' she said inelegantly.

'The Prince Khalim is downstairs waiting for you in the car,' he said quietly. 'Are you ready?'

Rose frowned. 'And you are?'

'My name is Philip Caprice. I am his emissary.'

'Really?' Rose drew her shoulders back. 'And did Prince Khalim not think it *polite* to come and call for me himself?'

Philip Caprice hid a smile. 'It is quite normal for him to send me to collect you.'

'Well, it is not *normal* for me!' said Rose heatedly. 'If he can't even be bothered to get out of the car, then perhaps you would be so kind as to tell him that *I* can't be bothered going downstairs!'

Philip Caprice frowned. 'Look—'

But Rose shook her head. 'I'm sorry,' she said firmly. 'I know you're only doing your job—but your boss's... *invitation*—' she bit the word out sarcastically '—leaves a great deal to be desired. It might have been more polite if he'd actually phoned me to arrange a time, instead of calmly announcing it the way he did! Either he comes up here, or I'm staying put.'

Philip Caprice nodded, his green eyes narrowing, as if recognising determination when he saw it. As if recognising that, on this, she would not be budged.

'I'll go and tell him,' he said. 'Perhaps you could leave the door open?'

'Having to ring the doorbell would be too much of an indignity, I suppose?' she hazarded, but she did as he asked.

She stood for a moment and watched him go, before stalking back into the sitting room where Lara, who had been listening to the entire conversation, was see-sawing between fascination and horror.

'Oh, Rose,' she whispered admiringly. 'You've done it now! Bet you anything he just drives away!'

'I sincerely hope he does,' said Rose coolly.

'Do you really?' came a deep, velvety voice from behind her, and Rose whirled round to see Khalim standing there, with such a glint in his black eyes that she was unable to tell whether he was amused or outraged.

'Y-yes! Yes, I d-do,' she said breathlessly, her heart clenching tightly in her chest as she saw how different he looked today. The eyes glittered with the same predatory promise, but there was not a flowing robe in sight.

Instead he was wearing an exquisitely cut suit in deep charcoal-grey—a modern suit with a mandarin collar which set off the exotic perfection of his face. And where the flowing silk had only hinted at the hard, lean body which lay beneath—the suit left absolutely nothing to the imagination and Rose just couldn't stop looking at him.

His shoulders were broader than she had realised, much broader, while the narrow hips were those of a natural athlete. And the legs...good heavens, those legs seemed to go on forever. Such powerful legs.

Rose opened her mouth to say something, but words just failed her.

'You want me to go away?' he prompted silkily.

Did she? 'It would probably be for the best,' she answered truthfully.

'But you've dressed for lunch,' he observed, his eyes sweeping over the elegance of the pale linen dress.

'Yes, I have.'

'So why waste all that effort?'

'It wasn't much effort.' She shrugged. 'It only took me a few minutes to change!'

'I'm flattered,' he said drily.

She fixed him with a reproving stare. 'I'm used to men being courteous enough to collect their date, and not sending a *servant* to collect them!'

His eyes grew flinty. 'Philip is no servant,' he said coldly. 'He is my emissary.'

'Let's not quibble about terminology!' she returned. 'Why didn't you come yourself?'

Khalim sighed. What would her reaction be if he told her that he had never had to? That all his life he had only had to metaphorically click his fingers and whichever woman he'd wanted would come—if not running, then walking pretty quickly.

'But I am here now,' he said, in as humble an admission as he had ever made. Because he suspected that Rose Thomas was not playing games with him, and that if he pushed her too far then she would simply refuse to come. And he wanted her far too much to even countenance that.

He turned to where a tousled-headed brunette was gazing at him in wonder from the other side of the crimson-painted room, and gave her a slow smile.

'Khalim,' he said, with a slight nod of his head.

Rose was infuriated to see Lara virtually dissolve into a puddle on the carpet—but who could really blame her? It was something outside both their experiences, having a man of this calibre here, exuding vibrancy and sheer physical magnetism.

'L-Lara Black,' she stumbled. 'And I'm very pleased to meet you…K-Khalim.'

Any minute now and her flatmate would start prostrating herself in front of him, thought Rose despairingly. She turned to find those impenetrable dark eyes now fixed on her.

'Shall we go?' he questioned quietly.

She knew that it would be impossible to backtrack, even if she had wanted to—and to her horror she discovered that there was no way she wanted to. She wanted one lunch with this magnificent man. One lunch to show him that she was his equal. That she wouldn't crumble and capitulate in the face of all his undoubted charms.

One lunch, that was all.

'Very well,' she answered, in a quiet tone which matched his.

Khalim very nearly allowed a small smile of triumph to creep onto his lips, until he drew himself up short. There was no victory to be gained from that coolly dispassionate acceptance! he reminded himself. But instead of feeling irritation at her unwillingness to co-operate, he found that his senses were clamouring to life, making his blood sing out that heated, relentless rhythm once more.

'Come, then, Rose,' he said, and gestured for her to precede him.

In the hallway, however, he halted, and Rose's mouth dried as she turned to see why. He was too close. The hall was too small. If she reached out her hand she could touch that proud, beautiful face. Could run her fingertips along his sculpted chin, and meet the faint rasp of shadowed growth there. She swallowed.

Khalim's eyes gleamed. So. He had not been mistaken. It was for her just as it was for him. She wanted him. He noted the coiled-up tension of repressed desire in her rigid frame. He could read it in the dark helplessness of her eyes, and in the fulsome pout of her soft lips.

'So,' he said unsteadily. 'Where would you like to go?'

'Haven't you booked anywhere?' asked Rose in surprise. She had assumed that he would want the best table in one of the best restaurants—and Sunday was traditionally a very busy day for eating out.

'No.' He shook his head.

'That will limit our choice somewhat.'

'I don't think so.' He saw the frown which had creased the milky-white space of skin between two exceptionally fine eyebrows. 'I never have to book,' he explained, and for the first time in his life he realised that he sounded almost apologetic.

And then Rose began to get her first glimmer of the implications of dating this man. She tried to make light of it and smiled. 'One of the perks of being a prince, I suppose?'

'That's right.' He found himself smiling back, unable to resist that sunny and unsettling curve of her mouth. 'Where would you like to go?'

Rose wasn't a head-hunter for nothing. Her 'people skills' were what kept her going in a competitive industry. She guessed that luxury would be second nature to Khalim—so wouldn't he be a little bored with luxury?

'There's a local Italian restaurant called Pronto! on Sutton

Street,' she said. 'Simple food—but good. And you can usually get a table there!'

He was pleasantly surprised, expecting her to plump for
somewhere much more up-market than her local restaurant.
'Then let's go and find it,' he murmured.

On the way downstairs, Khalim was hypnotised by the
proud set of her shoulders and the plaited hair of brightest
gold which had captivated him from the moment he had first
seen her.

Outside sat the most luxurious car Rose had ever seen—a
great black gleaming monster of a car, with tinted windows
and a liveried chauffeur who was standing beside it, and who
immediately sprang to open the door.

'Take us to Pronto!,' said Khalim. 'On Sutton Street.' And
the chauffeur inclined his head respectfully.

Rose climbed into the back seat, noting that Philip was
seated at the front, next to the chauffeur. And next to him, a
dark-suited and burly individual. A bodyguard? she wondered nervously. Probably.

The car cruised slowly through the traffic-snarled streets,
until it drew up outside a restaurant whose exterior was
adorned with a giant picture of the Italian flag.

'Vibrant,' observed Khalim softly as the chauffeur opened
the door for them and they both climbed out onto the pave-
ment.

'Isn't Philip joining us?' asked Rose.

Khalim suppressed a feeling very close to frustration, but
even closer to jealousy. *Jealousy?* So she wanted his cool
and handsome emissary to join them, did she? Was she attracted to him, he wondered in disbelief, or did she simply
want a chaperon?

His mouth hardened. 'No, he is not.'

Now, what had put *that* look there? puzzled Rose, shocked
by the sudden surge of relief which washed over her. She
wanted to be on her own with him, she realised sinkingly,
her growing attraction to him becoming all too apparent by

the moment. But with an effort she managed to shrug it away. 'Fine by me,' she said easily.

Inside the restaurant it was even more vibrant—with Italian music playing gently in the background.

The waitress gave Khalim an appreciative glance. 'Have you booked?' she asked him.

Khalim shook his head. 'Can you fit us in?'

'Sure can!' The waitress grinned, and winked at him.

Rose glanced at Khalim rather nervously. Obviously the woman had no idea that she was being so familiar with a member of Maraban's royal family—but would Khalim be forgiving, or outraged? I don't *care*, she thought fiercely. *I'm* going to enjoy my lunch!

But, strangely, Khalim found that he was enjoying the un-accustomed pleasure of anonymity. Normally he would not sanction such an intimacy—and particularly not from a wait-ress in a rather basic restaurant.

And yet Rose looked incredibly relaxed—even in the cool linen dress which gave her the outward appearance of an ice-maiden—and he wanted to relax *with* her. Not to pull rank.

'Thank you,' he murmured.

Something about the way he spoke made the waitress nar-row her eyes at him, for she suddenly looked rather flustered and led them to what was undoubtedly the best table in the room.

The only one, thought Rose rather wryly, which was not sitting right on top of its neighbours!

He waited until they were seated opposite one another and had been given their menus, before he leaned forward.

'So was this some kind of test, sweet Rose?' he wondered aloud.

She caught the tantalising drift of sandalwood and fought down the desire to let it tug at her senses. 'Test?'

'Mmm.' He looked around. 'Did you think I would baulk at being brought to such spartan surroundings?'

She raised her eyebrows and gave him a considering look.

'Oh, dear me,' she murmured back. 'You may be a prince, but must I also classify you as a snob, Khalim?'

A rebuke was almost unheard of. He could not think of a single other person he would have tolerated it from. But coming from Rose with that quietly mocking tone, it was somehow different. And to Khalim's astonishment, he found himself tacitly accepting it as fair comment.

'You haven't answered my question,' he returned smoothly. '*Was* it some kind of test?'

Why not be honest? Wouldn't a man like this spend his life being told what he *wanted* to hear, rather than the unadulterated truth?

'I thought that you might have had your fill of fancy restaurants,' she observed. 'I mean, surely luxury must grow a little *wearing* if it's relentless? I thought of bringing you to a place you would be least likely to eat in, had the choice of venue been yours. And so I brought you here,' she finished, and lifted her shoulders in a gesture of conciliation.

Guileless! he thought, with unwilling admiration. 'How very perceptive of you, Rose.'

The compliment warmed her far more than it had any right to. 'That's me,' she said flippantly, picking up her menu and beginning to study it, only to glance up and find him studying *her*. 'Shall we order?'

Khalim's black eyes narrowed. He had never had a woman treat him like this! Did she not realise that she should always defer to him? He felt a renewed tension in his body. Strange how such insubordination could fuel his hunger for her even more.

They both ran their eyes over the menus uninterestedly and ordered salads and fish.

'Wine?' questioned Khalim. 'Or would you prefer champagne?'

'But you rarely drink alcohol,' pointed out Rose. She crinkled a smile up at the waitress. 'Just fizzy water, please.'

'Or a fruit punch?' suggested the waitress.

Rose opened her mouth to reply, but Khalim glittered a glance across the table at her, and she shut it obediently.

'Fruit punch,' he agreed, and he began to imagine what it would be like to subdue her in bed.

When they'd been left on their own once more, Rose felt distinctly uncomfortable under his lazy scrutiny.

'Do you *have* to stare at me like that?'

'Like what?' he teased.

As if he would like to slowly remove her dress and run his hands and his lips and his tongue over every centimetre of her body. Rose shivered with excitement. 'You don't need me to spell it out for you. It's insolent.'

'To admire a ravishing woman? Rose, Rose, Rose,' he cajoled softly. 'What kind of men must you have known before me if they did not feast their eyes on such exquisite beauty?'

'Polite ones,' she gritted.

'How very unfortunate for you.' He saw the threat of a glare, and retreated. 'Are we going to spend the whole lunch arguing?'

Arguing seemed a safer bet than feasting her eyes on *him*, though maybe not. Didn't this kind of sparring add yet another frisson to the rapidly building tension between them? Rose felt a slight touch of desperation. Where were her 'people-skills' now, when she most needed them? 'Of course not,' she said, pinning a bright smile to her lips. 'What would you like to talk about?'

She sounded as though she was conducting an interview with him, thought Khalim, with increasing disbelief. By now she should have been eating out of his hand. 'Are you always so…' he chose his word carefully '…*arch* with men?'

'Arch?' Rose took the question seriously. 'You think I'm superior?' Her eyes glinted with amusement. 'Or is it just that you aren't used to women who don't just meekly lie on their backs like a puppy, where you're concerned?'

'Not the best analogy you could have chosen, sweet Rose,' he murmured mockingly. 'Was it?'

And to her horror, Rose started blushing.

He saw the blush. 'My, you *are* very sensitive, aren't you?'

Only with him! 'No.' She shook her head. 'I'm a big girl. I live in the real world. I have a demanding job. If I can't cope with a teasing little comment like that, then I must be losing the plot.' And that was exactly what it felt like. *Losing the plot.* 'Perhaps I *was* being a little arch. Maybe it's a reaction. I just imagine that most women allow you to take the lead, just because of your position.'

'Again, very perceptive,' he mused. 'It makes a refreshing change to have a woman who—'

'Answers back?'

He had been about to say *have a conversation with*, but he allowed Rose her interpretation instead. His own, he realised, would surely have sounded like an omission. What kind of relationships had he had in the past, he wondered, if talking had never been high on the agenda? He nodded. 'If you like.'

The waitress chose that moment to deposit their fruit punches in front of them, and they both took a swift, almost obligatory sip, before putting the glasses down on the table, as if they couldn't wait to be rid of them.

Rose leant forward. 'So where were we?'

Confronted by the pure blue light of her eyes, Khalim felt dazed. He wasn't sure. With an effort, he struggled to regain his thoughts. 'I suspect that it's time to find out a little about one another. One of us asks the questions, while the other provides the answers.'

'Okay.' She nodded, thinking *this* should be interesting. 'Who goes first?' she asked.

By rights, he did. He always did. It was one of the privileges of power. But, perversely, he discovered that he wanted to accede to *her*. 'You do.'

Rose leaned back in her chair. She spent her whole life interviewing people and she knew that the question most often asked was the one which elicited the least imaginative response. So she resisted the desire to ask him what it was *really* like to be a prince. She was beginning to get a pretty good idea for herself. Instead she said, 'Tell me about Maraban.'

Khalim's eyes narrowed. If she had wanted to drive a stake through the very heart of him, she could not have asked a more prescient question. For the land of his birth and his heritage meant more to Khalim than anything else in the world.

'Maraban,' he said, and his voice took on a deep, rich timbre of affection. He smiled almost wistfully. 'If I told you that it was the most beautiful country in the world, would you believe me, Rose?'

When he smiled at her like that, she thought she would have believed just about anything. 'I think I would,' she said slowly, because she could read both passion and possession in his face. 'Tell me about it.'

When he was distracted by the intuitive sapphire sparkle of her eyes, even Maraban seemed like a distant dream, Khalim thought. Did she cast her spell on all men like this?

'It lies at the very heart of the Middle East,' he began slowly, but something in the soft pucker of her lips made the words begin to flow like honey.

Rose listened, mesmerised. His words painted a picture of a magical, faraway place. A land where fig trees and wild walnut trees grew, its mountain slopes covered with forests of juniper and pistachio trees and where dense thickets grew along the riverbanks. He spoke of jackals and wild boar, and the rare pink deer. A place with icy winters and boiling summers. A land of contrasts and rich, stark beauty.

Just like the man sitting opposite her, Rose realised with a start as he stopped speaking. Dazedly she stared down at the table and realised that their meals had been placed in front of them, and had grown cold. She lifted her eyes to meet his, saw the question there.

'It sounds quite beautiful,' she said simply.

He heard the tremor of genuine admiration in her voice. Had he really spoken so frankly to a woman he barely knew? With a sudden air of resolve he gestured towards the untouched food.

'We must eat, if only a little,' he said. 'Or the chef will be offended.'

Rose picked up her fork. She had never felt less like eating in her life—for how could she concentrate on food when this beautiful man with his dark, mobile face made her hungry for something far more basic than food?

'Yes, we must,' she agreed half-heartedly.

They pushed the delicious food around their plates mechanically.

'Tell me about yourself now, Rose,' he instructed softly.

'Essex will sound a little dull after Maraban,' she objected, but he shook his head.

'Tell me.'

She told him all about growing up in a small village, about catching tadpoles in jam-jars and tree-houses and the hammock strung between the two apple trees at the bottom of the garden. About the life-size dolls' house her father had built beside the apple trees for her eighth birthday. 'Just an ordinary life,' she finished.

'Don't ever knock it,' he said drily.

'No.' She looked at him, realising with a sudden rush of insight that an ordinary life would be something always denied to him. And wasn't it human nature to want what you had never had? 'No, I won't.'

'You have brothers and sisters?' Khalim asked suddenly.

She put her fork down, glad for the excuse to. He really *did* seem interested. 'One older brother,' she said. 'No sisters. And you?'

'Two sisters.' He smiled. 'All younger.'

'And a brother?'

'No,' he said flatly. 'No brother.'

'So one day you will inherit Maraban?' she asked, and saw his eyes grew wary.

'Some far-distant day, I pray,' he answered harshly, aware that her question had touched a raw nerve. Reminded him of things he would prefer to forget. Things which simmered irrevocably beneath the surface of his life. His father's health was declining, and the physicians had told him that he would be unlikely to see the year out. The pressure was on to find Khalim a wife.

He stared at the blonde vision sitting opposite him and his mouth hardened. And once he married, then sexual trysts with women such as Rose Thomas would have to stop.

Rose saw the sudden hardening of his features, the new steeliness in his eyes. She shifted back in her seat, knowing that the atmosphere had changed, but not knowing why.

Khalim's breath caught in his throat. Her movement had drawn his attention to the soft swell of her breasts beneath the armoury of her linen dress. She could not have worn anything better designed to conceal her body, he thought, with a hot and mounting frustration—and yet the effect on him was more potent than if she had been clad in clinging Lycra.

In Maraban, the women dressed modestly; it had always been so. Khalim was used to Western women revealing themselves in short skirts or plunging necklines, or jeans which looked as though they had been sprayed on.

But Rose, he realised, had somehow cut a perfectly acceptable middle path. She was decently attired, yet not in the least bit frumpy. Contemporary and chic, and so very, very sexy...

He felt another swift jerk of desire. He must rid himself of this need before it sent him half mad. The sooner he had her, the sooner he could forget her. 'Shall we go?' he asked huskily.

Rose stared at him. The black eyes seemed even blacker, if that was possible, and she knew exactly why. The waves of desire emanating from his sleek physique were almost palpable. Her mouth felt suddenly dry; she knew instinctively what would be next on the agenda. She must resist him. She *must*. He was far too potent. Too attractive by far. Did she want to be just another woman who had fallen into Khalim's bed after a brief glimmer of that imperious smile?

No!

'Why, certainly.' She smiled. 'I have a lot of work back at the flat which needs catching up on.'

He ignored that, even though her offhand attitude inflamed him as much as infuriated him. She would be much more co-operative in a moment or two. He had not misread the signs, of that he was certain.

And Rose Thomas wanted him just as much as he wanted her...

He stood up, and Philip appeared at the door of the restaurant almost immediately.

'Come,' said Khalim.

'Aren't you going to pay the bill?'

'Philip will settle it.'

Rose walked out to the car, where the chauffeur was already opening the door. It was *unbelievable*! Did none of life's tedious little chores ever trouble him? 'I suppose you have someone to do everything for you, do you, Khalim?' she offered drily, then wished she hadn't. For in order to answer her question he had barred her way, and she could see the light of some glorious sexual battle in his eyes.

'I have never exercised my right to have someone bathe me,' he returned softly.

'Your *right*?' she questioned in disbelief. 'To *bathe* you?'

'Why, of course. All princes of Maraban have a master...or mistress of the bathchamber.' He shrugged, enjoying the spontaneous darkening of her eyes, the way her lips were automatically parting. As if waiting for the first thrust of his tongue. Yes, now, he thought. *Now!*

'So where do you want to go from here, Rose?' He dipped his voice into a sultry caress, allowed his mouth to curve with sensual promise. 'Back home to work? Or back to my suite at the Granchester for…coffee?'

His deliberate hesitation left her in no doubt what he *really* had in mind, and as she met the hard glitter of his eyes Rose couldn't deny she was tempted. Well, who wouldn't be? When every pore of that magnificent body just screamed out that Khalim would know everything there was to know about the art of making love and a little bit more besides.

But self-preservation saved her. That, and a sense of pride. One lunch and one arrogant invitation! Did he imagine that would be enough to make her fall eagerly into his bed? She stared into a face which had 'heartbreaker' written all over it.

'Home, please,' she said, and saw a moment of frozen disbelief. 'I have a mountain of work to do.'

CHAPTER FOUR

THE intercom on her desk buzzed and startled Rose out of yet another daydream involving a black-haired man in silken clothes, throwing her down onto a bed and...

'Hel-lo?' she said uncertainly.

'Rose?' came the voice of Rose's boss, Kerry MacColl. 'It's Kerry.'

'Oh, hi, Kerry!'

'Look, something rather exciting has come up and I need to talk to you. Can you come in here for a moment, please?'

'Sure I can.' Trying to project an enthusiasm she definitely wasn't feeling, Rose pushed away the feedback form she had been completing and went out into the corridor towards Kerry's room, which was situated on the other side of the passage.

Headliners was one of London's most successful small head-hunting agencies, and Rose had worked there for two years. It specialised in placing people in jobs within the advertising industry and was famous for its youth, its dynamism and eclectic approach—all highly valued qualities when it came to dealing with their talented, but often temperamental clients!

Their offices were based in Maida Vale, in a charmingly converted mews cottage. It had been deliberately designed so that their workplace seemed more like a home from home, and was the envy of the industry! The theory was that relaxed surroundings helped people do their job better and, so far, the practice was bearing out the theory very nicely.

Rose could see Kerry working at her desk and walked straight in without knocking, since she had always operated an open-door policy. And although, strictly speaking, Kerry *was* her boss—she was only a couple of years older than Rose—she had never found the need to pull rank. Headliners eight employees all worked as a team, and not a hierarchy.

She looked up as Rose came in, pushed her tinted glasses back up her nose, and smiled. 'Hi!'

Rose smiled back. 'You wanted to see me?'

Kerry nodded and fixed her with a penetrating look. 'How are you doing, Rose?'

Rose forced herself to widen her smile. 'Fine.' She nodded. And she was, of course she was. Just because she had spent the week since her lunch with Khalim thinking about him during every waking moment—it didn't mean there was anything wrong with her. And even if when she went to bed there was no let-up—well, so what? Maybe sleep *didn't* come easily, and maybe all her dreams *were* invaded by that same man—but that did not mean she was not fine. She wasn't sick, or broke, or worried, was she?

She had tried displacement therapy, and thrown herself into a week of feverish activity. She had spring-cleaned her bedroom—even though it was almost autumn!—and had gone to the cinema and the theatre. She had attended the opening of an avant-garde art exhibition and visited her parents in their rambling old farmhouse.

And still felt as though there was a great, gaping hole in her life.

'I'm fine,' she said again, wondering if her smile looked genuine.

Kerry frowned. 'You're quite sure?' she asked gently. 'You've seemed a little off colour this week. A bit pale, too. And haven't you lost weight?'

For a moment, Rose was tempted to tell her, but she never bought her problems into work with her. And, anyway, she didn't *have* a problem! she reminded herself. 'Oh, come on! Who *isn't* always trying to lose weight?' she joked.

'True.' Kerry indicated the chair opposite her. 'Sit down.'

'Thanks.' Rose wondered what all this was about, and

started to feel the first stirrings of curiosity. Kerry seemed terribly excited about something. And it must be something big because Kerry was the kind of seen-it-all and done-it-all person who wasn't easy to impress.

'What if I told you I'd just had lunch with a client—'

'I'd say lucky you—I just had a boring old sandwich at my desk!' And no need to mention that most of it had ended up in the bin.

'A client.' Kerry sucked in a deep and excited breath and then Rose really *was* surprised. Why, her sophisticated and sometimes cynical boss was looking almost *coquettish*! 'The most surprising and unbelievable client you can imagine.'

'Oh?'

'What would you say if I told you that we are being hired by a—' Kerry gulped the word out as if she couldn't quite believe she was saying it '—*prince*?' Kerry sat back in her chair and looked at Rose, her face a mixture of triumph and curiosity.

Rose felt as though she were taking part in a play. As though someone else had written the script for this scene which was now taking place. It was surely far too much of a coincidence to suppose that…that… Her heart was pounding unevenly in her chest. 'A prince?' she asked weakly, playing for time.

Kerry completely misinterpreted her strangulated words. 'I know,' she confided. 'It took me a little while before I could believe it myself! I mean, there isn't much that surprises *me*, but when a Lawrence-of-Arabia-type character walks into one of London's top restaurants and every woman in the room sat staring at him, open-mouthed. Well, suffice it to say that I was momentarily speechless!'

'That *must* be a first,' said Rose drily, and forced herself to ask the kind of questions she would normally ask if her brain weren't spinning round like a carousel inside her head. 'What did he want?'

'That's the funny thing.' Kerry picked up a pencil and twirled it thoughtfully around in her fingers. 'He wanted *you*.'

Disbelief and a lurching kind of excitement created an unfamiliar cocktail of emotion somewhere deep inside her. *'Me?'* squeaked Rose. 'What do you mean, he wanted me?'

Kerry frowned. 'Calm down, Rose—I'm not talking in the biblical sense!'

No, but you could be sure that *he* was, thought Rose, and her heart-rate rocketed even further.

Kerry smiled encouragingly. 'He—'

'What's his name?' put in Rose quickly, thinking that maybe, just maybe—there *was* another prince in London with dark, exotic looks.

'Khalim,' said Kerry, and her face took on an unusually soft expression. 'Prince Khalim. It's a lovely name, isn't it?'

'Lovely,' echoed Rose faintly. 'Wh-what did you say he wanted?'

'He wants to employ our agency to head-hunt for him! More specifically,' added Kerry, 'he asked especially for *you*.'

'D-do you know why?'

'Oh, yes,' said Kerry happily. 'He told me. Said he'd heard that you were probably the best head-hunter in the city, and that he only ever uses the best!'

The word *uses* swam uncomfortably into her mind and refused to shift. Rose frowned in genuine confusion. 'You mean he's in advertising?'

Kerry shook her head. 'Oh, no—it's nothing to do with advertising. He wants you to find someone to be in charge of his country's oil refinery. The man who has been there since the year dot is taking early retirement, apparently.'

Rose stared across the table in disbelief. 'But we don't *do* oilfields!' she protested. 'Our speciality is advertising.'

'That's exactly what I told him,' said Kerry smugly. 'I felt it was only professional to point that out. I said that my advice would be to consult someone who was familiar with that particular field.'

'And what did he say?' asked Rose, knowing that the question was in many ways redundant, and that she had a good idea of what was coming next.

She had.

'Oh, he said that the principles for finding the right person for the job were the same, no matter what the particular job,' Kerry explained airily. 'Matching skills with needs.'

'I'll bet he did,' said Rose dully. What Khalim wanted, Khalim had to have. And he wanted her, she knew that. The only trouble was that she wanted him, too—and she was only just beginning to discover how much...

Kerry gave her a piercing stare. 'This wasn't the kind of reaction I was expecting, Rose. I thought you'd be leaping up and down with excitement,' she said, and leaned forwards over the desk. 'When someone of this man's stature hears that one of your staff is about the best there is, and decides that no one else will possibly do. Well—' she shrugged, but there was no disguising her disappointment '—*most* people would be absolutely delighted! Is there something you're not telling me?'

Rose was a naturally truthful person, but this was her *boss*. And, anyway, even if she told the truth—how weak and pathetic would she sound if she came straight out with it? Kerry, I've met him and he desires me and I desire him too, but I'm reluctant to start anything that I suspect is only going to end in tears.

'No,' she said quickly. 'There's nothing of any relevance to the job.' And that much was true. If any of her ex-boyfriends had come to the agency requesting that she found someone to work for them—she wouldn't have had a problem doing it. Wasn't she in danger of letting Khalim tangle her life up into knots?

'Think of the opportunities this presents!' enthused Kerry. 'This could give us the chance to branch out into a completely different field. The world could be our oyster—and just think of our profile!'

Kerry spoke sense; the professional in Rose acknowledged that. There was no way she could turn down such a golden opportunity, even if she *had* been railroaded by the coolly manipulative Khalim into doing so. She put as much enthusiasm as she possibly could into her reply. 'I'd love to do it, Kerry.'

Kerry beamed. 'Good! He wants to see you first thing in the morning. Well, ten o'clock, to be precise.'

'Where?' But Rose knew the answer to this, too.

'At his suite. The *penthouse* suite! At the Granchester Hotel.' Kerry winked. '*Very* posh! Just make sure you wear something nice!'

Rose opted for the cover-up. A silk trouser suit in a sugar-almond pink. And the complete opposite of a come-and-get-me look, with her hair caught back in a stark pony-tail and her make-up so sparing that it was virtually non-existent.

She arrived at the Granchester at precisely five to ten and the first person she saw standing at the other end of the vast foyer was Philip Caprice. As expected.

She saw his hand move to the breast pocket of his suit, and then, with a slightly wary smile, he walked across the foyer towards her.

'Hello, Rose.' He smiled.

It wasn't *his* fault that he worked for a man who used his untold influence to control events, she supposed, and she gave him a returning smile.

'Hello, Philip. Khalim sent you down to collect me, I suppose?'

'No, Khalim has come down to fetch you himself,' came a smooth, velvety voice from just behind her, and Rose turned round to find Khalim standing there, the black eyes glittering with some unspoken message. Was that triumph she read there? She supposed it was. He had got exactly what he wanted. Or so he thought...

'And I suppose I should be flattered, should I?' she asked spikily.

Khalim gave a hard smile. 'Actually, yes, perhaps you should. After all, most women find it a pleasure to be in my company.'

'But, presumably, they haven't been manipulated into it, like I have?'

Khalim stilled. 'Are you intending to make a scene in the middle of the foyer?'

'You classify giving a legitimate opinion as making a scene?' Rose smiled. 'What spineless women you must have known in the past, Khalim!'

And looking at the feisty sparkle which was making her blue eyes shine like sapphires, Khalim was inclined to agree with her. 'Shall we go upstairs?' he asked pleasantly.

The words came blurting out before she could stop them. 'Why, so that you can seduce me?'

The black eyes narrowed, but then his mouth curved in a slow, speculative smile. 'Is that what you would like, then, sweet Rose?'

And, to Rose's horror, that smile had the most extraordinary effect on her. She found her skin warming under that unmistakable look of approbation, as if she had found herself beneath the gentle heat of a spring sun. Her heart began to patter out an erratic little dance and little shivers of sensation skittered all the way down her spine.

With a supreme effort, she said firmly, 'No, what I would *like* is to have been given some choice in taking this job!'

'I'm sure you were perfectly free to turn it down.' His shrug was disarming, but the steely intent behind his words remained intact.

'Yes, that would have gone down very well with my boss, wouldn't it? Sorry, but I don't want to take this highly lucrative contract, because...'

'Because?' he questioned so silkily that the hairs on the back of her neck began to prickle, and she stared at him indignantly.

'Because a man who is capable of such underhand—'

But her words were waylaid by long, olive-coloured fingers being placed on her arm. She could feel their gentle caress through the thin silk of her suit jacket, and at that moment felt as helpless as a rabbit caught in the glaring headlights of an oncoming car.

'Let us continue this discussion upstairs,' he instructed smoothly. 'I am not certain that I am going to like what I am about to hear—and, if that is the case, then I most assuredly do not wish for all the staff and guests of the Granchester to be privy to it.'

Rose opened her mouth to protest, then closed it again. What was the point? She was here to do business, after all. 'Will Philip be accompanying us?'

Dark eyebrows were raised in mocking query. 'Ah! Once again you have need of a chaperon do you, Rose?'

Her own look mocked him back. 'Of course not! I'm a professional—and our business will be conducted on just that footing. I know that I can rely on you to abide by that, can't I, Khalim?'

Her attempt to dominate made him ache unbearably, and Khalim felt the slow pull of sexual excitement. What untold pleasure it would give him to subjugate her fiery insurrection!

'A word of warning, Rose,' he murmured. 'A Marabanesh is master of his own destiny. Rely on nothing and you shall not be disappointed.' He turned his dark head. 'Come, Philip,' he drawled. 'The lady requests your company.'

Philip Caprice seemed slightly bemused by the interchange. 'I'm honoured,' he replied.

But Rose could barely think straight. All the way up in the lift, Khalim's words kept swimming seductively around in her head. *Master of his own destiny.* Why should that thrill her so unspeakably? Because the quiet Englishmen of her acquaintance would never have come out with such a passionate and poetic phrase?

His suite was something outside Rose's experience, even though her work had taken her to plenty of glamorous places in her time. But this was something else! She looked around in wonder. It was absolutely vast—why, she could imagine two football teams feeling perfectly at home here! And it was furnished with sumptuous understatement.

She didn't know quite what she had expected—Middle-Eastern opulence, she supposed, with golden swathes of material, and mosaics and richly embroidered cushions scattered on the floor, perhaps even a water-pipe or two!

And she couldn't have got it more wrong, because Khalim's suite was so very English. Comfort, with a slight modern edge to it; it was thickly carpeted in soft pale cream with three enormous sofas coloured blood-red. On the wall hung some magnificent modern paintings—huge canvases whose abstract shapes took the mind on surprising journeys.

But it was the view which was the most stunning thing the suite had to offer—because along the entire length of the room ran floor-to-ceiling windows overlooking London's most famous park. She gazed down, thinking that it was so unexpected to see a great sward of green right bang in the middle of a bustling city.

And when she looked up again, it was to find Khalim watching her.

'You like it,' he observed, and the pleasure in his voice was unmistakable.

'It's beautiful,' she said simply. 'Absolutely beautiful.'

And so was she, he thought. So was she. Quite the most beautiful woman he had ever seen, with her pale blonde hair and milky-white skin, and a pert little nose offset by the most sinful pair of lips imaginable. Again, he felt the irresistible pull of desire, but he quashed it ruthlessly.

At his English boarding-school, he had sometimes liked to fish—the calm and the quiet and the splendid isolation had soothed his homesick soul during the times he had been missing his homeland quite desperately. And early on he had learnt that the most prized fish were those which proved the most difficult to catch.

And so it was with Rose. He acknowledged that she wanted him, too, and he suspected that she was perceptive enough to have recognised it herself. But she was not like other women, he knew that with a blinding certainty. She would not fall easily into his arms, no matter how much she wanted him.

He smiled, not oblivious to the impact of that smile. 'Please sit down, Rose. Shall we have coffee?'

His tone was so courteous and his manner so charming that Rose was momentarily captivated. She completely forgot about giving him a piece of her mind. Why, for a moment, she felt almost *flustered.*

'Er, thank you,' she said, and slid down onto one of the blood-red sofas, astonished when a middle-aged woman, who was obviously a Marabanesh herself, carried in a tray of fragrant-smelling coffee.

Had someone been listening for his command? she wondered rather helplessly, before realising that *yes*, they probably had! He *was* a prince, after all, with people hanging onto his every word.

And then she remembered. He might be a prince, but he was also a devious manipulator who had used his money and position and power to get her here today!

With a smile, she took one of the tiny cups from the woman, and put it down on the floor so that she could delve into her briefcase.

She extracted a sheaf of papers and fixed him with a bright, professional smile. 'Right, then. Let's get started!'

'Drink your coffee first.' He frowned.

She gave another brisk smile. 'You're not paying me to drink coffee, Khalim!'

His frown deepened. 'What do you want to know?' he asked sulkily.

Rose almost smiled again. Why, right then, she got a fleeting glimpse of the little boy he must once have been! And a very handsome little boy, too! 'You went to school with Guy, didn't you?' she asked suddenly.

Satisfied that she had fallen in with his wishes, and was postponing the start of the meeting in deference to him, Khalim nodded. 'A very English boarding-school,' he said and sipped his own coffee.

'How old were you?'

His face suddenly tensed. 'Seven.'

The way he shot that single word out told her it had hurt. And why brush those feelings under the carpet? Wouldn't a prince be 'protected' from so-called prying questions such as those. And if you bottled things up, didn't that mean you would never be able to let them go? 'That must have been very difficult for you,' she ventured cautiously.

Khalim regarded her thoughtfully. Brave, he reasoned. Few would dare to ask him such a personal question, and there were few to whom he would give an answer. But on her angelic face was an expression of genuine concern, not just mere inquisitiveness.

'It wasn't…' He hesitated. A Marabanesh man of his stature would never admit to human frailty. 'Easy,' was all he would allow.

Understatement of the year, thought Rose wryly.

He saw her take her pen out of her briefcase, and suddenly found that he didn't want to talk business. 'It was the tradition,' he said abruptly.

She glanced up. 'The tradition?'

'For princes of Maraban to be educated in England.'

'Why?'

He gave a rather speculative smile and Rose was suddenly alerted to the fact that this man could be ruthless indeed. *Remember* that, she told herself fiercely.

'So that it is possible to blend into both Eastern and Western cultures,' he replied.

And sitting there, with his immaculately cut suit and his handmade Italian shoes, he did indeed look the personification of Western elegance. But the deep olive skin and the glittering black eyes and the decidedly regal bearing bore testament to the fact that his roots were in a hot, scented land which was worlds away from this.

And remember that, *too*, thought Rose.

'Maraban sells oil all over the world,' he continued. 'And wherever I go, I am aware that I am my country's ambassador. It has always been to my advantage that I am able to merge into whichever culture I am with at the time.'

'So you're a chameleon?' asked Rose thoughtfully.

He gave a slow smile. 'I prefer to describe myself as a man of contrasts.'

Hadn't she thought exactly that, the very first time she had met him? Rose shifted uncomfortably. It felt slightly disconcerting, alarming even—to be echoing Khalim's thoughts.

She took a sip from her coffee, then put the cup back down on the floor.

'So, to business. And I need you to tell me, Khalim— exactly what is it you want?' she asked him crisply.

For once it was difficult to focus on business—he couldn't seem to kick-start his mind into gear. He wondered what she would say if he told her that what he *wanted* was to make love to her in such a way that every man who ever followed him would be like a dim memory of the real thing. He felt the powerful thundering of his heart in response to his thoughts.

'Let me give you a little background first,' he began softly. 'Maraban has substantial reserves of oil in—'

'The Asmaln desert,' she put in quickly. 'And other natural resources include deposits of coal, sulphur, magnesium, and salt.'

Khalim looked at her in astonishment. 'And how, for an

Englishwoman, do you know so much about my country?' he demanded.

Rose's mouth pleated with disapproval. 'Oh, *really*, Khalim! Once I knew that I had to take the wretched job, I approached it in exactly the same way as I would any other! Information is power, and I spent until late last night finding out everything I could about Maraban!'

His eyes narrowed with unwilling admiration. 'What else do you know?'

'That only four per cent of the country is cultivated, nearly all of which is irrigated. I also know,' she added, 'that Marabanesh pistachio nuts are considered to be the finest in the world!'

'And do you like pistachio nuts?' he asked seriously.

Her mouth lifted at the corners. 'Oh, I wouldn't dream of having a gin and tonic without one!'

Such flippancy was something he was unused to as well— at least from anyone outside his inner circle. Yet his mouth curved in response to that frankly mischievous smile. 'Then I must arrange to have some sent to you, Rose,' he murmured. 'A whole sackload of Maraban pistachios!'

It was distracting when his hard face softened like that. It started making her imagine all kinds of things. She tried to picture him doing ordinary things. Going to the supermarket. Queuing up at the petrol station. And she couldn't. She tried to picture him on holiday, swimming…

Oddly enough, that was an image which imprinted itself far more clearly and Rose saw glorious dark limbs, all strength and muscle as they submerged themselves in warm and silken waters. With almost painful clarity, she recalled just how it had felt to move within the sandalwood-scented circle of his arms at the wedding reception.

Khalim saw the sudden tension around her shoulders. 'Something is wrong?'

Had he noticed the hectic flush which was burning its way along her cheekbones? She stared fixedly at the pristine papers on her lap, unable to meet his gaze, terrified that his slicing black stare would be able to read the unmistakable longing in her eyes.

'No,' she said, with slow emphasis, until she had composed herself enough to meet that challenging look head-on. 'Nothing is wrong, Khalim. But I'm still waiting for you to tell me what it is you're looking for.'

Khalim recognised her determination, and a will almost as forceful as his own. It was a heady discovery, he thought as he began to speak.

'Maraban has one of the world's most well-run oil refineries and the man who heads it up is taking early retirement.'

'And you want someone to replace him?'

Khalim shook his dark head. 'No one could ever replace Murad,' he said thoughtfully. 'He has been there for many years, and there have been many changes in the industry during that time. No, I need someone to take oil production into the first third of this century and there are two likely candidates working there at present. I need a man with vision to head it up—'

'Or a woman, of course?'

Jet sparks heated the onyx eyes, bathing her in an intensely black light.

'No,' he contradicted resolutely. 'Not a woman. Not in Maraban.'

Rose bristled; she couldn't help herself. She thought about all she had striven to achieve in her life. 'So women aren't equal in Maraban?'

'I think you are intelligent enough to know the answer to that for yourself, without me having to tell you, Rose,' he remonstrated quietly.

'It's disgraceful!' she stormed.

'You think so?' His voice was dangerously soft.

'I know so! Women in this country died to have the right to vote and to call themselves equal!'

'And you think that makes them happy?'

Her eyebrows shot up. 'I can't believe you could even ask me a question like that!'

He smiled, savouring the rare flavour of opposition and conflict. 'I just did.'

Rose very nearly threw her pen across the room in a fit of pique, before remembering herself. Since when had she taken to hurling missiles? She steadied her voice with a deep breath instead. 'Of course equality makes women happy! What woman worth her salt wants to spend her life living in a man's shadow?'

The woman he would marry would be only too glad to. His mind skipped to the women currently being vetted as eligible wife material, then thought how unlike them this woman was. Their very antithesis. He felt the thrill of the forbidden, the lure of the unsuitable, and it heated his blood unbearably. 'You should not judge without all the facts available to you, Rose,' he remonstrated softly. 'Women in Maraban are very highly respected and they are treated with the utmost reverence—because they are seen as the givers of life. Come and see for yourself whether the women of Maraban are happy.'

She stared at him, furiously aware that wild hope was vying with indignation. 'What do you mean?'

In that moment, he had never rejoiced in his position quite so much. How perfect that whatever he desired should be granted to him without effort. And he desired Rose Thomas more than anything in his life to date. He gave a cool and glittering smile. 'You will accompany me to Maraban,' he purred.

CHAPTER FIVE

'YOU *are* kidding, Rose?'

Rose stared at her flatmate, still slightly reeling from Khalim's unarguable statement. 'I wish I was!'

Lara cocked her head to one side and grinned. 'Oh, no, you don't! What other woman do you know who wouldn't want to be whisked off in a private jet with a prince—a *prince*, no less, who looks like Khalim does? And acts like Khalim does!'

'High-handed!' grumbled Rose.

'Masterful,' sighed Lara.

Of course, Lara wasn't entirely wrong—not about Khalim, nor Rose's attitude to being whisked off in such an extraordinary fashion. Because if she examined her feelings honestly, wasn't there a part of her—and quite a large part of her—which was feeling almost sick with excitement at the thought of being taken to Maraban by its overwhelmingly attractive prince and heir? Any minute now she would wake up and find that the alarm had just gone off!

'So tell me why you're going again,' said Lara, screwing her face up, as if she hadn't understood the first explanation, which Rose had blurted out. 'Just to find out about how women in Maraban live, compared to their Western counterparts? Is that it?'

Rose shook her head. 'No. That was just the provocative way he phrased it.' Along with the even more provocative look which had gleamed with such dazzling promise from those inky eyes. 'But the fact is that I'll probably be recruiting from within Maraban itself, or the surrounding countries if that fails. There are two possible candidates there already, so I really do *need* to go.'

68

'Oh, you poor thing!'

She'd phoned Kerry to broach the subject of her journey, and her boss had sounded bemused.

'Of course you must go, Rose. You're in charge of the job, aren't you?' Kerry had said, her voice sounding slightly puzzled. 'Go where you need to go; the prince is paying.'

Oh, yes, the prince was paying all right, and in paying the prince was also managing to demonstrate just how wide-reaching were his influence and power.

And power was, Rose had to concede with a guilty shiver, a very potent aphrodisiac indeed. She must remember that. Khalim would not be blind to that fact either, which meant that she would have to be very, very careful not to let it all go to her head. She thought back to how she had greeted his suggestion.

'Where will I be staying?' she demanded, not caring that Philip had sucked in a horrified breath at the tone she was using. 'In a hotel, I hope?'

Khalim stilled. She really could be most insolent! If she were not quite so beautiful, he really would not have tolerated such disrespect. 'Maraban has internationally acclaimed hotels,' he told her smoothly. 'But as my guest you will naturally stay in my father's...'

Rose looked up as she picked up on his hesitation—the last man she would have expected being stuck for words. 'Your father's what?'

'Palace,' he said reluctantly.

Rose widened her eyes. His father's palace, no less! Well, of *course* he would have a palace, wouldn't he? Royal families did not generally live in trailer parks! She looked at him with interest, her indignation dissolving by the second.

Had his reluctance to speak been motivated by the fact that palaces were what really drew the line in the sand? Palaces were what emphasised the unbreachable differences between Khalim and ordinary people like her. And, if that was the case, then didn't that mean that there was a thoughtful streak running through him? Despite her reservations, she smiled.

'And is it a beautiful palace?' she asked him softly.

An answering smile curved the edges of Khalim's hard mouth. Most people rushed onto another subject—seeing his home simply as some kind of status symbol, forgetting that palaces tended to be designed with beauty in mind. But then Rose, he suspected, had a very real sense of the beautiful.

'Very.' His reply was equally soft. 'Would you like me to describe it to you, or will you wait and see for yourself?'

Rose swallowed down temptation. The very last thing she needed was that deep, sexy voice painting lyrical pictures for her. A voice like that could suck you in and transport you away to a magical place and make you have foolish wishes which could never come true. And Rose needed her feet set very firmly on the ground.

'No, I think I'll wait and see for myself, thank you,' she said primly, tucking her still pristine papers back into her briefcase. Khalim had promised to fill her in about the oil refinery on the plane and she was glad to agree. At least it would give them something to talk about, other than the kind of irritating questions which kept popping to the forefront of her mind, such as, Khalim, why are your lips so beautiful? Or, Khalim, did anyone ever tell you that you have a body to die for?

'Rose!'

Rose blinked out of her reverie to find Lara staring at her as if she were an alien who had just landed from the planet Mars. 'Wh-what is it?' she stumbled.

'You looked miles away!'

'I was.' In Maraban and in Khalim's arms again, to be precise. Wondering if the land he had described could ever possibly live up to the richness of his description of it. I hope not, she thought distractedly. I really do.

'When are you going?' asked Lara.

'The day after tomorrow.' Khalim had wanted to fly out

first thing the next morning, but Rose had put her foot down. She might have a wardrobe which could cope with almost any eventuality, but a trip such as this required a dash round London's biggest department stores! And hadn't it been immensely pleasurable to see his incredulous expression when she had opposed his wishes to leave when *he* wanted? She'd heard Philip's disbelieving snort as she'd refused to back down!

Who knew? Khalim was a man used to always getting his own way, and thwarting his wishes occasionally might just be good for him! Why, he might even thank her for it one day!

'Very well,' he had agreed coldly. 'The day after tomorrow.'

She spent the next day shopping and on impulse bought a new evening gown far more glittering and ostentatious than any of her normal purchases. But once she'd packed she felt almost sick with nerves, and realised that she'd better tell her parents she was going abroad. She rang and rang their old farmhouse, but there was no reply, and so she phoned her brother instead.

'Jamie? It's me, Rose!'

'Well, hi! How much do you want to borrow?' came back the dry comment.

'Very funny!'

'But you never seem to ring me these days, sister dearest—'

'You've lost the use of your dialling finger, have you? Men are notoriously bad at communication and I don't see why it should always be the women who stay in touch!'

Jamie sounded indulgent. 'Fair! So is this just a friendly chat with your favourite brother?'

'My only brother.' Rose smiled, and then grimaced at her reflection in the mirror. 'Well, actually, no—I've been trying to ring Mum and Dad—but there's no reply.'

'That's because they're up in the Lake District—'

'They're *always* going somewhere!'

'But it's good, isn't it? That they're enjoying their retire-ment—I hope *I'm* still having such a good time, at their age!'

'Yes,' said Rose thoughtfully. 'I wanted to tell them that I'm going abroad for a couple of days.'

'Oh? Anywhere nice?'

Rose removed a speck of dust from the mirror with her fingernail. 'Have you heard of a place called Maraban?'

There was a pause. 'Isn't it in the Middle East?'

'That's right.'

'So is it work? Or a holiday?'

'Oh, work. I've, er, been asked to find someone to head up their oil refinery.'

She could hear the frown in Jamie's voice. 'Really? But I thought you only worked in advertising?'

'Usually I do.' She scowled in the mirror again as if Khalim's reflection was mocking back at her. 'But this is special, or rather the client is. He's a...um...he's a prince.'

'Sorry? Must be a bad line—I thought you said he was a prince.'

How far-fetched it sounded! Her voice sounded almost apologetic. 'I did. He's Prince Khalim of Maraban.'

There was a moment of astounded silence before she could hear Jamie expelling air from between pursed lips—an ex-pression of bemusement he had had since he was a little boy. Then he said, 'Wow! Lucky girl!'

'Aren't I?' she agreed, just hoping that it sounded con-vincing, because most women *would* be thrilled and excited by the idea, wouldn't they? 'You can tell all your friends I'm going to stay in a palace!'

'Heck,' he said softly, still sounding slightly stunned.

'And the other thing—'

'Mmm?'

'It's just that Lara's going to be away filming, and I just wondered whether you would pop your head into the flat on your way home from work—just check that there aren't any free newspapers or letters making it look like the flat is empty?'

'Course I will,' he replied cheerfully. 'You should try living somewhere that doesn't have such a high quota of burglars!'

'I know.' Rose let out a small sigh. 'Listen, thanks, Jamie.'

'Sure.' There was another pause. 'Rose, this trip—it *is* all perfectly above board, isn't it?'

'Of course it is! What else would it be? It's business, Jamie, strictly business.'

But as she replaced the receiver, Rose wondered if she had been entirely honest with her brother...

The following morning, she opened the door and her mouth fell open when she discovered that it was Khalim himself who stood there.

He saw the pink pout of her lips and smiled a predatory smile. 'Surprised?' he murmured. 'Were you expecting Philip?'

Well, yes, she was surprised, but not because he hadn't sent his emissary to collect her. Mainly because he had switched roles again. Gone was the exotic-looking businessman in the beautifully cut suit. Instead, he was dressed in a variation of the outfit he'd been wearing at the wedding—a flowing, silken top with loose trousers of the same material worn underneath. But today the robes were more silvery than gold. A colder colour altogether, providing an austere backdrop to the dark, proud features. Oh, but he looked magnificent!

'You've ch-changed,' was all she could breathlessly manage.

'Of course I have. I'm going home,' came the simple reply. 'Are you ready?'

She'd packed just one suitcase, and it stood in readiness in the hall. She gestured to it and then *was* surprised when he picked it up.

He saw the look and correctly interpreted it. 'You imagined that I would send someone up to collect it? That I should never carry anyone else's bags?'

'I suppose I did.'

Astonishingly, he found that he wanted to enlighten her—to show her that he was not just a man who had been cosseted by servants from the moment of his birth.

'There were reasons behind me being sent to boarding-school other than to learn to blend into both societies,' he told her softly. 'Like cold showers and rigorous sport and the discipline of learning to stand on my own two feet.'

She stared at him, all too aware of the dark luminosity of his eyes. 'And was it hard?' she questioned. 'To adapt to a new culture and all that went with it?'

Her direct questions went straight to the very heart of the matter; impossible to ignore or to brush aside. He shrugged. 'Little boys can be cruel.'

'Yes, I know.' She wondered if he was conscious that remembered pain had clouded the amazing black eyes. 'And how did you cope with that?'

He pulled the door open and motioned for her to precede him. 'You have to appear not to care. Only then will you cease to become the butt of playground mockery.'

She saw a picture of a beautiful young boy with hair as black as his eyes. Outstanding in more than just looks and an easy target for boys who had not had so many of life's gifts conferred on them.

'Khalim—'

She was close enough for him to feel the sweet warmth of her breath. Close enough for him to have coiled his fingers around the narrow indentation of her waist and to have pulled her to him, and kissed her.

Would she have resisted? He doubted it. No woman who had ever been kissed by him had failed to follow it up by tumbling into bed with him. But the timing was wrong. Why begin something only to have it end unsatisfactorily? If he made love to her now, then it would be a swift coupling in her bedroom—with no guarantee that the flatmate would not suddenly return. And Philip and the chauffeur sitting waiting downstairs in the car. That would do her reputation no good at all, he realised—shocked that it should matter to him.

'Let's go,' he said, and moved away from her before his body picked up any more of her enticing signals.

The long black car soon picked up speed once they were out of the clutches of the city itself and heading towards Heathrow Airport.

Khalim, rather surprisingly, took out a laptop computer and sat tapping away at it for the entire journey, leaving Rose with little to do other than to pull out a book to read, which was at least a distraction from the unnerving presence of the man by her side.

She was reading *Maraban—Land of Dreams and Contrasts*, by Robert Cantle, a weighty book and, apparently, the definitive work on the country, which she'd bought on yesterday afternoon's shopping trip. She'd expected to have to wade through it, but she couldn't have been more wrong. It was, she thought to herself dreamily, absolutely *fascinating*.

Khalim glanced over at where she sat engrossed, and raised his dark brows.

'Not exactly what you'd call light reading,' he observed.

She heard the surprise in his voice. 'You expected me to sit flicking through magazines, I suppose?'

'Never suppose, Rose,' he returned softly. 'Never with me.'

In the confines of the luxurious car, his proximity overwhelmed her and she found herself edging a little further up the leather seat away from him. 'I'm enjoying it,' she told him solidly.

'You *do* take your work seriously, don't you?' he commented drily.

She looked up and treated him to a cool stare. 'Please don't patronise me, Khalim. The more I know about Maraban, the better I am able to do my job.'

He smiled, and settled back to his screen, thinking that Rose Thomas was proving to be much, much more than a pretty face. A *very* pretty face.

His eyes flickered to where one shapely thigh was outlined beneath an ankle-length skirt in a filmy, pale blue material which matched the simple cashmere sweater she wore. She'd dressed appropriately, he thought with pleasure.

He'd had many Western lovers, but none who seemed to have such a genuine interest in his country. Plenty who had *pretended* to, he remembered. His mouth hardened. But they had been the matrimonially ambitious ones, and as easy to spot as the glittering sapphire—as big as a swan's egg—which dominated the crown he would one day inherit.

He glanced out of the window, knowing that he would soon have to face the reality of his destiny. For that very morning had come news from Maraban that his father was frailer than before. Pain etched little lines on his brow as he acknowledged that the mantle of responsibility had slipped a little closer to his shoulders.

Would this be his last, delicious fling before it descended completely? he wondered.

Rose had never been on a private jet before and the interior of the Lear matched up to her wildest expectations. Most of the seats had been removed to provide a spacious interior, and two stewardesses were in attendance.

Very much in attendance, thought Rose grimly, suspecting that both had been chosen for their decorative qualities as much as for their undoubted efficiency. And both, like herself, were blonde—though these blondes had not had their colouring bestowed on them by nature.

Khalim introduced her to the pilot, who was obviously a fellow Marabanesh, and once they had effected a smooth take-off he turned to her, studying her mutinous expression with amusement.

'Does something displease you, Rose? Is something wrong?'

She certainly wasn't going to tell him that in her opinion the stewardesses could have done with wearing something which resembled a skirt, instead of a pelmet. She met his eyes, and once again her heart thundered in her ears. 'Wrong?' she managed, as smoothly as she could. 'What on earth could be wrong, Khalim?'

He had hoped that she was jealous; he wanted her to be jealous.

In fact, he had slept with neither of the attendants, even though it would have taken nothing more than a careless snap of the fingers to do so. He suspected that the two women would have been game for almost anything—and that even a *ménage à trois* would have been greeted with delight, instead of derision. But he would never have sullied himself with such a dalliance, even though he knew that many of his cousins enjoyed such debauchery.

'Shall we eat something?' he questioned as the taller of the stewardesses approached them.

She remembered what he had said to her in the restaurant. She'd never felt less like eating in her life, but to refuse would surely be an insult to his chef? 'Yes, please.'

'And we will drink mint tea,' he instructed.

'Sir.' The stewardess inclined her blonde head respectfully.

The two attendants began laying out a feast on the low, circular table. Rose looked down at the engraved bronze plates, enjoying the colour and variety of the different foods which they held—tiny portions which pleased the eye and tempted the palate.

'You like these things?' asked Khalim as he offered her a tiny pancake stuffed with cheese and doused with syrup, resisting the urge to feed her, morsel by morsel, then have her lick his fingers clean.

'I've never tried food like this before.' She bit into it. 'Mmm! It's yummy!'

'Yummy?' He smiled as he observed her, enjoying the unconscious sensuality of watching her eat. 'Then you have many pleasures in store, Rose,' he told her, his voice deepening as he thought of the ultimate pleasure she would enjoy with him.

Something in his voice drove all thoughts of food clean out of her mind, and she lifted her head to find herself imprisoned in the black gleam of his eyes. She put the half-eaten pancake down with fingers which were threatening to shake.

He hadn't touched a thing himself, she thought, as he chose just that moment to languidly stretch his long legs out, and the brush of the silk as it defined the muscular thrust of his thighs was positively *indecent*.

'Something is troubling you, Rose?' he murmured.

'Nothing,' she lied and directed her gaze to his chest instead, but that wasn't much better. She found herself imagining what his torso would be like without its silken covering—hard and dark, she guessed, with the skin lightly gleaming like oiled satin. 'N-nothing at all.'

He saw the swift rise of colour to her cheeks and the sudden darkening of her eyes. He could order everyone to clear the main salon now, he thought heatedly. And take her quickly before this hunger became much more intense.

But what if she cried aloud with pleasure? Sobbed her fulfilment in his arms as women inevitably did? Did he really want the two attendants exchanging glances as they listened at the door while he made hard, passionate love to her?

'Eat some more,' he urged huskily.

'I…I'm full.'

He glanced at his watch. 'Then I shall order for these plates to be removed—'

'And then you'll tell me all about Maraban's oil refinery?'

she put in quickly, because at least that would take her mind off things. Him.

The oil refinery? He threw her a look of mocking bemusement as he leaned back against the cushions. Never had a woman surprised him quite so much as Rose Thomas and surprise was rare enough to be a novelty! 'That is what you would like?' he questioned gravely.

'More than anything in the world!' she agreed fervently, but the gleam of discernment in the black eyes told her that they both knew she was lying.

He spoke knowledgeably for almost an hour, while Rose butted in with intelligent questions. The first time she asked him something, he raised his eyebrows in a look which would have made most people freeze and then retreat.

'I need to *ask* you these things,' explained Rose patiently, reminding herself that maybe it wasn't *his* fault that people usually hung on adoringly to every word he said.

'Such pertinent questions,' he conceded in a murmur.

'There you go again, patronising me!' she chided.

'That was not my intention, I can assure you.'

She paused, unsure whether to frame the question she *really* wanted to ask, and then remonstrating with herself for an uncharacteristic lack of courage. 'Khalim?'

His eyes narrowed, some instinct telling him that this was not another query about Maraban's oil output. 'Rose?' he returned softly.

'Just why *did* you want me to act as your head-hunter?'

He curved her a slow, almost cruel smile. 'I had to have you.'

Rose froze. 'You mean—'

He shook his head. 'I was informed that you were the best head-hunter in town—I already told you that.'

'Thank you.'

Her blue eyes shone a challenge at him and he found himself smiling in response. 'You also asked me whether I had employed you so that I could seduce you.'

Some of her customary grit returned and she didn't flinch beneath his mocking gaze. 'But you neatly avoided answering me, didn't you, Khalim?'

'Did I?'

'You know you did.'

He narrowed her a speculative glance, then shrugged. 'I can't deny that I find you beautiful, or that I want you in my bed, but—'

She sucked in a breath which was both shocked and yet profoundly excited. The men she knew just didn't *say* things like that! 'But what?'

'Sleeping with me isn't a prerequisite for landing the contract.'

'But will I get a bonus if I *do* succumb to your charms?' she asked flippantly.

Khalim's face darkened and he very nearly pulled her to him to punish her with a kiss which would dare her to ever mock him so again. But he stopped himself in time; instead, he forced himself to imagine how sweet the victory would be after such a protracted battle!

'Put it this way,' he warned her silkily, 'that as a man I will attempt to seduce you—no red-blooded Marabanesh would do otherwise.' A slow, glittering look. 'But you are perfectly within your rights to turn me down.'

Rose stared at him as she felt the irrevocable unfurling of desire, knowing that his words were iced with an implicit boast. That no woman Khalim attempted to lure to bed would ever be able to resist him.

And Rose had spent her life resisting men who saw her as just a trophy girlfriend, with her blonde hair and her bright blue eyes. Just you wait and see, Prince Khalim! she thought.

He was intrigued by the defiant little tilt of her chin, and his need for her grew. He controlled his desire with an effort and distracted himself by flicking another glance at his watch.

'Do you want to look out of the window?' he asked unsteadily. 'We're coming into Maraban.'

CHAPTER SIX

SUNLIGHT danced and shimmered across a wide expanse of water, and Rose was spellbound—enough to be impervious to the sudden build-up of tension which his silken words had produced.

'Water!' she exclaimed as the beauty of the scene below momentarily drove all her newly learned facts about the country straight out of her head. 'But I thought—'

'That you would be coming to a barren and desolate land with not a drop of water in sight?' he chided. 'That is the Caspian Sea, Rose, and the borders of Maraban lie on its Western shores.'

'Oh, but it's beautiful!'

'You seem to think everything *about* Maraban is beautiful,' he commented indulgently.

'But it is!'

He thought how wonderfully uninhibited her appreciation was, and how her eyes sparkled like the blue waters of the Caspian itself.

'Fasten your seat belt,' he murmured gently. 'The heat can sometimes make the landing turbulent.

But, in the event, their descent to Maraban was as smooth as honey, and as the plane taxied down the runway Rose could see a large number of men standing in line, all in flowing robes which fluttered in the small breeze created by the aircraft.

'Gosh, it's a deputation,' she observed.

Khalim leaned across her and glanced out of the window, and her senses were invaded by the subtle persuasion of sandalwood.

'I shall go out alone,' he told her. 'If you want to go and freshen up.'

'So you don't want to risk being seen with me, Khalim?' she asked wryly. 'Are you planning to smuggle me off the plane with a blanket over my head?'

He wondered if she had any idea how privileged she was to accompany him in this way! If it had been anyone else, he would have flown them over separately. But he had not wanted to take the risk of her refusing to come...

'I don't imagine that you would wish to be subjected to the wild conjecture which your appearance would inevitably provoke.' His tone was dry. 'The less we announce your presence, the less tongues in the city will gossip.'

She got some idea then of how public his life had to be, and how rare the opportunity to play any of it out in private, and, in spite of everything, she felt her heart soften.

'Yes, of course. I understand.' She nodded. 'I'll go and freshen up as you suggested.'

He laughed. 'Why, Rose—that's the most docile I've ever heard you be!'

She put on a suitably meek expression. 'And you like my docility do you, Oh, Prince?'

The breath caught in his throat and dried it to sawdust and his heart clenched inside his chest. 'No. I like you fiery,' he told her honestly. 'You make a worthy combatant.'

Which pleased her far more than remarks about the colour of her hair or the sapphire glitter of her eyes. Her looks she'd been born with and were just the luck of the draw—her personality was a different matter. And if Khalim approved of certain facets of her nature...now, that really *was* a compliment!

Just don't get carried away by compliments, she reminded herself.

She enjoyed the luxury of the aircraft's bathroom, which contained the most heavenly sandalwood soap. Rose picked it up and sniffed it, her eyes closing for a moment. It smelt of *him*. She washed her hands and her face with it, and it was as though the essence of Khalim had seeped into her skin itself.

Stop it, she told herself as she brushed her hair and slicked on a little lipstick. You're walking straight into his honeytrap.

She stepped back to survey the results in the mirror, thinking that at least she *looked* cool and unflappable. Only the slightly hectic glitter of her eyes betrayed the fact that inside she was churned up by conflicting emotions—and the most disturbing one of all was the fact that Khalim was beginning to grow on her.

Grow on her? Who did she think she was kidding? Why, it was as if he had taken up root inside her mind and managed to invade most of her waking thoughts. Whatever had she thought about before Khalim had entered her life?

After twenty minutes, he returned to the aircraft, by which time Philip had joined her in the main salon.

'Rose and I will go in the second car with the bodyguard,' said Khalim imperturbably. 'Will you take the first car and prepare them at the palace for my arrival?'

'Of course.' Philip gave Rose a curious glance, before bowing to the prince.

'Why does he look at me that way?' asked Rose, after he had gone.

For a second he experienced a rare moment of indulgence. 'What way is that, sweet Rose?'

'You saw.'

Khalim sighed. Would the truth go to her head? Fool her into believing that her presence here had an ultra-special significance? Or a future?

'Because you are the first woman I have ever brought here to Maraban,' he admitted, on a growl.

She didn't react. 'Should I be flattered by that?' she questioned drily.

He found her coolness utterly irresistible. Even though it *was* rather galling to be shown nothing in the way of gratitude! 'I would not dare to presume it—not of you,' he murmured. 'Come, Rose—enough of this sparring—let me show you my country.'

The hot air hit her with a heated jolt, even though it was now September and Khalim informed her that the temperatures were already cooling down towards the icy winter which followed.

And the drive to the palace was a feast to the senses! Rose stared out of the limousine window with fascination at the scenes which unfolded before her. Maraban's capital was absolutely heaving with people and there were cars and carts and camels all vying for space along the congested roads of the city. She could see dusty boxes of oranges, and live chickens in a cage.

The main thoroughfare had obviously been cleared for Khalim's arrival, and she could see crowds jostling to catch a glimpse of the enigmatic profile through the smoked-glass window.

The palace was some way out from the main drag of the city, and Rose's first sight of it was unforgettable. In the distance, tall mountains reared up in jagged peaks, and against the cloudless blue cobalt of the sky stood the palace itself—gleaming purest gold in the honeyed light of the afternoon sun.

Rose was silent and Khalim looked at her, taken aback by the rapture which had softened her features into dreamy wonder.

'You like my home?' he asked, knowing deep down that such a question was redundant.

It seemed unbelievable that such an extraordinary building could ever be described by the comfortable word 'home'.

'How could I not like it?' she questioned simply.

Khalim's mouth hardened. Was she really as guileless as she seemed? Or was she cynically aware that her eyes were like dazzling blue saucers when she spoke with such emotion, their light lancing straight to his very heart?

He shook his head slightly in negation. He wanted her body, that was all.

That was all.

'Tell me what to expect when we arrive,' said Rose, wondering why he was scowling when all she had done was tell him she liked his home.

Sometimes, he reflected ruefully, she sounded as if *she* were the one expressing a royal command! 'My mother and sisters have their own section of the palace—we will join them for dinner and you will meet them then. You will have your own suite of rooms, and a girl will be assigned to look after your needs.'

'And your father?'

'My father lives in a different section of the building.'

She hesitated. 'Because he's sick, you mean?'

Khalim frowned. 'You are very persistent, Rose! No, not simply because he is sick—it is our royal custom. Princes of Maraban do not sleep with their women, not even their wives.'

Rose looked at him in disbelief. 'You mean that they just go and have *sex* with them, and then go back to their own apartments?'

'*Sometimes* they remain there for the night,' he informed her benignly, though he could not imagine leaving *her* alone for one precious second of the night.

'Lucky old them!' said Rose sarcastically.

'Actually,' he iced back, 'they *would* show gratitude, yes!'

'For being downtrodden, you mean?'

'I think you forget yourself, Rose!' he snapped.

'I think not! I am not your royal subject, Khalim! And if I have an opinion which happens to differ from yours—well, that's just *tough*!'

He had never felt so turned on by a woman in his life and the desire to kiss her was overwhelming. But by then the car was driving slowly into the inner courtyard where trees provided a welcome shade—the sunlight dappling through broad, verdant leaves. Khalim clicked his tongue with irritation as the chauffeur opened the door for her.

But when Rose alighted from the car, she was hit with the most unforgettable and heady fragrance, so powerful that it halted her in her tracks.

'What is that amazing scent?' she whispered, their disagreement forgotten.

A sense of destiny whispered disturbing fingers over his flesh. 'It is the fragrance of the roses which bloom in the palace gardens,' he murmured, watching as the sun turned her hair into a gold just a shade lighter than the palace itself. 'The sweetest scent in the world—but you must wait until the evening time, when the perfume is increased by a hundredfold.'

But as they walked side by side towards a pair of vast, ornate doors, he thought that no scent could be sweeter than the subtle perfume which drifted from her skin, more beguiling than any siren.

Robed figures awaited them, and Rose was introduced, certain that she would never be able to remember all these new and unusual names. The men all bowed courteously but she could detect flashes of curiosity on their hard, dark faces. I wonder if they approve of me, she thought, but then found Khalim's gaze on her face, more encouraging than she could have believed it would be, and she felt the warmth of his protection.

And all the while she felt that they were surrounded by other watchers, by unseen eyes. She caught a brief glimpse of a young woman, spectacularly clad in crimson silk, but when she turned her head to get a better look the woman had disappeared again.

Khalim followed the direction of her gaze. 'Fatima!' he called, and the young woman reappeared, only her eyes visible above a scarlet yashmak.

She performed an elaborate sort of bow, and Khalim said,

'This is Rose Thomas. I have brought her here to do a job for me. I want you to make sure that she has everything she needs. Say hello now, Fatima.'

'Good afternoon,' said Fatima, in a soft, halting English accent. 'I am pleased to meet you.'

Khalim laughed. 'Fatima is learning English!'

'I'm impressed,' said Rose gravely. 'And rather ashamed that my Marabanese only amounts to about five words.'

Khalim glimmered her an onyx gaze. 'I will teach you,' he promised softly. Oh, yes. He would teach her the many words of love. She would learn to please him in his own language. 'Now Fatima will show you to your rooms—and you shall bathe and change—then later I will come for you.'

She wanted to ask him exactly what he meant by such a masterful and yet ambiguous expression as that—*I will come for you*—but it didn't really seem appropriate, not with Fatima hanging onto every word. He probably meant that he would come to take her down for dinner. So why did that make her heart crash against her ribcage in disappointment?

'Come, please,' said Fatima, with a shy smile.

Rose followed her through a maze of silent marble corridors, thinking that unless she had a guide she would get hopelessly lost.

At last Fatima opened a set of double-doors leading into a large, cool room and Rose looked around her, her eyes feasting themselves on the richly embroidered cushions which were scattered over a wide, low bed covered in a throw of embroidered gold. A carved wooden chest stood in one corner, and the room smelt faintly of incense—though a bronze vase which was crammed full of crimson roses only added to the perfumed atmosphere.

One wall contained bookshelves and closer inspection showed a variety of novels and textbooks, some in Marabanese, but mostly in English. Well, at least she would not be bored!

The shutters were closed but Fatima went over to the window and opened them, and outside Rose could see a profusion of blooms of every hue and their scent drifted in to bewitch her.

The rose garden!

Had Khalim deliberately put her in here, to enchant her with their fragrance? To remind her of the flower she had been named after?

She shivered as a sense of the irrevocable washed cool temptation over her skin.

'You will bathe?' asked Fatima, and gestured towards a door leading off the enormous room.

'Yes, yes, please—I will.'

'And you wish me to assist you?'

Rose shook her head, and smiled, thinking how different Maraban hospitality was! 'No, thanks, Fatima—I'm used to managing on my own,' she answered gravely.

Fatima nodded and gave another shy smile. 'I will bring mint tea in an hour.'

'That will be wonderful. Thank you.'

After the girl had left, Rose went into the bathroom to find a deep circular bath, inlaid with exquisite mosaics in every conceivable shade of blue. There were fragrances and essences from Paris, and fluffy towels as big as sheets. East meets West, she thought with approval, and turned the taps on.

It was the best bath she had ever had. Lying submerged in scented bubbles in the high, cool splendour of the vaulted bathroom, she felt that the real Rose Thomas was a very long way away indeed. So why did she suddenly feel more *alive* than she had ever felt before?

By the time she had dried her hair, it was getting on for seven o'clock. When would Khalim come, and what should she wear for dinner? Would her gorgeous new evening gown make her look like some kind of houri?

In the end, she decided on a simple silk dress which brushed the floor when she walked. The sleeves were long and loose and it was the soft, intense colour of bluebells. Her hair she left loose and shining, and as she stared at herself in the long mirror she thought that she could not possibly offend anyone's sensibilities in such a modest gown.

Fatima came, bearing a bronze tray of mint tea. In true Eastern style, Rose settled herself on an embroidered cushion on the floor, and had just poured herself a cup when there was an authoritative rap on the door. Her heart began to thunder.

'Come in,' she called.

The door opened and there stood Khalim. He, too, had changed, and he must also have bathed, for his black hair was still damp and glittered with a halo of stray drops of water. His robes were coloured deepest claret—like rich, old wine—but his face looked hard, his expression forbidding as he quietly shut the door behind him.

'Do you always invite men so freely into your bedroom, Rose?' he questioned softly.

She put the cup down and looked up at him, knowing that she was not prepared to tolerate his insulting implication. Nor prepared to admit that she had known it was him, simply from the assertive way he had knocked on the door! She shrugged her shoulders in a devil-may-care gesture. 'Oh, they usually come in two at a time! At least!'

'Please do not be flippant with me, Rose!' he exploded.

'Well, what do you expect?' she demanded. 'I *presumed* that no one would come here, except for you! And I *presumed* that while I was here I would be under your protection, but maybe I was wrong!'

'No.' His voice was heavy. He was used to obedience, not passionate logic from his women. 'No, you were not wrong.'

'Well, then—don't imply that I am loose with my favours—'

'Rose—'

'And don't you *dare* make a value judgement about me, when you barely know me, Khalim!'

Barely *know* her? Why, his conversations with Rose Thomas had been more intimate than those he'd had with any other woman before! He felt he knew her *very* well, and he had certainly told her more about himself than was probably wise. His voice gentled as he slid onto a cushion opposite her. 'Do you want me to know you better, Rose?'

Shockingly, she did—she wanted him to know her as intimately as any man could. She wanted to see the contrast of his long-limbed dark body entwined with the milky curves of her own. She wanted to feel the primitive thrust of his passion, the honeyed wonder of his kiss. She stared down at the clear chartreuse colour of her mint tea, afraid that he would see the hunger in her eyes.

'Rose?'

His voice was beguiling, but she resisted it. 'What?'

'Look at me.'

Compelled to obey by the command in his voice, she slowly lifted her head to find herself dazzled by a gaze of deepest ebony.

The pink flush which had gilded her pale skin pleased him, as did the darkened widening of those beautiful blue eyes. 'Do you want me to know you better?' he repeated on a sultry whisper.

The question was laced with erotic expectation, and a passive side she never knew existed wanted to gasp out, Oh, yes. Yes, *please!* But such capitulation must be par for the course for a man like Khalim. She would never win his respect if she fell like a ripe plum into those tempting arms. And his respect, she realised with a start, was what she wanted more than anything.

His body he would give her freely; his deference would be a far more elusive prize.

'Obviously—' she forced a breezy smile '—we will get to know each other better during my stay here. I have no objection to that, Khalim.'

It was such a deliberate misunderstanding that, instead of

feeling indignant, he began to laugh softly. 'You wilfully misunderstand me, Rose,' he murmured. 'You are quite outrageous.'

How rare the sound of his laughter, thought Rose with a sudden pang of compassion. How often could a man like this really let himself go?

She smiled and lifted up one of the china cups. 'Tea, Khalim?' she enquired.

He was still laughing when they went down to dinner.

As he guided her through the maze of marble corridors towards the dining hall, Rose wondered how he had spent his afternoon. Would it seem prying if she asked? 'Have you seen your father yet?' she asked softly.

His face tightened with pain and if she could have wished the words unsaid, she would have done so.

'I'm sorry, I didn't mean to—'

'No.' He shook his dark head. 'We cannot ignore reality, however painful it is. Yes, I saw him.' He paused. He could not talk freely to his mother or his sisters about his father's failing health, for they would begin to weep inconsolably. Nor Philip either. Philip was a man, and men discussed feelings only with discomfort. But Khalim had a sudden need to express himself—to articulate his fears. This was death which he was soon to encounter and he had known no close deaths other than his grandparents' when he had been away at school in England.

'He is fading.' He forced himself to say the brutal words, as if saying them would give life to them. Or death to them, he thought bleakly.

'I'm so sorry.' For one brief moment he looked so vulnerable that she longed to take him in her arms and lay his proud, beautiful face down on her shoulder and to hug him and comfort him. But surely such a gesture would be misinterpreted—even if it *was* her place to offer him solace, which it certainly wasn't.

But then the moment was gone anyway, for the face had resumed its proud and haughty demeanour as he inclined his head in wordless thanks for her commiseration.

'Let us go and eat,' he said.

Dinner was a curious affair, made even more so by the fact that Rose felt as though she was on show—which she guessed she was. But even more curious was Khalim's mother's initial reaction to her.

Khalim ushered Rose into the room where a very elegant woman aged about sixty sat with her two daughters at the long, rectangular table.

The three women wore lavishly embroidered robes, and Rose noticed that Khalim's mother's sloe-shaped black eyes narrowed and her shoulders stiffened with a kind of disbelief as Rose walked rather nervously into the ornate salon. She said something very quickly to her son in Marabanese, and Khalim nodded, his eyes narrowing thoughtfully.

But once Khalim had introduced them, she relaxed with a graciousness which disarmed her and shook Rose's hand and bid her welcome.

'What should I call you?' asked Rose nervously.

'You should call me Princess Arksoltan.' His mother gave her a surprisingly warm smile. 'My son must respect your work very much if he has accompanied you to Maraban.'

Khalim scanned his mother's face, but it bore no trace of disapproval. And why should it? She knew him well, and, yes, he *did* respect Rose's professional skills. His mother also read voraciously and that had, in its way, made her outlook unusually unfettered by tradition.

Perhaps she suspected that he would consummate his relationship with Rose while she was here. But that would not worry her either—she was as aware as he was that he must marry a woman of Maraban blood. She would turn a blind eye to any dalliances which occurred before that marriage would take place. As soon it must, he reminded himself, remembering the prospective brides who had been paraded before him just before he had flown out for Guy's wedding.

A host of dark-eyed virgins, their faces concealed by their yashmaks. Young and exquisitely beautiful, not one had dared meet his eye. He had asked himself whether he found any of them attractive, and the answer had been yes, of course he did. A man would have to have been made of stone not to. But their inexperience and respect for his position would make them merely hostages to his desires. By definition, it would be a submissive and unequal marriage.

He looked at Rose, at the proud way she bore herself and the confidence with which she returned his stare. He felt the muffled acceleration of his heart and cursed it.

'And these are my two sisters,' he said huskily. 'Caiusine and Enegul.'

His two sisters were impossibly beautiful with black eyes and the thickest falls of ebony hair imaginable. And none of the women wore yashmaks, Rose noted in surprise as she took her place at the table, with Khalim on one side, his mother on the other.

Soundless servants brought platter upon platter of food, while candles guttered on the table, blown by the scented breeze which drifted in through the open windows.

'Will you drink wine, Rose?' Khalim asked her softly, watching the rise and fall of her breathing and the way it elevated her magnificent breasts.

She shook her head. 'I won't, thank you. I'll have what everyone else is having.'

Khalim poured her juice, silently applauding her for her diplomacy, while Rose chatted about the purpose of her trip in answer to his sisters' interested questions.

'Tomorrow we're going to the oil refinery,' she told them.

'And Khalim is letting *you* choose Murad's successor?' asked Enegul in astonishment.

Black eyes glittered at her through the candlelight and his

sister's question only crystallised what Rose had suspected all along.

'I think that Khalim has already decided who he wants to replace Murad,' said Rose slowly as the absurdity of the situation dawned on her. As if a man of Khalim's power would rely solely on *her* judgement! 'And I'm just here to confirm his decision.'

He felt the dry beat of desire. Obviously, she was nothing but a witch—well schooled in the art of sorcery! 'How very perceptive of you, Rose.'

'That's my job,' she answered sweetly.

'And what if you and Khalim disagree?' asked Arksoltan. Black clashed with blue in visual duel.

'Then it's whoever argues the case for their choice best, I guess,' said Rose.

'Khalim, then!' put in the younger sister loyally.

'Do not underestimate the power of Rose's debating skills,' came his dry response.

He accompanied her back to her room, and the corridors were echoing and silent, empty save for the ever-constant presence of his bodyguard who followed at a discreet distance behind them.

Her senses were full of him as they walked side by side. The whisper of the silk as it clung and fluttered around the hard, lean body and the faint drift of sandalwood from the warmth of his skin. But there was an unmistakable tension about him, and it had transmitted itself to her so that her breathing had become unsteady, her heart rate erratic as she thought of what *could* lie ahead.

Would he try to kiss her tonight? And didn't she, if she was being honest—and she spent her life trying to be honest—didn't she want that more than anything else?

'You have enjoyed your evening with my family, Rose?'

She nodded. 'I thought it very good of your mother to entertain me when she must be so worried about your father.'

'To be royal means to learn to hide your feelings.' He

shrugged. 'And it would be unforgivable not to show hospitality.'

She nodded, and thought of his mother's initial reaction to her. 'When I walked into the dining room, your mother looked…'

He stilled. 'What?'

'I don't know—shocked—surprised.' She shrugged. 'Something, anyway.'

'Is there anything which escapes those perceptive eyes of yours?' he demanded.

'And she said something to you, too—something in Marabanese which I couldn't understand.'

He nodded.

'What was it, Khalim?'

He gave a painful sigh, knowing that he could not be evasive with her, could not resist the sapphire appeal in her eyes. Was this destiny he was about to recount, or simply history? Coincidence, even? 'You bear a strong resemblance to a woman my great-great-grandfather knew.'

She stared at him, wondering what he wasn't telling her.

He seemed to make his mind up about something. 'Come with me,' he said, and changed the direction in which they were walking.

Intrigued, Rose quickened her step to match his. 'Where are you taking me?' she whispered.

'You will see.'

The chamber he took her to was so carefully hidden that no one could have found it, certainly not unless they were intended to. A small, almost secret chamber containing nothing other than books and a desk, with a carved wooden stool.

And a portrait.

'Look,' said Khalim, very softly, and pointed to the painting. 'Look, Rose. Do you see the resemblance now?'

The air left her lungs of its own accord, and Rose sucked in a shuddering gasp of astonishment.

A portrait of a woman, whose flaxen hair was contrasted

against a gown of crimson silk, her blue eyes capturing the viewer—mesmerising, bright blue eyes which seemed to see into your very soul. Her face was pale, almost as pale as Rose's own skin and she knew without a doubt that this was no Marabanesh woman.

'Wh-who *is* it?' she whispered, and she only just prevented herself from saying, Is it *me*?

'A woman that Malik loved,' he told her tonelessly.

'And lost?' she guessed.

He shook his head sadly. 'She was never his to be had, Rose,' he said. 'The cultural differences between them were too great. And they discovered that love, in this particular case, could not conquer all. She returned to America and they never saw one another again.'

'Oh, but that's terrible!' she breathed.

'You think so? It was the only solution open to them, my sweet, romantic Rose.'

She discerned in his voice the emphatic acceptance of his own destiny, and she didn't say another word as he ushered her out of the room and back towards her own apartments.

'We are here.' He stopped outside her door and stared down at her for one long moment. 'And now...' he was aware of the sudden rapidity of his breathing, the erratic thundering of his heart '...you must sleep, or...'

'Or what?' she asked breathlessly.

He didn't answer at first, just raised his dark hand to lift a strand of the blonde hair which rippled down over her shoulders. 'So pale. Pale as the moon itself,' he whispered.

She stared up at him, too excited to be able to say a single word, other than his name. 'Khalim?' And it came out like a prayer.

He looked down into her eyes, read the unmistakable invitation in them and felt a heady rush of triumph wash over him, knowing that she wanted him, that he could pin her up against the wall and make her his.

He felt himself grow exquisitely hard in anticipation, until he drew himself up short and reminded himself that this was no ordinary woman. She was more beautiful than most, for a start. And a woman like this would surely spend her life warding off advances from men. Not that she would ever reject *him*, of course—but how many times would she have been made to wait for something she wanted? To simmer with desire? Until the slow heat of need became unbearable and boiled over into a heated fire?

And hadn't he become curiously *intimate* with this Rose? Confided in her in a way which was unknown to him? He had heard men say that sex combined with intimacy was the most mind-blowing experience of all. Could he not taste that pleasure once, just once, before his inevitable marriage?

He curved his mouth into a slow, almost cruel smile as he bent his head and briefly touched his lips to hers, feeling her instinctive shudder of elation being quickly replaced by one of disappointment as he swiftly lifted his head away from hers.

'Goodnight, sweet Rose,' he said softly, resisting the soft, blue temptation of her eyes. And he turned back along the wide, marbled corridor, the shadowy figure of his bodyguard immediately echoing his movements, and she watched him go with a sense of disbelief.

Had she been mistaken, then? Imagining that Khalim's not-so-hidden agenda had been to seduce her? And she had actually *accused* him of that? Oh, Lord! She leaned her forehead against the cool of the wall, recognising that she had just succeeded in making a complete and utter fool of herself.

CHAPTER SEVEN

BUT by the time she was dressed the following morning, Rose had recovered most of her equilibrium. The morning sun always had a habit of putting things into perspective. Okay, so Khalim hadn't made a pass at her—why, she should be celebrating, not moping around the place! Falling into his arms—which she had been all too ready and willing to do last night—was a sure-fire recipe for a broken heart. Her head had already told her that in no uncertain terms.

His authoritative rap sounded just after nine, but she went through the pantomime of asking, 'Who is it?' and hearing the reluctant trace of amusement in his voice as he replied. 'Khalim.'

She opened the door to find the ebony eyes mocking her. 'Good morning, Khalim,' she said innocently.

'I see you learn your lessons well,' he told her softly as he scanned her face for the tell-tale signs of crying. But there were none, and he was taken aback by a sense of disappointment that she had not wept in the night for his embrace.

And Rose knew exactly what he was thinking! Had he hoped to find her despondent? she wondered wryly. 'That depends on whether or not I have a good teacher!' she murmured.

'And am I?' he purred. 'A good teacher?'

She walked past him, knowing how dangerous this kind of conversation could be if she allowed it to continue. The seductive tilt to his question made her want to melt into his arms, and that was *not* on his agenda—he had made that *quite* clear. 'It doesn't require a lot of skill to tell someone not to open the door without first finding out who's there!'

Khalim's mouth hardened. Such impudence! So—today

she was refusing to play the game, was she? He wondered anew why had he not tasted the pleasures she had been all too willing to offer him last night, tasted them over and over again until he had grown bored with them?

'Let us go and eat breakfast!' he growled.

'Lovely,' she murmured.

They broke bread and ate fruit on a terrace which overlooked the tiered rose-gardens and the scent and sight of the flowers were almost too distracting. Just as Khalim was. And where had her appetite gone? Rose picked undisinterestedly at a pomegranate and drank juice instead.

'You aren't hungry?' he demanded irritatedly, because of his restless night racked with frustrated dreams.

'It's too hot.'

Too *something*, he thought, shifting slightly in his chair as if mere movement could dispel the rapidly building ache of longing deep inside him. 'We shall drink some coffee, and then leave.' He glanced down her long legs which were modestly covered in sage-green linen, matching the short-sleeved safari shirt which gave no emphasis to the curve of her bosom beneath. 'I see you have worn trousers.'

'I knew you would not want me showing any flesh.'

He bit back his instinctive comment that she could show him as much flesh as she wanted, and whenever she wanted.

'And I didn't know if I would have to climb stairs at the refinery,' she continued animatedly. 'So I played safe.'

'Yes.' His pulse hammered as he imagined her walking upstairs, worrying about her modesty. Affording him the occasional tantalising view of lace panties. A pulse began to hammer at his temple. She *would* wear lace, he was certain of that. And once they were lovers he would buy her a tiny little skirt and she would wear no panties at all, and he would demand that she climb the stairs in front of him...

'Khalim? Is something wrong?'

Her face was an enchanting picture of genuine concern, and Khalim glared. 'Nothing is wrong!' he snapped as his erotic daydream didn't *quite* do the decent thing of leaving him alone. 'But the sooner we get out to the refinery, the better!'

They drank their coffee in uncomfortable silence and then walked around to the front of the palace, where two gleaming four-wheel drives sat awaiting them.

Khalim went to the first and opened the passenger door for her and Rose looked over her shoulder to see that the second vehicle had a burly and shadowy figure at the driving seat.

'Who's in the other car?' she asked as he climbed in and turned the key in the ignition and the second vehicle started its engine in synchrony.

'My bodyguard,' he said shortly.

The ubiquitous bodyguard! 'Doesn't your bodyguard have a name?'

He gave a thin smile. 'I am monitored twenty-four hours a day, three hundred and sixty-five days a year, Rose,' he said. 'There are a team of them—faceless, nameless and invisible to all intents and purposes. It is better that way—if I build a relationship with any of them then it makes me...' He had been about to say vulnerable, but changed his mind. Khalim *vulnerable*? Never! 'Familiarity makes them more accessible to bribery,' he compromised.

She tried to imagine being watched all the time. 'And don't you ever feel trapped?'

'Trapped?' He considered the question as he turned right onto a wide, dusty road surrounded by sand which was the pale silvery colour of salt. 'I have never known any different,' he explained slowly. 'Even at school, I had someone there, a figure always in the background.'

'But don't you ever want to break free?' she asked wistfully.

Her voice held a trace of disquiet, and something in the way her face had softened made Khalim feel a sudden overwhelming sense of regret for what could never be. 'This is freedom of a kind,' he said simply. 'To be alone in a car with a beautiful woman, here in Maraban.'

She thought about this as the car effortlessly negotiated the pock-marked road. 'Why have you never brought a woman here before? There must have been...' She tried to be sophisticated but, stupidly, her voice threatened to crack. 'Lovers.'

There had been women, yes—many lovers in his thirty-five years. So why was it that he could not picture a single one of their faces? Nor recall one conversation which had enthralled him enough to stay locked in his memory?

'My family and my people would disapprove if I flaunted Western permissiveness in their faces.'

Rose flinched at his choice of phrase, but his attention was on the dusty horizon ahead of them, and he did not notice. Did he classify *her* as a permissive Westerner, then?

He tried to give her a brief picture of his existence. 'I live two types of life, Rose. The man who jets around the world and wears suits and stays in all the major cities—he is not the same man who dwells here in Maraban.'

'A man of contrasts,' she said slowly. 'From a land of contrasts.'

He was unable to resist a slow smile of delight. 'A few hours in my country and already you are an expert!'

That smile tore at her heart. Wasn't he aware of its devastating impact? Didn't he know he could ask for the moon with a smile like that—and very probably be given it on a shining golden platter? It just wasn't fair, thought Rose as she stared sightlessly out at the unforgiving desert. 'That's another part of my job,' she said. 'I learn very quickly.'

He wondered what had made her renew that flippant tone, or to sit so rigidly in her seat, but at that moment he saw the gleam of reflected light which heralded the first view of the refinery.

'Look, Rose,' he urged softly.

She forced herself to look interested, forcing herself to put thoughts of Khalim out of her mind. He wasn't hers. He never *could* be hers. What would Kerry say if she knew that her finest head hunter was sitting staring dismally ahead like a lovesick schoolgirl?

But the smile she had pinned onto her face became genuine as she stared at the maze of silver towers and pipes which appeared on the stark horizon.

'It's so modern!' she exclaimed. 'Like a space-age city!'

'You imagined camels, did you?' he questioned drily. 'Robed figures rolling barrels of crude oil around?'

'Maybe a bit,' she admitted.

'Maraban's refinery is one of the world's finest,' he told her, with a quiet pride. 'It takes billions to build a refinery and millions to maintain. Cost-cutting inevitably leads to breakdowns in the system, and we must be one hundred per cent reliable if we are to stay ahead of our competitors.'

There was a tough, uncompromising note to his voice, and in that moment she realised that he was far more than just a figurehead. He was *involved*. Caring. Passionate. About his country and its industry, if nothing else.

The guards at the heavily barred security gates, who had obviously been alerted to their arrival, bowed and ushered them through and Khalim drew up outside the simple but beautifully designed main entrance. Huge tubs of fleshy-leaved shrubs gave a welcoming flash of green.

He turned to look at her, thinking how wonderfully cool she looked with her hair caught back in that sophisticate pleat. Almost aloof—like some exquisite ice maiden. An ice maiden he would one day make take fire, he vowed silently, and then cursed the answering kick of excitement in his loins.

'I have arranged for you to interview both men in the director's office.'

She nodded as she picked up her briefcase from the floor of the car. 'Good. I'll meet you afterwards.'

His smile was bland. 'I don't think you understand, Rose. I will, of course, be present during the interviews—'

'You will not.'

His eyes narrowed with displeasure. 'Quite apart from the fact that I am not used to having my wishes so flagrantly flouted—my family *own* this refinery. Any decisions will ultimately come back to haunt me. I should like to observe each man's interaction with you.'

'Fine.' Rose flashed him a fake-pleasant smile and put her briefcase back down on the floor just as Khalim jumped out of the vehicle and pulled her door open.

'Come on,' he said, seeing that she sat there, so still that she could have been carved from marble.

'I'm not going anywhere.'

Frustration and recognition of that stubborn streak of hers very nearly made him lose his temper. 'Oh, yes, you are,' he contradicted softly. 'I happen to be paying you to—'

'You're paying me to do a job!' she snapped. 'And I cannot do it properly if you happen to be sitting in the room like some great big spectre!'

'Spectre?' he repeated faintly. So she was openly insulting him now, was she?

'You're not just the boss—so to speak—you're their *ruler*, for goodness' sake! How can I expect them to answer me honestly, when all they'll be concerned about is saying what they think *you* want to hear?'

He glowered at her, because he knew she was right—and the only conclusion he could draw from that was that *he* was wrong. And he was never wrong! 'Are you getting out?' he asked dangerously.

'Not unless you agree to my terms,' she answered sweetly.

There was a short, tense silence. He wondered what would happen if he exercised his royal prerogative and picked her up and carried her to the director's private dining room and ravished her there and then? And then shook his head in disbelief at the answering throb of need his thoughts had produced.

Was she going to drive him *insane*, this Rose Thomas?

'Very well,' he agreed tightly. 'It shall be as you wish.'

'Thank you,' she said, but as she slid from the car he caught her wrist, bringing her up close so that black eyes dominated her vision, burning like coals brought up from the depths of hell. And she shivered in response to his touch, even though the temperature was soaring.

'You may find me a far more daunting adversary than you imagine, Rose,' he warned her softly.

Something in his face told her they weren't talking oil refineries now and excitement and fear fused in the pit of her stomach. 'But we aren't fighting any more,' she protested.

'Now you've got your own way, you mean?' he mocked. 'Oh, yes, we are. We've been fighting one way or another since the moment we first met.' And maybe there was only one way to get this confounded conflict out of his system once and for all. He felt another heated tug of desire, provoked by the irresistible darkening of her eyes.

She stared at him. And the stupid thing was that all she wanted right then was for him to kiss her. To kiss her and never stop kissing her. 'K-Khalim?' she said falteringly, shaken by the depths of his anger—an anger which was surely disproportionate to the crime of having the courage to stand up to him? Especially when her professionalism was at stake.

'Come inside,' he said with silky menace as he steeled his heart to the appeal in her eyes, 'and I'll introduce you.'

He showed her into the director's office, which looked like any other high-ranking executive's hidey-hole, with the exception of the pictures on the wall which were both exotic and vaguely erotic. And the desk looked like something out of a museum, with its dark, old wood inlaid with gold.

'Murad Ovezov, the present incumbent, has agreed to speak to you first. He should be able to give you a good idea of what the job entails.'

She hated this new coldness in his eyes, the new *distance* in his attitude towards her. Well, tough! He had hired her to do a job, and do it she would—to the very best of her ability. And that definitely did not include having his powerful and disapproving person present at the interviews!

She gave him a cool smile. 'Thank you, Khalim—you can send him in now.'

It was *unbelievable*, he fumed as he went off to find Murad. She was dismissing him like a servant! She answered him back! Well, she would not be answering him back for much longer. Soon she would be agreeing to everything he said! He would satisfy her as no other man had, and she would be enchained to him for ever!

Murad Ovezov was a man of sixty years, and, although age had painted its inevitable lines around his black eyes, he still exuded a certain *power*. He had worked at the Areeku refinery since it had opened, gradually working his way up until he held the highest position within the factory.

'It's very good of you to see me,' said Rose politely.

He gave a wary bow. 'I was not expecting intervention,' he said, in faultless English.

'I think that you and Khalim have probably decided for yourselves who you wish to replace you.' She smiled, noticing him start when she used the prince's first name. 'I'm here as the fail-safe mechanism—a third party often sees different qualities. Or failures.'

He nodded in comprehension. 'Where would you like to begin?'

She spent half an hour with Murad and then Serdar Kulnuradov was brought in. He was aged forty, confident and knew the refinery inside out. He quoted figures and projections with such fluidity that Rose was left reeling with the breadth of his knowledge.

'Thank you for your time,' she said as he stood up to leave.

Serdar gave a short bow. 'It is my pleasure.' He paused. 'Though it is not usual in Maraban to be interviewed by a woman.'

'Especially a foreign woman?' suggested Rose, with a wry smile. 'I can imagine.'

Oraz Odekov was ushered in next—and a different breed of man entirely. For a start he was aged just thirty and Rose's line of questioning produced quite different answers from those of Serdar.

'And how do you see the future of Areeku?' she asked him at the end of the interview.

And where Serdar had basically said that he wanted more of the same, Oraz was concerned with minimising the effects of pollution.

'You think that's important?' enquired Rose.

'I know so,' he answered simply. 'That is the way of the world today. Countries who do not fight to keep the planet clean will ultimately be discriminated against.'

'Thank you,' she said, and scribbled it down.

He hesitated by the door, and his handsome young face gave a small smile. 'May I be so bold as to say how refreshing it is to have a woman involved in the selection procedure? This, too, is the way forward.'

Go and tell Khalim that, thought Rose irreverently as she smiled back.

Khalim appeared just seconds later. Had he been waiting out in the corridor? thought Rose in wonder. Like a boy waiting outside the headmaster's study.

'Made your mind up?' he asked.

Well, he was certainly to the point when it came to business, thought Rose with some admiration.

'Yes.'

'And?'

'It has to be Oraz.'

There was silence. 'Because he's young and good-looking, I suppose?'

'Please don't insult me, Khalim!'

He sighed. 'Because Serdar is set in older ways than yours and because you are a feminist, is that it, Rose?'

She looked at him steadily. 'I never bring my own personality or prejudices into the selection process—whether or not *I* think I could get on with them is irrelevant. I'm not going to be here, am I? And please don't start calling me a "feminist", Khalim, especially in that derogatory tone.'

'Oh?' His eyes held a mocking challenge. 'You're saying you're not?'

'I'm saying that I don't like labels! Of any kind! I'm just a woman, who believes in equality, that's all.'

The very *last* kind of woman he should be attracted to! And yet he was intelligent enough to realise that her unsuitability was part of what *made* her attractive to him. Her lively mind and keen wit and her refusal to be cowed were qualities he was unused to. Qualities which were proving more aphrodisiac than plump oysters!

'So you're in a dilemma now, aren't you, Khalim?'

He looked at her from between narrowed eyes. Had the minx now managed to read his mind? 'A dilemma?' he stalled.

'Of course. You clearly want Serdar to be the next director, while my advice to you is to appoint Oraz.'

'Because?'

'You want my reasons?'

His smile was coolly assessing. 'That *is* what I'm paying you for.'

She didn't react, but why should she? He spoke nothing but the truth. She *was* here on a professional basis—solely on a professional basis, she reminded herself—and he *was* paying.

'Okay. Serdar has the greater experience, I grant you that, but Oraz has vision. A vision to carry the Areeka well into the middle of this century, and to make it a refinery to be reckoned with.'

He smiled again. 'My very sentiments.'

She stared at him a moment before the gleam in his black

eyes told her exactly what he meant. 'You mean…that you *agree* with me?'

He sighed, almost wishing that she had chosen contrary to his own instincts. 'Yes, Rose. I am entirely in accordance with your wishes.' He glanced at his watch. 'Now let me take you back to the palace for lunch, and afterwards…'

His words tailed off in a silken caress and Rose's heart began to pound uncomfortably in her chest.

'Afterwards?' she asked, relieved that her voice didn't sound *too* eager.

'Afterwards I shall take you riding.'

'I don't ride.'

There was something sensual and uncompromising in his answer.

'But I do,' he said.

CHAPTER EIGHT

THE stables were almost like palaces themselves—huge and cavernous and completely spick and span. Rose knew little of horses, but she knew enough to realise that these bright-eyed animals were well cared for. And that the black stallion whose ear Khalim was tickling—surprisingly gently—was like no other horse she had ever seen, with its fine, narrow body, long legs and slender neck.

'What an unusual creature,' she breathed.

He paused mid-stroke, and Rose found herself wondering what it would be like to have those long, sensuous fingers stroking *her* with such a light caress.

He had changed from his silk robes into close-fitting jodh-purs and a gauzey white shirt, and had borrowed a similar outfit from one of his sisters for Rose. She thought that now he looked like some tousled buccaneer—wild and carefree. Contrasts again, she thought as she watched him.

'This is an Akhal-Teke,' he purred. 'One of the oldest breeds in the world—bred and raced for almost three thousand years. These horses are prized for their desert hardi-ness—with their remarkable endurance and resistance to heat.'

A sense of history and longevity wrapped dreamy arms around her, and her voice was dreamy as she asked, 'And is this *your* horse?'

'Yes, indeed.' His voice deepened with pleasure. 'This is Purr-Mahl. The name means literally, "Full Moon"—'

'And he was born by the light of it, I presume?'

'You presume correctly, Rose.' He smiled. 'I sat and watched the birth, saw the contrast between the silvery-pale gleam of the moon and the night-dark colour of the foal, and I named him there and then. Come, let me sit you upon him.'

'But I don't ride, I told—'

Her protest was already lost on the warm, sultry breeze as he swung her up into his arms, and she wished that he could carry on holding her like that for ever, but he carefully placed her in the saddle instead.

'Press your thighs hard against his body,' he urged and felt a renewed awakening of need. 'Let him know you are there.'

She did as he instructed while he took the reins and led the horse out into the yard where a bodyguard stood, his face inscrutable in the glaring heat of the sun.

Khalim led her round and round the yard for a while and then he murmured something in his own language to the bodyguard, who gave a small bow in response.

Picking up a small leather bag, which he slung over his shoulder, he led her out through the gates to where the stark, shimmering vista of the desert awaited them, with the vast mountains dominating the skyline.

'What did you say to the bodyguard?' she asked him curiously.

'Just that you did not ride, and that I wanted to show you the view from the gate. He is new,' he added casually.

He led the horse a little way into the silvery-white sand, and then suddenly, without warning, he sprang up behind her, and pulled her close into his body at the same time as he seized the reins to urge the horse forward with a murmured word of command and a light slap to the shank.

And they were off!

'Khalim!' Her startled word streamed out like the wind which whipped through her hair.

'Do not be frightened, sweet Rose,' he murmured against her windswept hair.

But it was not fear she felt, it was something far closer to exhilaration. He held her tightly against the hard, lean column of his body, and he handled the horse with such control and mastery that Rose instinctively felt safe.

Safe? Was she mad? Galloping full-pelt across an unforgiving landscape towards the mountains with this dark, enigmatic prince who was taking her who knew where?

Yes, safe. As if this was somehow meant to be. As though all along this had been meant to happen.

As the mountains grew closer, time and distance lost all meaning for her, she had no idea how far they had ridden, or for how long, when, just as suddenly as he'd begun, he steered the horse to a halt in some kind of valley.

Rose could see fig plants and forests of wild walnut trees. And surely down there was the silver glimmer of water?

He jumped down from Purr-Mahl and held his arms up to her and there was a moment of suspended silence while she stared into the enticing glitter of those ebony eyes before sliding down into his arms.

'Sweet Rose,' he said softly.

Had she thought he would kiss her then? Because she was wrong. Instead he took her by the hand and led her towards where she thought she had seen water, and indeed it was, with dense dark thickets of green growing alongside.

He sat down where it looked most hospitable, and patted the ground beside him.

This is a dream, thought Rose. *This is a dream.* And why not? Was Maraban not the land of dreams as well as contrasts?

He pointed to the distant peak of one of the towering mountains.

'When I was a boy,' he said, and his voice softened with memory, 'my father and I used to wait for the first thaw of spring to melt the snow on those mountain peaks, and to flow down to swell the icy river. And we would ride here and drink the crystal waters from a goblet—'

'Why?'

He turned and smiled, and she had never thought that he

could look so impossibly carefree. 'Just for the hell of it.' He shrugged, sounding as English as it was possible to be. He took the leather bag from his shoulder and drew out a small golden goblet, studded with rubies as wine-dark as the robes he had been wearing the other night. 'Always from this goblet.' He smiled.

Rose took it from him and studied it, turning it round in her hands. 'It's very beautiful.'

'Isn't it? Thousands of years ago my ancestors carried it along with many other treasures, when they trekked to this fabled mountain oasis to establish their kingdom.'

But even as he painted beauty with his words, he also painted sadness. For in that moment Rose gleaned some sense of his tradition, his history. He was not as other men. He could not make the same promises as other men. She'd been right from the very first when she had said to Lara that he was not able to offer commitment. And as long as she could accept that...

He put his hand inside the bag again, and drew out a flask in the same gold and claret-coloured jewels as the cup. 'When I was seventeen, he brought me here as usual, only this time we did not drink water; we drank wine.' He smiled. 'Rich, Maraban wine, made from the wild grapevines which grow in the mountain valleys.' His eyes grew soft. 'Will you drink some wine with me, Rose?'

She knew a little then how Eve must have felt when the serpent had offered her the apple, for the question he asked was many-layered. 'I'd love to.'

He tipped some of the ruby liquid into the cup and held it up to her lips. 'Not too much,' he urged gently. 'For Maraban wine is as strong as her men.'

She closed her eyes as she sipped and felt its warm richness invade every pore of her body, and when she opened them again it was to find Khalim staring at her with such a transparent look of hunger on his face that she started, and a droplet of wine trickled from her lips and fell with a splash onto her wrist.

It lay there, a tiny crimson-dark star against the whiteness of her skin and they both stared at it.

'Like blood,' said Khalim slowly. 'The rose has a thorn which draws blood.'

She raised her head and so did he and the look they shared asked and answered the same question, and the goblet fell unnoticed to the ground as he bent his head to kiss her.

Her lips fell open to his velvet touch and she heard herself making a little sound of astonished delight, because she had wanted this for so long. Oh, too long. Much, much too long.

He tangled his fingers in the silken stream of her hair and deepened the kiss. 'Rose,' he groaned against his sweet plunder of her mouth and they fell back against the coarse, desert grass. 'Beautiful, beautiful Rose.'

Her fingers greedily explored the magnificent musculature of his torso through the thin, billowing shirt he wore, kneading her hands against his back as though he were the most delicious kind of dough.

Khalim felt that he might explode with wanting. But more than that—he knew that this woman above all others deserved his honesty. And that had to come now, before it was too late.

He lifted his head from hers and gazed down at her, feeling the heated flush of desire as it snaked its way across his cheekbones. Saw her matching response and the longing which darkened her eyes into twin eclipses.

He drew a long, shuddering breath. 'I have to tell you something,' he began unsteadily.

But Rose was proud. And she was also perceptive—they both knew that. She shook her head. 'I know.'

'You can't know!' he protested.

She wanted to say it *her* way—because she suspected that his words could wound her more deeply than any dagger. 'There can't be any future for us; I know that. This is this, and nothing more than this, and I mustn't read anything else into it.' She actually smiled at his expression of perplexity, recognising that this was a man who was used to calling the shots! 'Don't worry, Khalim,' she finished huskily. 'I won't.'

He shook his head and made a silent curse. By withdrawing emotionally, as she had just done so neatly, she had succeeded in making him want her even more! Impossible! And his need was made all the more poignant by knowing that he could never really have her!

She saw the look of pain etched on his features, and lifted a wondering hand to smooth it down over the hard jut of his jaw. 'Khalim?' she questioned softly. 'What is it?'

He gave a muffled groan as he bent to kiss her neck, his fingers moving to swiftly unbutton her thin shirt, his groan deepening as his hands found and cupped the curved perfection of silk-and-lace-covered breasts.

He peeled the shirt open and levered himself up to stare down at her, his eyes as wild and as black as the stallion they had just ridden. He didn't speak another word until he had slithered down the jodhpurs past her ankles and impatiently removed each sock, until she was lying there in just her bra and panties.

'Lace.' He swallowed as his gaze raked from her face, down over her bosom, and down further still until it came to rest with rapt fascination at the flimsy little triangle of silk and lace which was all that kept him from her greatest treasure. 'I always knew you would wear lace, Rose.'

'And you?' She turned the tables as she reached her hand up and scraped her fingernails against his nipples through the white voile of the billowing shirt. 'What about you, Khalim?'

He was used to complete mastery. 'Me?' he questioned unsteadily, an unmistakable note of surprise in his voice. 'What about me, Rose?'

'Take it off,' she ordered softly.

Her words sent the blood coursing heatedly around his veins. 'Is that a…command?' he demanded unsteadily.

She revelled in the sense that something here was different for him. 'It most certainly is.'

The sight of her head pillowed on the flaxen satin of her hair, and her big blue eyes and soft pouting mouth, was almost as much of a turn-on as her near-naked body. Khalim began to unbutton his shirt with fingers which threatened to tremble.

'You have me in your thrall, sweet Rose—see how my hands shake,' he murmured as the shirt was flung onto the desert scrub. 'Now name your next command.'

'Take it off,' she instructed, revelling in the heady sensation of having such power over this man. *This* man.

'What?' But the attempted tease came out in a kind of strangled plea.

'Everything.'

His long black riding boots were kicked off, and then he fingered the button of his jodhpurs, seeing from the automatic thrusting of her breasts that she was hurtling towards a stage of almost unbearable excitement. You and me both, he thought, with a helpless kind of rapture.

He made his undressing as slow and as deliberate as he could, and Rose was shocked, startled and unbearably aroused to see that he wore nothing beneath the jodhpurs, absolutely nothing. Nothing to disguise the awesome power of his erection. She swallowed, wondering whether... whether...

He read the expression in her eyes as the jodhpurs joined the shirt. 'You worry that I am too much of a man for you?'

She laughed in soft delight at the arrogant boast. 'Maybe you worry that I am too much of a woman for you!'

For answer he pulled her panties down with more speed than grace, and then his hand reached behind her to unclip her bra with one deft movement, freeing the tumultuous splendour of her breasts.

He took one breathless look at her nakedness, before coming to lie on top of her, dipping his head to suckle greedily

at her breasts, his fingers moving between her thighs to flick
at her slick heat.

Rose's head fell back. 'Oh! Khalim!'

'You want me to stop?' he suggested, lifting his head away
from her nipple so that she almost fainted with disappointment.

'Yes! No!'

'What, then?'

'I want to savour it. Savour you.' She wanted this feeling
to go on and on and on and never stop. Khalim *hers*, in her
arms, as she had dreamed of him being since the moment
she had first seen him.

'Next time,' he promised. 'This has been too long in the
waiting. Now we will satisfy our hunger—later we will attend to the feast.'

She felt the caress of his fingers and shuddered. 'This is
feast enough, Khalim.' She sighed. 'Feast enough.'

'Oh, Rose.' He smiled as her body responded instinctively
to his touch. 'Sweet, beautiful Rose.'

But he could wait no longer, his desire for her too intense
to bear. In that moment just before the communion of their
bodies, he felt as though he were about to embrace life in a
way in which he had never embraced it before.

He parted her thighs with eager hands and she felt the
unbelievable power of him moving against her. Surely it was
too soon? Surely she was not ready? But she dissolved into
honeyed heat at just that first touch, and her thighs parted
wider of their own accord and as he took one long, sweet
thrust he made a low moan.

He filled her in every way he could—physically, mentally,
emotionally. Joined in a fundamental flow, while the hot desert sun beat down on them, he was no longer Prince Khalim
and she no longer Rose Thomas, the woman of his employ.
Now he was just a man, and she was just a woman, locked
in the most basic rhythm of all.

She couldn't remember the kisses, or the murmured things

he whispered in her ear—some in English and some in a far more thrilling foreign tongue which she recognised as Marabanese. She only knew that the stars were beckoning her, that her world was about to explode.

And his.

He lifted his head to stare down at her, as helpless at that moment as he had ever been, sensing her release in conjunction with his own.

And then it happened, on and on and on, until their cries were replaced by the soft sound of the desert wind, their stricken breathing calming at last and their sweat-sheened bodies glued together.

Rose felt her eyelids drifting downwards, but he shook her awake.

'No, Rose,' he murmured. 'You must not sleep.'

'*Must* not?' she questioned automatically, even as a lazy yawn escaped her.

He smiled, but it was a rueful smile. Even in the midst of their mutual pleasure—still she challenged him! He kissed his finger and placed it over her lips to silence her. 'They will come for us very soon,' he said.

That had her sitting up immediately, and she saw his eyes darken at the unfettered movement of her bare breasts. 'Who will? When?'

'My bodyguards.' He shrugged, leaning over to rescue her discarded panties and bra.

She shook the stray grains of sand out of her underwear and turned to glare at him. 'And they'll know where to find you, of course?' she demanded crossly. 'This is the usual location for your little *trysts*, is it?'

'Rose, Rose, Rose,' he murmured. 'Fiery, beautiful, argumentative Rose! I have never brought a woman here before—'

No, of course he hadn't. No other Western woman had ever accompanied him to Maraban. And no Maraban woman would have cavorted with such abandon on the ground with the heir to the throne.

'How will they find us, then?' She stood up and pulled her panties all the way over her slender thighs, enjoying the brief look of frustration which clouded his eyes. 'Are they clairvoyant, or something?'

He zipped up his jodhpurs with difficulty. Impossible that she should have aroused him again so quickly, but somehow...somehow, she had. 'They will follow the trail of the horse,' he said shortly, and roughly pulled his shirt on.

Rose was struggling into her clothes. 'What must I look like?' she moaned. 'Won't they take one look at us and know exactly what we've been doing?'

He gave a rueful shrug. Rose cherished honesty, didn't she? Then honesty she would have. 'They would take one look at you and think that I was the worst kind of fool if we had *not* been doing what they suppose.'

'Oh!' Her cheeks were burning. 'And what will they think of me?'

He gave her a cool, steady look. 'Do you seek the approval of my bodyguards?' he questioned. 'Or my approval?'

'Neither!' she snapped. 'I'm thinking about my professional reputation!'

'But your job is done. You are here now as my guest. My *lover*.' He lingered on the last word with a sense of treasures to come, and then looked at her with a question glittering from his black eyes. Would she voice her objection to the term of possession without any promise of commitment?

But Rose simply stared back at him without regrets. She had given herself to him freely. Completely. In a way she had given herself to no man before. She had never known that love-making could be that intense, that profound, that...*fundamental*. She shivered with the memory.

And he had not told her lies. On the contrary, he had been totally open with her. Had told her before he'd made love to her that there could be no long-term future—and she had accepted that and given herself to him as he had given himself to her.

So why not enjoy these exotic fruits of temptation for as long as they were available? To treasure and store up memories which would see her into old age. For she knew without a doubt that no man could ever follow Khalim.

'Will you be my lover, Rose?' he asked softly.

She opened her mouth to speak just as she heard the dry beat of hooves on the sand, and looked up into the distance to see four horsemen on the horizon, galloping fast towards them.

And then she smiled, deliberately enticing him with a slanted look of remembered pleasure. 'Yes, Khalim. I will be your lover.'

CHAPTER NINE

ROSE felt as though she had been taken prisoner on the ride back to the Palace.

There had been a short, sharp exchange between Khalim and a man she had never seen before, a formidable-looking man in rich robes, whose bearing immediately distinguished him as someone of substance. Rose couldn't understand a word of what they were saying, but she guessed that the man's quietly restrained anger was an admonishment to Khalim for breaching security.

Khalim lifted her gently onto his mount and she held on tightly to his waist, longing to turn her head and to steal a glance at him, but she resisted, relieved when the golden gleam of the palace came into view.

Khalim dismounted and lifted her down, and in one single, suspended moment their eyes met and in his she read, what…?

Longing. Yes. And surely a brief dazzle of tenderness. But something else, too—something which stirred a wistful fear deep inside her—for wasn't that regret there? A regret which told as clearly as words would have done that she must accept the limitations of their affair. And never hope.

'I'll see you to your rooms,' he said in a low voice.

The man in the rich robes said something and Khalim turned his head and made a snapped reply.

'Come!' he said to Rose, and led her through the courtyard and into the palace.

'Who was that man?' she asked him once they were out of earshot.

'My cousin, Raschid,' he said.

'He's angry with you?'

Khalim allowed himself a small smile. 'Furious,' he agreed. But making love to Rose had been worth any amount of fury.

'And will you get into trouble?'

He raised his dark brows. 'I think not. I am the prince, after all,' he said autocratically.

He spoke with an arrogance that no other man could have got away with, thought Rose, guiltily acknowledging the thrill of pleasure that his mastery gave her. 'Of course you are,' she murmured.

They reached her rooms and he paused, reaching his hand out to cup her chin, wanting to kiss her above all else, and to lay her body bare once more. He bit down the dull ache of frustration.

'I will have food sent to you here for I cannot be with you this evening,' he told her shortly.

She opened her eyes very wide as her heart pounded with disappointment, but she was damned if she would let it show. 'That's a pity,' she said calmly.

A *pity*? Had he thought she would beg him to stay? Or interrogate him about where he was going? And didn't her lack of jealousy make him want her all the more? 'But I will come to you later, sweet Rose.'

'I might be asleep.'

'Then I will wake you,' he said on a silken promise, and he planted a sweet, hard kiss on her mouth before sweeping away.

Rose slowly got out of her rumpled clothes and took a long, scented bath before slipping into a pair of pure white trousers made out of finest cotton-lawn, and a little shirt of the same material.

Fatima appeared with a tempting array of food—a type of tomato stew with baby okra and lamb accompanied by a jewel-coloured rice dish. And a platter of pastries, glistening with syrup and stuffed with nuts and raisins. There was pomegranate juice and mint tea to drink.

But once she had gone, Rose only picked uninterestedly at the dishes on offer.

How could she concentrate on something as mundane as food, when her mind and her senses were filled with the memory of Khalim and his exquisite love-making? He had been everything. Tender and yet fierce. His kisses passionate and cajoling. He had moaned aloud in her arms, had not held back on showing her his pleasure—and that in itself felt like a small victory.

With disturbing clarity she recalled the vision of their limbs entwined, his so dark and so muscular, contrasting almost indecently with her own milky-white skin, and then she sighed, wondering if she would ever be able to concentrate on anything other than her Marabanesh prince ever again.

More as diversion therapy than anything else, she picked up Robert Cantle's book on Maraban, and read the chapter on Khalim's forefathers, and the establishment of the mountain kingdom.

There were richly painted portraits of his recent ancestors—and one in particular which had her scanning the page avidly. Malik the Magnificent, she read. It was him! Khalim's great-great-grandfather whose thwarted love had borne such a striking and uncanny resemblance to Rose herself.

She studied a face almost as proudly handsome as Khalim's with its hard, sculpted contours and those glittering black eyes and luscious lips, and she sighed again. Don't start getting all hopeful, Rose, she told herself fiercely. You could not have had it spelt out more explicitly that love affairs like this have no future.

At eleven, she put the book down, telling herself that he would not come tonight. She began pulling the brush through her hair, telling herself not to be angry, but she *was* angry. Was this a taste of things to come? How he thought he could treat his women? Keep them hanging around *at his convenience*?

She flung the hairbrush down just as the door slowly

opened, and there stood Khalim in robes of deepest sapphire, his eyes narrowing with undisguised hunger as he caught the unmistakable outline of her body through the thin material of her clothes.

Rose bristled. 'I didn't hear you knock.'

'That's because I didn't,' he said, shutting the door softly behind him.

'Why not?'

He stilled as he heard the reprimand in her voice, and he turned to meet the blue blaze of accusation which spat from her eyes. 'Because we are now lovers, Rose. This afternoon you gave yourself to me with an openness which suggested that we have no need for barriers between us. Do I need to knock on your door?'

The voice of reason in her head told her to back off, but she had missed him, wanted him, and felt hurt by his unexplained disappearance, and so she ignored it. 'Damned right you need to knock!' she retorted. 'I may be mature enough to realise that this is a very grown-up affair with no promises or expectations on either side—but that does not mean that I'm prepared to be trampled on like some sort of chattel!'

If he hadn't wanted her so much, he would have walked out there and then. No woman had ever spoken to him with such a flagrant lack of respect—especially when he had had her gasping and sighing in his arms on the desert grass!

'I do not treat you as a chattel,' he answered coldly.

'No? You just make love to me and then waltz off for the evening without bothering to tell me where you are going?'

He hid a smile. Ah! So she was *jealous*, was she? Good! 'But you just told me that neither of us have any expectations, Rose,' he demurred.

'That's not an expectation!' she declared wildly, wondering where all her powers of logic had flown to. 'That's just simple courtesy. Where were you?'

He had been foolish to imagine that he would not have to tell her. He had not wanted to hurt her, but now he saw that by not telling her he must have hurt her more. He was not used to analysing what effect his actions would have on a woman's feelings. Usually, he did what the hell he liked, and was allowed to get away with it. With anything.

'I had dinner with my mother and my father,' he said softly. 'My father is too frail to accommodate—' he very nearly said 'strangers' but bit the word back in time '—guests,' he finished heavily.

Rose stared at him. 'And that's all? Why didn't you tell me that?'

She would never be able to find out, and yet Khalim realised that if he was anything less than truthful with his fiery Rose, he would lose her.

'No, that isn't all.' He sighed. 'There was a young woman there, too.'

Rose froze as some new and unknown danger shimmered into her subconscious. 'I'm not sure that I understand what you mean.'

'My father is very frail—'

'I know that.'

'Soon he will die,' he said starkly, and there was a long, heavy pause. 'And I must take a bride when the year of mourning is complete.'

It was the most pain she had ever felt and she felt like smashing something—anything—but somehow, miraculously, she managed to keep her face composed. Why crumple when this was what her instincts and her common sense should have told her? 'And this—young woman—was, I presume, one of the *suitable* candidates being lined up for you?'

How preposterous it sounded coming from his beautiful, English Rose! 'Yes.' He thought back to the girl being brought in by her mother, her slim, young body swathed in the finest embroidered silks. Only her eyes had been visible, and very beautiful eyes they had been, too—huge, and doe-like, the deep rich colour of chocolate.

But she had been tongue-tied at first, and then so docile

and submissive—so adoring of her prince and heir. He had seen his mother's approving nod, and the sharp look of pleasure on the face of the girl's mother, and had tried to imagine being married to a woman such as this.

She would bear him fine Marabanesh sons and in time she would grow fat and he would grow bored. Had his mother and his father noticed his distraction with the idea? he wondered now.

'So is she going to be the lucky one?' asked Rose, only just preventing herself from snarling.

'No, she is not.'

'Oh? Did she discover how you'd spent your afternoon, then? Lying with me under the hot desert sun? Making love to *me*?'

The taunt triggered memory, fused and exploded in a fury of anger and almost unbearable passion. He pulled her roughly into his arms, though he saw from the instant dilation of her eyes that she was not objecting. Not objecting one bit, he thought as he drove his mouth down hard on hers.

And only when he had slaked a little of his hunger for her did he lift his head and gaze down into her dazed face as her eyelids fluttered open to stare up at him.

Her lips opened to frame his name, but no word came.

'Rose,' he said gently, his breath warm and soft on her face. 'How can we be lovers if you make such unreasonable demands on me?'

Her fingers bit into the hard strength of his shoulders beneath the sapphire silk. 'Most people wouldn't call them unreasonable!'

'Most people, most people,' he chided. 'Rose, Rose, my sweetest Rose—I am not most people. We both know that. I told you that right from the very beginning.'

She shook her head sadly. 'No, not right from the beginning, Khalim. You told me just before you made love to me, when making love had become as inevitable as night following day. You did everything in your not inconsiderable power to get me to arrive at that point. You played me as you would—' memory flashed into her subconscious as she recalled something he had told her about his schooldays, his love of fishing '—a *fish*! That's what you did! Yes, you did, and don't deny it! Teased me and tempted me, and—'

He cut short her protests with a forefinger placed softly on her lips, feeling them tremble beneath his touch, and he felt a surge of something far greater than mere desire. How well she knew him! How was this possible in so short a time?

'Yes, I plead guilty to your accusations,' he admitted slowly. 'Every one of them.'

Her anger was mollified by the triumph of knowing that she understood him a little too much for his liking, and her fingertips curled spontaneously into the nape of his neck, like a kitten's claws.

He felt her capitulation in the instinctive sway of her body, her hips folding into his, where fire and desire were building and burning, and he groaned.

'So can we not just enjoy this...now, my sweet, sweet Rose? To take what many pleasures are ours?'

It was, she recognised, an expression of need as much as lust, and the closest that Khalim would ever come to...not begging, exactly, because a man like Khalim would never, ever beg. But beseeching, certainly. She stared up into his face, and all her objections withered into dust.

'Yes, my darling,' she said shakily. 'We can.'

His hand was unsteady as he traced a slow line with his finger, from neck to navel, the filmy white material of her blouse moulding itself to the slim curves beneath.

'I want to see you naked,' he said huskily. 'Properly naked against satin, not sand.' He drew the cotton top over her head, his breath freezing with pleasure as he saw the unfettered lushness of her breasts and the flaxen hair which streamed down over them. He bent his head to kiss one puckered, rosy nipple.

'Oh!' she sighed, squirming her hips in helpless pleasure. 'You are a wicked, wicked man, Khalim.'

'You bring out the wickedness in me,' he murmured.

'The feeling is mutual,' she murmured back. 'So, so mutual.' Rose's hands slid underneath the sapphire silk of his gown, fingertips feasting on the feel of the satin skin which lay over the muscular definition of his torso. She felt him shudder beneath her touch and knew another moment of triumph, suspecting that once again he was close to the edge. And that was a heady feeling. This man of control and power—*hers*!

'I wanted to make this a long, slow undressing,' he said, bending his head to whisper in her ear.

'I sense a "but" coming.'

'Mmm. I think it will take many days before I can bear to prolong the pleasure in that way. Shall we…?' He paused, and trickled a finger down to rest possessively in the small dip of her navel. 'Shall we quickly remove these constraining garments, so that we can come together without barrier?'

But the word stirred an uncomfortable thought which had occurred to him over dinner that very night.

'And I have brought with me—' he scowled as he forced himself to say the abhorrent word, but only abhorrent when used in connection with Rose '—*condoms*! We were too reckless and too hungry for one another earlier.' When, for the first time in his life, he had made love without protection. It had also occurred to him that she might have become pregnant, and an intense and primitive yearning had swept over him. Only to be replaced by a fervent prayer that it should not be so.

For it would be impossible if Rose Thomas were carrying his child. Impossible!

Rose shrugged the slippery silk impatiently over his shoulders and let it flutter to the ground.

'You don't need them,' she told him.

Black eyes iced instantly at the implication. 'What don't I need?' he questioned softly.

She met his gaze without flinching. 'Condoms. We won't need them.' She hesitated. Surely she wouldn't have to spell it out for a man of the world such as this?

'Why not?'

Apparently she did.

'I'm on the pill,' she said bluntly.

'No!' His mouth formed the denial as if he had been stung.

'Yes,' she insisted quietly.

His heart pounding with an unendurable jealousy, he tightened his grip on her. 'So this is the way of Western women, is it?' he demanded. 'Always prepared, is that so? *Just in case?*'

'Don't be so hypocritical, Khalim,' she answered with dignity. 'I happen to be on the pill because my periods were heavy and irregular—'

'Your *periods*?' he demanded incredulously.

She guessed correctly that women did not speak of such matters with Khalim. So they were allowed certain intimacies with him such as sex, were they? But nothing in the way of *real* intimacy. Of women as they really were. Well, she had taken him on *his* terms; now let him take her on *hers*. She tried to make allowances for his upbringing and his culture. 'It's a very effective remedy,' she explained patiently.

'And also very convenient if you happen to just want to fall into bed with someone?' he scorned.

She wrenched herself away from him and fixed him with a withering stare. 'If you believe *that*, then you can get out of here right now, and don't bother coming back!'

He could see from the fire in her blue eyes that she meant it, and he forced himself to draw a steadying breath. 'I shouldn't have said that—'

'No, you're right—you shouldn't!' Her breathing came fast and rapid and indignant. 'How many lovers have you slept with in your life, Khalim?'

'You dare to ask me *that*?' he questioned dangerously.

'I'll bet it's a whole lot more than *I* have—which is precisely *two!*'

He flinched again and his mouth hardened. How dared there have been another before him? How *dared* there!

'*Two!*'

'Yes, two. Actually not terribly shocking considering that I'm twenty-seven years old and have grown up in the kind of culture I have! I have *never* gone to bed with anyone indiscriminately! Can you look me in the eye and honestly say that *you* haven't, either?'

He stared at her, torn between fury and admiration. His beautiful, logical Rose! Applying the same rules of life for her as well as him! He bit down the pain of jealousy and a slow light began to glimmer at the back of the black eyes.

'You have never actually been to bed with *me* either, have you, sweet Rose?' he murmured, taking her unresisting hand and raising it to his lips to kiss it. 'And I think that is a situation which we should remedy now, with all seemly haste.'

How powerful he looked. How masterfully dark and virile and proud. Rose wondered half wildly whether she should have prevented him from scooping her up into his arms and carrying her over to the low mattress. A victor with his spoils, she thought weakly.

But then she was the victor, too. Because to have provoked that look of sensual promise coupled with a barely restrained impatience to make love to her was the most potent sensation she had ever encountered.

She let the last of her misgivings go as he laid her down on the embroidered coverlet, tugging at the silk cord which bound his loose trousers so they fell to the floor.

My heavens, but he was aroused! Darkly and magnificently aroused. Her mouth began to tremble as he slid her cotton trousers all the way down her legs and tossed them aside with an impatient disdain.

'Khalim,' she gasped as he came to lie beside her, his arms snaking possessively around her waist while his eyes burned down at her like smouldering coal.

'What is it, sweetest Rose? You want me to kiss you now?'

It was exactly what she wanted—the touch and the warmth and the security of his lips caressing hers. So that for one mad and crazy moment she could imagine that it was not lust which made this kiss such magic, but fool herself into thinking it was something as elusive and as precious as love.

CHAPTER TEN

KHALIM stayed with her for most of the night, but slipped out as dawn began to paint a pink and golden light on the horizon.

He swiftly dressed, then bent his head to kiss her, his lips lingering regretfully on her pouting mouth. 'The plane leaves at midday,' he murmured. 'Be ready to leave at ten.'

'Mmm?' she questioned groggily.

It had been the night of her life. His love-making had known no boundaries—nor hers, either. She'd given herself to him without inhibition. But with love, she realised with a sinking heart as she acknowledged the emotion which had first crept and then exploded deep inside her.

She loved him.

The realisation gave her no real pleasure—for what pleasure could ever be gained from a love which was doomed right from the start? But she *had* taken him on her terms, and she *did* want him, and because of that she pinned a sleepy smile onto her face.

'Mmm?' she questioned again, stalling for time, time to be able to react in the way expected of her, and not with the gnawing feeling of insecurity which had started to overwhelm her every time she thought about losing him.

'Be ready by ten,' he instructed softly, wishing that he could lie with her here until the morning sun filtered its way in precious golden shafts through the shutters.

She nodded and watched him go, all elegance and grace as he swished out of the room in the silken robes.

She ate the fruit and bread which Fatima brought to her room for breakfast and was ready by nine when there was a knock on the door and she opened it to find Khalim standing

131

there, changed from his robes into one of his impeccably cut suits, ready for the flight back to London, and with an unusual expression on his face.

He looked perplexed.

'What is it?' she asked him quickly.

He shrugged. 'My father has requested that he meet you.'

Rose opened the door a little wider. 'You sound surprised.'

He was. Exceedingly. It was inconceivable—to *his* mind, in any case—that his father should express a wish to meet his Western blonde. But he would not tell Rose that.

'He is so frail,' he told her truthfully, 'that he sees few visitors.'

Except for prospective brides, thought Rose bitterly—bet he sees *loads* of those. 'Then I must be honoured,' she answered.

He nodded absently, his mind far away. 'I will arrange to have your bags taken out to the car,' he said. 'Now, come with me.'

She thought how distracted he seemed as he led her through the maze of marble corridors into a much larger and grander part of the palace. Past silent figures who watched them with black eyes which were unreadable, until at last an elaborately ornate door was flung open and they were ushered into a bedchamber.

At the far end of the room was a large and lavishly decorated bed, and, lying on it, a man whose unmoving rigidity proclaimed the severity of his illness.

'Come,' said Khalim softly.

By his father's bed sat his mother, her face troubled, and she nodded briefly at Khalim and then, not quite so briefly, at Rose.

'Father,' said Khalim. 'This is Rose Thomas.'

In a face worn thin by illness, only the eyes remained living and alert. Keen, black eyes, just like his son's. He gave a small smile and Rose was overwhelmed by the graciousness of that smile.

'So,' he said slowly. 'I believe that I must thank you for confirming Khalim's chosen successor for the oil refinery.' Another smile, this time rather more rueful. 'An opinion which differed from my own. And therefore Khalim said that we must bring in an independent arbitrator to decide.'

Rose looked up at Khalim in surprise, and met a mocking glance in return.

'Thank you. It is a great honour to meet you, sir,' she said quietly, and bowed her head.

The old man nodded and said something very rapid to Khalim, in Marabanese, and then Khalim tapped her arm. 'Come, Rose,' he said. 'Will you wait in the outer chamber while I bid my father farewell?'

Rose slipped silently from the room, her heart clenching as she read the pain in Khalim's face. Did every departure seem like the last time he would ever see his father? she wondered as she sat on a low couch outside the bedchamber.

It seemed a long time before Khalim came out again, and when he did his face was grave and Rose sprang to her feet.

'Is everything…okay?' she asked. It seemed a stupid question under the circumstances, but Khalim did not seem to notice.

'His physician is with him now,' he said slowly. 'Come, Rose—we must go to the airport, where the plane awaits us.'

They walked back along the corridor and he glanced down at her. 'The way you looked at me back there,' he mused.

Rose's eyes opened very wide. Had he seen the tell-tale signs of love? she worried. And wouldn't that be enough to send him fleeing in the opposite direction?

'When?'

'When my father told you that we had agreed to bring in an outsider to arbitrate, you looked surprised. What was the matter, Rose—did you imagine that I had invented the job as a ploy to get you out to Maraban?'

'It would sound insufferably arrogant of me to say yes,'

she answered slowly. 'But maybe just a little, then, yes—yes, perhaps I did.'

He admired her honesty—it would have been easy for her to have been evasive, and to lie. And, in truth, had not such a vacancy existed—then might he *not* have manufactured an excuse to bring her on such a trip? He smiled. 'You have fulfilled all my expectations, Rose. In every way and more.'

The limousine whisked them to the airport at Dar-gar and they were immediately escorted onto the plane, where Philip Caprice and the two glamorous air stewardesses were waiting for them.

And it wasn't until the plane had taken off into a cloudless blue sky and Khalim found his eyes wandering irresistibly to her pure, beautiful profile that he began to experience some of the misgivings which his father had already expressed so eloquently.

He had not wanted to leave her this morning, and now he felt like dismissing Philip and making love to her again. Rose Thomas was getting under his skin, he acknowledged—and he seemed to be hell-bent on breaking every single rule which mattered.

His mouth hardening, he deliberately picked up his brief-case and pulled a sheaf of papers out.

Rose interpreted the body language. The almost impercep-tible way he turned away from her. Oh, yes! He'd been vir-tually silent in the car on the way to the airport, and now she was getting the cold freeze. Was he having second thoughts? Had he thought more about the heinous crime of her being on the pill and decided that she was the worst kind of woman?

Was this the reality of being Khalim's temporary woman?

She got to her feet and met the hard, dark question in his eyes. 'I'm going to freshen up,' she said, and picked up the smaller of her two bags.

When she emerged a whole half an hour later, Khalim froze.

While in Maraban she had dressed most appropriately, in trousers or long skirts—clothes which modestly concealed her delectable shape. But now she had changed into a strappy little sundress in a golden colour which matched her hair, and which showed off far more brown and shapely leg than he was comfortable with.

He shifted in his seat. Not at *all* comfortable with. He waited until she had decorously taken her place beside him before challenging her.

'What is the meaning of this?'

She turned her head and raised her eyebrows. Now he was *talking* to her as though she were his concubine! 'The meaning of what?'

'This…this…vulgar *display* of your body,' he grated, realising that he did not want her body on show for anyone. Anyone but *him*!

'But this is exactly the kind of dress I was wearing when we first met,' she pointed out reasonably. 'You liked it well enough then, as I remember.'

'But now,' he said coolly, 'I do not.'

'Oh?'

He lowered his voice to a sultry whisper. 'I do not want other men looking at you in that way!'

'You mean the way *you're* looking at me?' she enquired innocently.

'That is *different!*''

'I fail to see how!' she answered wilfully.

He drummed his fingers impatiently against the arm rest. Well, short of marching her back into the bathroom and insisting that she put something decent on, there was little he could do.

He made a terse and impatient sound beneath his breath, feeling the uncharacteristic tug of frustration—and not solely sexual frustration, either. No, this was a frustration born out of the knowledge that he had finally met a woman who would not bend to his will! His match!

'Wear what you like!' he gritted.

'I intend to!'

The rest of the journey was completed in a stony silence, while Rose fumed and wondered how she could ever have thought herself in love with such a tyrant of a man.

Then she stole a glance at that beautiful, dark profile and thought of his tenderness and his passion during the night, and once again her heart pained her as though someone had driven a stiletto into it, then slowly twisted it round.

By the time they had disembarked into the waiting limousine at Heathrow Airport, Khalim was in the rare quandary of not knowing what to do. Or, rather, of knowing exactly what he *wanted* to do—which was to rush Miss Rose Thomas straight back to his suite at the Granchester Hotel and ravish her to within an inch of her life. So that for ever after she would comply with every demand he ever made!

He sighed. The trouble was—that he did not want that at all. Her fire and her independence inspired him almost as much as it frustrated him. What a hollow victory it would be to have Rose in the compliant position he usually expected of his women!

The car slowed as it approached the busy thoroughfares of London and he forced himself to look at her.

Forced, indeed! As if looking at her could give him nothing but untold pleasure!

'Would you like to come home with me?' he murmured.

For Khalim, he sounded almost biddable, Rose thought. But not quite.

'You mean to the Granchester?' she enquired coolly.

'Of course!'

She shook her head. She had had enough of his surroundings and their influence. 'Why don't you come back with me?' she questioned innocently.

To that flat she shared with the other girl? Unthinkable!

And then he thought of the alternative, which was even more unthinkable—that he went home without her!

'Very well,' he answered.

'There's no need to make it sound as though I'm leading you into the lion's cage!' said Rose crossly.

'Not a lion, no,' he agreed, a hint of humour lightening the night-dark eyes. 'More some beautiful and graceful cat!'

She wasn't sure whether it really *was* a compliment—but she found herself basking in it anyway.

But as the car began to approach her road, Rose began to wonder whether it had been such a good idea to invite him. What if Lara had a load of her out-of-work actor friends around, lying all over the place and drinking wine and smoking cigarettes?

Or what if Lara had had a heavy night, and had left the place in a state of disarray—a common enough occurrence when Rose wasn't around to tidy up after her.

They left the bodyguard sitting in the car outside and went upstairs to the flat.

It was rather better than Rose had anticipated, but not much. There weren't a *crowd* of Lara's friends—just her on-off boyfriend, Giles, whom Rose always thought of as *very* off.

Giles had been born into a wealthy family, imagining that the world owed him a living. He had fluked his way into drama school and then coasted through the course—only just managing not to be asked to leave by the skin of his teeth.

Unfortunately he had the kind of blond-haired, blue-eyed looks and carved aristocratic cheekbones which meant that he could get any woman that he wanted—and Lara wanted him far more than he wanted her.

Which meant, thought Rose grimly, that she waited on him as if he were an invalid. Cooking up various little treats for him and pouring him glasses of wine at all hours of the day.

Like now.

So why was he polishing off a glass of Chardonnay in the middle of the afternoon? And looking at Khalim with a kind of jealous incredulity.

But then, Rose decided with more than a little satisfaction, Giles rarely met men who transcended *his* good looks so completely!

She looked around at the plates and cups and wineglasses littered around the sitting room and saw Khalim's lips curve with undisguised displeasure. Well, *let* him judge her, she thought proudly as she bent to pick up an empty wine bottle which was in danger of tripping someone up!

'Lara, you've already met Khalim,' she said shortly. 'Khalim, I don't believe you've met Giles, who is Lara's—'

'Lover,' drawled Giles arrogantly.

Khalim's facial muscles didn't move an inch. 'It is my pleasure,' he said smoothly and looked at Rose with a question in his eyes.

Now what? thought Rose helplessly. Did she take him to her room? No, she couldn't—she just *couldn't*. Not with Giles smirking like that and Lara affecting that puppy-dog expression whenever she looked at Khalim.

'Would you like some coffee?' she asked weakly.

'Thank you,' he replied, without enthusiasm.

The kitchen looked as though someone had tried to start World War Three in there—with every surface covered in used crockery and glasses.

And Lara had used up all the real coffee, thought Rose in disbelief as she picked up a nearly-empty jar and held it up to him.

'Is instant okay?' she questioned.

'Instant?' he echoed, as though she had just started speaking in Marabanese.

'Coffee,' she elaborated.

'Do you have any tea?'

'Yes. Yes, I do.' She made them two cups of herb tea and then cleared the table so that they could sit down and drink it.

They sat facing one another warily across the rising steam from their cups.

Now what? thought Rose again, before getting back some of her customary spirit.

'You don't *have* to stay, you know,' she bristled.

'No, I don't,' he agreed calmly, thinking that Rose—*his* Rose—should not have to live amidst such outrageous chaos. 'But you will not come back with me to the Granchester either, will you?'

'No.'

'Do you mind telling me why?'

How to explain that his costly surroundings only emphasised their inequality, and that if she was to spend the tenure of their fragile relationship always on *his* territory, then it would always seem a little tainted.

'Can't we just be like a normal couple?' she demanded. 'I don't always want to be surrounded by your bodyguards and the awe in which people hold you. Everyone always defers to your status—it's always there. A barrier.' She nearly said, A barrier towards getting to know you, and then stopped herself. Maybe he didn't *want* to get to know her on the level she craved to discover him.

He stared across the table at her. 'Then we seem to have reached some kind of stalemate, don't we, Rose? What do you suggest?'

The idea hit her like a thunderclap. If only they *could* be an 'ordinary' couple. The idea grew. 'Why don't you rent a flat of your own?' she suggested. 'A flat where we can meet as equals?'

'A *flat*?' he repeated.

'Why, yes.' Of course, they would never be *quite* the same as a normal couple. Khalim would never have to go begging to the bank manager for a loan, for example. But neutral territory would give them some kind of equality, surely?

'There are loads of—' she forced herself to say the hateful word '—short-let flats on the market in London. Furnished or unfurnished—suit yourself. Wouldn't it be…nice…' she gave him a kind of feline smile '…to have a place where we were free to be ourselves? Within reason, of course,' she added hastily. 'Obviously there would have to be some provision for your bodyguard.'

He raised his eyebrows. Good of her! And then he thought about it. And thought some more. Didn't her words have more than a kernel of truth in them? Wouldn't a rented flat give him a fleeting kind of freedom? The kind of freedom which most men of his age took for granted? The freedom…and he swallowed as he imagined a whole place of their own. Where Rose could wander around wearing what she wanted.

Where they could watch a video and eat their supper lolling around on a sofa, as he had seen his friend Guy do with Sabrina on so many occasions.

'Very well.' He nodded, and his mind started ticking over. 'I can see the wisdom behind your idea. I will get Philip to start looking immediately—'

'No, Khalim!' she said, interrupting him. 'You have to do it like other people do! *You* go and look at flats. You find the one you want and *you* do all the transactions. Do it yourself for once! Forget Philip!'

Her feisty challenge drove the blood heatedly around his veins and in that moment his desire to possess her made him feel almost dizzy. But he would have to wait. He would not bed her here with the feckless actor and her sweet but rather untidy flatmate listening to them.

'I most certainly will, Rose,' he promised. 'And with haste.' He lowered his voice into a sensual whisper. 'Because believe me when I tell you that I cannot bear to wait for you much longer.'

CHAPTER ELEVEN

IT WAS not a flat, of course. It was a magnificent, four-storey house in Chelsea.

'A flat would have caused too many problems for my security,' explained Khalim as he showed her through a wealth of magnificent, high-ceilinged rooms. And his Head of Security still had not forgiven him his breach when he had galloped off across the desert sand with Rose locked tightly against him! 'So what do you think?' he murmured. 'Does my Rose approve?'

How could she do anything but? Rose let her gaze travel slowly around the main drawing room. Everywhere she looked she could see yellow and blue flowers—saffron roses and lemon freesias, and the splayed indigo fingers of iris— and she was reminded of the bouquet he had sent her, when he'd first been trying to...

To what? To seduce her? She turned her head, so that he could not see her eyes. Had that been his only intention? Maybe it had, she acknowledged, but something else had grown from that intent. You didn't share a house with a woman if sex was the only thing on your mind.

Oh, *stop* it, Rose, she remonstrated with herself. Stop playing Little Miss Wistful.

'I love it. It's beautiful,' she said, and hoped that her voice didn't *sound* too wistful. Because they were *playing* house, not setting up house together, and she must never let herself forget that. But at times like this it wasn't easy.

She stared in slight awe at the two white sofas with their jade-green cushions, and the low bleached oak coffee-table. 'It all looks brand-new,' she commented with approval.

'That's because it is.'

141

Rose raised her eyebrows. Heaven only knew how much he would be paying per month for a place like this. She asked the question she had been dreading asking. 'How long is the let for?'

There was a momentary pause. 'I am not renting it,' he said quietly. 'I bought it.'

'You *bought* it? What, just like that?' she asked incredulously, until she realised how preposterous she must have sounded. A place like this would be nothing to a man of Khalim's wealth.

He saw her look of discomfiture. 'And for security reasons, all the furniture had to be brand-new—'

'What, in case there was an explosive device stashed behind the sofa?' she joked, then wished she hadn't.

'Something like that,' he agreed wryly.

'Sorry. That was a stupid thing for me to say!'

He smiled. 'How very magnanimous of you, Rose.'

When he smiled like that she was utterly lost. 'So you've bought a house,' she observed slowly.

'Well, to be honest—nothing I looked at to rent—' he remembered the bemusement of house-owners when he'd turned up with his bodyguard in tow '—came up to—'

She met his glittering black gaze. 'Palace standards?' she questioned drily.

How he loved it when she teased him that way! 'Mmm.' He swallowed down the desire which had been bubbling over all week. 'Anyway,' he finished, 'it will be a good investment.'

A good investment. Of course. That was how the rich made themselves richer, wasn't it? They invested.

Trying not to feel a little like a commodity herself, Rose wandered over to one of the huge picture windows which overlooked an intensely green square surrounded by iron railings and looked out.

'A very good investment, I'm sure,' she echoed.

'My bodyguard will have the self-contained unit downstairs,' he explained, watching the sudden stiffening of her shoulders and wondering what had caused it. 'And the upper three storeys will be entirely for you…and for me.'

Rose swallowed down the excitement that his words had produced. For the past week—was it only a *week*? It had seemed like a century in passing—she had thought of nothing else. Tried to imagine the reality of sharing a flat with Khalim, and every time she had failed to make that final leap of faith. To think that they actually would. That he would arrange it all himself. And then bring her here to live with him. Because when she had suggested that she simply visit him on occasional evenings and stay the night, he had swiftly censured her suggestion with arrogant assertion.

'No!'

'No?'

His black eyes gleamed. She could fight him on this, but she would not win. Oh, no. 'I do not want you to bring cases of clothes here, or have one toothbrush here, and another at your flat. You will live here, Rose, with me.'

For how long? her heart wanted her to cry out, but she steeled herself against its plea. She probably only thought she loved him. Wanted him because he was so completely unattainable. She must not place emotional demands on him which he couldn't possibly meet, because in time it would wear down whatever it was they had between them.

And what was that?

'Rose?' He broke into her reverie with a silky question.

Well, now was the time of reckoning, she told herself as he drew her into his arms and lowered his dark, beautiful head to hers. Now they would be able to see what they had between them.

His kiss was fierce and hard and long, whipping her up into a frenzy of need which matched his.

He found himself wanting to rip the little sundress from her body, to lay her down on the floor and impale her there. But there had been little restraint in his physical dealings with her so far. Little desire to show her the mastery of which he was proud.

For he had learned his sexual skills well. His eighteenth birthday present from his cousin had been a trip to Paris, to a hotel which had been the last word in luxury. And there, awaiting him, had been his 'present'—a stunning redhead in her forties, with a body which most men only dreamed of. A woman of the world, of a certain age. And in the three days and nights which had followed, she had taught him everything there was to know about the act of love.

The most important being, she had purred with satisfaction, the ability to give a woman pleasure.

He looked down into Rose's milky-pale face, where her sapphire eyes shone out at him like bright stars, and he felt an unrecognisable kick of emotion. He wanted to pleasure his Rose, he realised. To give her more pleasure than she had ever dreamed of. He smiled with the heady anticipation of it.

'Come and let me show you the bedroom now.'

She took his proffered hand, feeling oddly shy as he took her into a white and blue bedroom which was dominated by a vast bed.

He was watching her carefully. 'Rose,' he said, almost gently. 'Why do you blush?'

She certainly wasn't going to tell him that his smile had made her feel almost like… She shook her head at the ridiculousness of it all. Like a virgin bride on her wedding night. Who the hell was she kidding?

Oh, I *wish*, she thought helplessly as he drew her into the circle of his arms. How I wish.

'Now.' His voice deepened as he ran his ebony gaze over her. 'At last.'

He undressed her slowly, and with infinite care, his fingers teasing and tantalising her as they unbuttoned the sundress and then peeled it from her body. And then, as though he had all the time in the world—off came her lacy brassière.

And finally, with his fingertips flicking light and teasing movements which thrilled her to the very core—he slowly removed her little lace panties.

'Now let me look at you,' he commanded softly.

She should have felt shy in her nakedness, when he still stood so formidably clad in his dark grey suit—but how could she feel anything but pride under that warm look of approval? Instinctively, she lifted her shoulders back and the movement emphasised the lush thrust of her breasts.

He felt the unmistakable wrench of desire. 'Get into bed,' he commanded softly. 'You're shivering.'

Shivering, yes—but her tremble had nothing whatsoever to do with the cold, but with the tingling sense of expectation which washed over her as he began to unknot his tie.

He unhurriedly slipped his jacket off, and hung it over the back of the chair.

Come on, she thought. Come *on*!

But if he read the hunger in her eyes he chose to ignore it, his dark gaze not leaving her face as he slowly began to unbutton his shirt.

The shirt joined the jacket on the chair, and he unbuckled his belt before unzipping his trousers.

'You could strip for a living,' she told him throatily, unable to keep her thoughts to herself any longer.

He smiled. 'So could you. What say we make a living of it together?'

It was an outrageous fantasy, tinged with a poignancy produced by that elusive word 'together'. But she lost the sadness as he climbed into bed to join her, and pulled her into his arms, his warm, living flesh making her feel on fire where they touched.

'Just you and me,' he murmured, and cupped her breast in his hand, feeling the nipple thrust and jut against his palm in instant reaction. 'How do you like that?'

'What—*that*?' She jerked her head jokingly towards her

breast, where his hand looked so shockingly dark against the whiteness of her skin.

But he shook his head, a rare kind of tenderness filling his voice. 'No,' he demurred. 'I meant the you and me bit.'

'Oh, that!' She was about to make a flippant comment, the kind of comment which would keep her safe from hurt. But she read in his eyes an elemental truth—that right at that moment he was holding nothing back from her. And didn't such a truth deserve another? 'Oh, that is a prize beyond rubies,' she told him huskily.

He groaned as his mouth replaced his hand, locking his lips hungrily against the rosy nub which sustained all life. He wondered if these breasts would ever suckle a child.

A child that could never be his!

'Rose,' he groaned again, and the slick lick of his tongue made her feel almost weak with longing, so weak that she gave into her most primitive desire and slid her hand down between the muscular thighs until she had found what she was looking for.

'Rose!'

Her wanton capture of him made him feel as weak as water in her hands. And so did the way she was touching him, her hands lightly caressing the rock-hard shaft of him. His eyes closed and his head fell back against the pillow. Never, since that first induction to the pleasures of the flesh, had he allowed a woman such freedom with his body.

'Stop, Rose,' he begged.

'You don't like it?' she asked him innocently.

'I like it.' He said a single word in Marabanese he hadn't realised he knew, and then gently closed his hand over hers to stop her. 'Too much.'

She realised how much she had enjoyed seeing him look as dreamily helpless as that. To see him fighting for control. It made her feel strong. *Equal.* 'Well, then?' she whispered close to his mouth, so close that he touched his lips to hers.

'This is intended to be traditional love-making, Rose,' he told her sternly.

'And no demonstration that I have a certain amount of experience—and that you aren't my first lover?'

There was no flippancy in her voice now, Khalim recognised—with a flash of insight which dispelled the black clouds of his jealousy. Nothing but a wistful trace of insecurity, as though he would be judging her and finding her wanting. He tipped her chin upwards, so that their eyes locked on a collision course.

'You push me far, Rose,' he told her. 'Sometimes too far, I think.'

'You went mad when you found out I was on the pill!'

He had to force himself to stay calm and drew a deep breath. 'My harsh words on the subject in Maraban were based on...jealousy,' he grated, spitting out the unfamiliar word. 'Jealousy that I was not your first lover—'

'And I was jealous that you weren't mine,' she said softly, filled with a sudden boldness—because what was to be gained by hiding the truth from him?

Khalim expelled a long, low breath, remembering the newness, the vitality and sheer power of their first encounter, and he sought to honour it in some way. 'I felt like your first,' he said.

'And I yours,' she whispered back.

'You are more my equal than any woman I have ever met, Rose. You live by different rules to the women in my country, and the life you have lived makes you the person you are today. And I like the person you are today.'

A person who could get him running halfway around London to find a place for them to live, much to Philip Caprice's bemusement and his bodyguard's outrage!

'So don't you like your women to be subservient?' she asked him teasingly, wondering what she had said that was so wrong, because his face darkened with a simmering look of bitterness.

He thought of the unknown woman who would one day become his wife. And his eyes flickered down to where Rose lay—so pale and so beautiful—her hair spread like a moonlit fan across his pillow.

He shook his head. 'I never want subservience from you, Rose,' he whispered. 'Never from you.'

And all her thoughts and doubts and questions were driven from her mind as he began to stroke her, as if she were some pampered feline, and she wrapped her arms around him, kissing his neck and the bare warm flesh of his shoulders.

Khalim found that he wanted to touch her for ever, to run his fingertips over the creamy satin of her skin, to explore her body until he knew every curve and every dip of it. It was a new sensation for him—the wish to prolong the waiting, until it reached such a fever-pitch that neither of them would be able to resist it.

'Khalim!' gasped Rose, as his skilful touch took her down erotic pathways she had never encountered before, so close to the edge that if he didn't... 'Khalim!'

'Mmm?' What exquisite pleasure it gave him to see his Rose lying there, her hips in frantic grind, powerless to resist him. The sight of a woman yielding to him had never before had the power to make his heart thunder as though it really *were* the very first time. He knew then that he could make her beg for him, and knew also that it would leave a bitter taste in his mouth. For he was as much in her thrall as she was in his. 'It is time,' he whispered against her hair.

He moved to lie above her, dark and dominant and utterly, utterly in control as he parted her thighs, smiling as he felt her honeyed moistness.

And he entered her not with the powerful thrust of that first time in the desert—as though he would die if he didn't join with her as swiftly as possible. No, this, thought Rose as an unstoppable warmth began to unfurl deep within her— this was a long, slow movement which seemed to pierce at the very heart of her.

They moved in conjunction, in perfect synchrony, her pale, curving flesh complementing the hard, lean lines of his. Each lingering thrust set her trembling, until her whole body seemed to shimmer with some unexpected light.

Khalim felt as though he were enveloped in some dark, erotic enchantment, and he had to use every once of self-restraint he possessed to hold back. Until he saw the sudden arching of her back, the inevitable stiffening and then indolent splaying of her limbs as rapture caught her in its silken net.

And only then did he let go, with a moan which seemed to be torn from his soul itself.

Only then did he shudder with the pleasure of fulfilment, until he came to a perfect stillness—and allowed his head to fall upon the cushioned splendour of her breast.

They dozed on and off for most of the afternoon, and then he made love to her again. And again. Until she sat up in bed with her blonde hair all tousled and falling in disarray around her shoulders, while he sucked erotically on her fore-finger.

'Khalim?'

'Mmm?' He loved the salty-sweet taste of her skin.

'I'm hungry.'

'Hungry?' The thought of food had not occurred to him, not with such a feast here in his arms, but then he had taught himself to transcend hunger. When reaching puberty he had been sent into the desert with his tutor and taught to go without food for days. Existing on a little water and what few berries were available. It was the simple code of the desert: that you should learn to do without, because you never knew when you might need to.

'Yes, starving, actually!' complained Rose.

He released her finger and lay back on the pillow, the sheet rumpled by his ankles, his dark body gloriously and proudly naked. 'You want that we should ring out for some food?'

She opened her mouth to say yes, when she remembered,

and shut it again. They were trying to be ordinary, weren't they? And if they were an ordinary couple who had just moved into their first home, then they would certainly not have an excess of cash to throw about.

'No. Let's have something here,' she said and tossed her hair back over her shoulder. 'I brought a load of groceries with me, remember?'

Khalim shrugged, and gave a satisfied smile. 'Whatever you wish to prepare will taste like manna, Rose.'

She was about to get out of bed when she frowned at his easy assumption that *she* would cook. 'Why don't *you* make us something to eat, Khalim?'

'*Me?*' he questioned. '*Me?*'

'Yes, you! I'm not asking you to run naked up and down Park Lane—just make us a cup of tea and a sandwich!'

'A cup of tea and a sandwich,' he repeated, on a low growl, damned if he was going to admit to her that he hadn't ever had to prepare a meal for himself in his adult life! He swung his long legs out of bed and stood naked in front of her, a mocking question in the dark eyes as he saw her unconscious little pout. He put his hands low on his hips, in a gesture of pure provocation.

'Sure?'

Rose licked her lips. So he was trying to use his sexuality to get out of making her a sandwich, was he? What place equality now? 'Quite sure,' she answered primly, but immediately turned over to lie on her stomach so that he wouldn't see the sudden tightening of her breasts.

He returned after so long that Rose was certain he must have fallen asleep in the kitchen, carrying a loaded tray with him. And he still hadn't bothered to get dressed!

But to her surprise, the sandwich was creditable.

'That looks really good, Khalim!' she exclaimed.

He sizzled a look at her. 'Don't patronise me, Rose,' he warned.

'I wasn't!'

'Oh, yes, you were!' His eyes glittered. 'Just because I haven't had to fend for myself doesn't mean I don't know what to do, if I need to—and you wouldn't need to be a culinary genius to be able to cut off two slices of bread and wedge a little salad between them.'

Round one to Khalim, thought Rose with unwilling admiration as she bit into the most delicious sandwich she had ever eaten.

CHAPTER TWELVE

LIVING with a prince wasn't a bit as Rose had expected—though, when she stopped to think about it, what *had* she expected? It wasn't exactly the kind of situation where you could rummage through your life's memory box and come up with a comparable experience, was it?

But there was only one word she could use to describe it. Bliss. Sheer and utter bliss.

She had never lived with a man before—had never felt any desire to make such a commitment to anyone before Khalim—and she was amazed at the way they just kind of slotted together as though this had always been meant to happen.

To her astonishment, the same things made them laugh—though for all the wrong reasons. Television game shows and badly made sitcoms, for example. And corny jokes which Khalim had apparently never grown out of since his schooldays.

'It is enjoyable to have someone to share them with,' he murmured to her one morning, when she was about to leave for work.

She heard the trace of wistfulness in the deep timbre of his voice. 'What an isolated life you have led, Khalim!'

He shrugged. 'Of course. It goes with the territory.'

And the territory in his case was real, not imagined.

And the other aspect of their life which was as close to perfection as Rose could imagine was their love-life. Their *sex*-life, she corrected herself automatically.

Just because Khalim sometimes astonished her with amazing tenderness during the act of love, didn't mean that he actually *felt* love. Sex *was* sometimes tender, just as sometimes it was fast and furious, or deliciously drawn-out. In fact, it had a hundred different expressions, and Khalim seemed intent on exploring each and every one with her.

On the downside, there was no doubt that Khalim had been spoiled—both physically and spiritually. There was often a tussle as to who got their own way, with Khalim often expecting her to accede to *his* wishes, simply out of habit.

'No!' she protested one evening, when she walked into the kitchen to find that the breakfast cups and plates still hadn't been stacked in the dishwasher. 'It's *your* turn to sort out the kitchen, Khalim!'

Khalim's eyes narrowed. This was fast turning into the farce of a camping trip he had been forced to endure at school at the age of thirteen! 'Haven't we taken this living a normal life to the extreme?' he demanded fiercely. 'Surely even normal couples get someone in to do the housework!'

'Yes, they do,' said Rose patiently. 'But that doesn't include general tidying up, does it? And anyway—' she looked up at him in appeal '—isn't that more of the same of what you're used to? People waiting on you, so that you don't live in the real world at all?'

Khalim gave an impatient little snort. Didn't she realise that when she opened those great big baby-blue eyes at him like that, he would agree to almost anything? He walked over to where she stood, like some bright and glorious vision in a short white skirt and a clinging scarlet T-shirt, and pulled her into his arms.

'Khalim, no!'

'Say that like you mean it!'

'I do!' she said, half-heartedly.

He shook his head as he lifted her face to his. 'Oh, no, you don't, my beauty,' he murmured, and bent his lips to hers.

She responded to him the way she always responded— with complete and utter capitulation, opening her mouth greedily to the seeking warmth of his, and tangling her fingers luxuriantly in the thick, black hair.

He gave a groan as he cupped her T-shirted breast, thinking how he had longed to hold her in his arms like this all day. She was like a fever in his blood, a fever he must purge before too long. He *must*. 'Let's go to bed,' he demanded heatedly.

'No!'

'No?' His black eyes glittered. Why was she saying one thing, while her body was saying the precise opposite? 'You mean you want me to do it to you here, standing up?'

Rose felt the instant pooling of need. He was outrageous! Irrepressible! She loved him—oh, how she loved him. 'No,' she said again, and with an effort disentangled herself from his arms, knowing in her heart of hearts that she was going a little bit over the top about this. But for heaven's sake—there was a *principle* at stake here! 'Well, really I mean yes—but *not until after you've stacked the dishwasher*!'

'If you think I'm going to allow domesticity to start dominating the *important* things in life, then you have made a very poor judgement, Rose,' he'd said, with a silky and sexual threat, and kissed her again, very soundly.

She lost that particular battle—but the crazy thing was that she didn't particularly care. She didn't care about anything, she realised.

Except for her dark lover with the soul of a poet, who would never truly be hers.

They went out—of course they did—just like any other couple. Except that they were not—and excursions into the outside world brought that fact crashing home. For trips to restaurants or the theatre were always shadowed by the discreet but ever vigilant bodyguard, who was never more than a few steps away from Khalim. Several times they ate with Sabrina and Guy, and Rose found herself glancing at Sabrina's shiny new wedding band with more than a little envy.

And each morning they both left for work, just like any other couple.

'Do you *have* to go to work?' Khalim demanded sleepily from their bed one morning, when the thought of having her in his arms for the rest of the day was just too much to resist. Philip could deal with all the most urgent matters, he thought hungrily. He threw her a sizzling look. 'I mean, *really*?'

'I most certainly do!' she replied crisply, steeling herself against the promise in those night-dark eyes. 'Why, are you offering to "support" me from now on, Khalim?'

He smiled, knowing that her challenge was an empty one. That his feisty, independent Rose would sooner sweep the streets than accept money from him! 'Any time you like,' he mocked. 'Any time at all.'

And it said a lot about her emotional state for Rose to realise that the offer actually *tempted* her for a moment. She spent one heady moment thinking how wonderful it would be to be 'kept' by Khalim, before swiftly taking herself out of the flat and heading off for her offices in Maida Vale.

Each day, Khalim went to his suite at the Granchester to join Philip Caprice where he locked himself into matters of state affecting Maraban, settling down to study the papers which had been sent for his attention.

And lately there were more and more of them, he acknowledged as he began to accept that the burden of his inheritance began to creep ever closer.

The heady, pleasure-filled weeks crept stealthily by. Each night he received reports on his father's health, and the physicians assured him that he was weak, but stable.

But one evening he replaced the telephone receiver with a heavy hand, tension etching deep lines on the dark, beautiful face, and Rose's heart went out to him, even as a cold feeling of the inevitable crept over her. 'Don't you want to go out to see him?' she asked softly. 'Shouldn't you be there, with him?'

He met her troubled gaze, her foreboding echoed in his

own eyes as he saw their fantasy life coming to an end. He nodded. 'I shall go at the weekend,' he told her. 'Once I have concluded the American oil deal.'

Her heart began to pound as she heard something new in his voice. Something she would have preferred not to have heard. Distance. She had heard it once before in Maraban and it had frightened her then.

Distance.

She stumbled over the words. 'And you may...you may stay there, I suppose?'

There was a long pause. 'That depends—'

'Please be *honest* with me, Khalim! Otherwise what good will this whole...' she couldn't think of a single word which would sum up the magic of their weeks together, and so she plumped for the prosaic '...*affair* have been, if the truth deserts us when it really counts?'

'Affair?' he echoed thoughtfully and then nodded slowly. 'Yes. I may have to stay. And I won't be able to take you with me, you know, Rose.'

'I know that. I never expected you to.'

'No.' She had placed no demands on him whatsoever, apart from a stubborn determination for him to do his share of the household chores. Would it have made him happier if she had broken down? Wept? Begged him not to go, or to smuggle her back to some anonymous house in Maraban? Because that at least might have given him some indication of her true feelings for him.

Never before had he encountered a woman who didn't demand words of love and commitment—particularly in the aftermath of love-making. But Rose had not. Did she not want emotional reassurance from him, then? Or was her eminently practical side simply telling her that such words meant nothing. That actions were what counted—and that soon he would have to leave.

'Then we'd better make the last of these two days,' she said unhappily.

He nodded, wishing that he could take the sadness from her eyes. 'Let's start right now.' And he pulled her into his arms and kissed her, dazed by the emotional effect of that sad, sweet kiss. 'A kiss like there was no tomorrow,' he murmured.

I wish tomorrow never *would* come, thought Rose as she kissed him back with a hunger which verged on desperation, a desperation which grew into a storm of passion which left them shaking and helpless in its wake.

They were slavish in their attention to detail, to try to make their last hours together as perfect as possible. The meals they cooked were their favourite meals; the music they played the most poignant.

And their love-making took on an extra dimension—the sense of inevitable loss they both felt making it seem more profound than it had ever done before.

She played with his body as she would a violin, fine-tuning every single one of his senses until he would moan with helpless pleasure beneath her hands and her lips.

The night before he was due to leave, they ate a sensual supper in bed and she was just licking off the strawberry yogurt which she had trickled on the dark matt of hair which sprinkled his chest when the phone rang.

'Leave it to the machine,' he instructed, his eyes tight shut with the pleasure of what she had been doing with her tongue.

She shook her head and sat back on her heels, wearing nothing but an exquisite wisp of scarlet silk he had bought her and then fought to make her accept. 'It might be Maraban,' she whispered. 'It might be news of your father.'

Guilt evaporated his pleasure instantly and Khalim reached his hand out and snatched up the phone.

'Khalim!' he said.

As soon as he started speaking in rapid Marabanese, Rose knew that something was very wrong—even if the dark look of pain which contorted his features hadn't already warned her.

He spoke in an unfamiliar, fractured voice and nodded several times, and when he put the phone back down Rose knew without being told that the worst had happened.

'He is dead?' she asked, in a shaking voice.

He didn't answer for a moment, shaking his head instead. The inevitable. The expected. And yet no less hard to bear because of that.

'Yes, he is dead,' he answered, in a flat, toneless voice. 'He died unexpectedly an hour ago.'

'Khalim—' she went to put her hand out to him, but he had already swung his long, dark legs over the bed and begun to dress. 'Can I *do* anything? Do you want me to phone Philip?'

'Philip is already on his way over,' he said, still in that strange, flat voice. 'The plane is being fuelled—and we will leave for Maraban immediately.'

Rose bit her lip. 'I'm so sorry, Khalim.'

He turned then and she was shaken by the bleak look of emptiness on his face.

'Yes. Thank you.'

He looked forbidding, a stranger almost, but Rose didn't care. She couldn't stop herself from moving across the room and putting her arms around him in a warm gesture of comfort. His body felt stiff, as if it was trying to reject the reality of what he had just heard, but she hugged him all the tighter.

'I should have been there,' he told her brokenly. 'I should have *been* there!'

'You couldn't have known! You were planning to leave first thing! It was unexpected, Khalim. Fate!'

'Fate,' he echoed, and tightened his arms around her waist.

Let it go, she urged him silently. Let it *go*.

And maybe her unspoken plea communicated itself to him in some inexplicable way, for she heard him expel a long, tortured breath and then his arms came round her, his head falling onto her shoulder, and she felt his long, drawn-out shudder.

They stood like that for moments—minutes, aeons, perhaps—until the insistent jangling of the doorbell could be heard.

He raised his head to look at her, and there was the unmistakable glimmer of tears in the black eyes.

'Khalim?' she whispered.

The great black cloud of grief which was enveloping him lifted just for a moment as he met the soft sympathy in her eyes, and grief became momentarily guilt.

This was the moment, he realised. The moment of truth. He would have to let her go.

And he didn't want to.

'May the gods forgive me for saying this at such a time,' he whispered, knowing that there would never be another moment to say it, 'but I do not wish to lose you, Rose.'

Oh, the pain! The spearing, unremitting pain of imagining life without Khalim. 'It has to be.' How rehearsed the words sounded, but that was because they were. She had been practising a long time for this very moment. 'It *has* to be.'

The doorbell rang again.

He lifted her chin, sapphire light blinding from her eyes. 'I must be in Maraban,' he told her, and then he said very deliberately, 'but I can come back.'

She stared at him as hope stirred deep within her, even while logic told her that any hopes she harboured would be futile. 'How?' she whispered.

'When things are settled.' He shrugged his shoulders. 'I will be able to visit you from time to time. It won't be the same, but...' His words tailed off as he saw the frozen expression on her face.

'What, and become your English mistress, while you take a bride back in Maraban?'

'I have no bride in Maraban!' he grated.

'Not yet! But soon you will!' She let out a deep sigh.

'Having to be content with little bits of you, when I've had…had…' Only now her words tailed off, too. She had been about to say that she had had all of him, but that hadn't been true, had it?

She had had his company and his laughter and his body, but there had never been any mention from Khalim of the most important thing of all.

Love.

She shook her head, fighting to keep her dignity. He would remember her as his proud, independent Rose, not a snivelling wreck of a woman. 'No, Khalim,' she said firmly. 'It won't work.' She pictured a life where she would always be waiting. Waiting for the infrequent phone call. Waiting for news that he had taken a wife at last. News of his wedding. Or of his baby, perhaps… She shook her head as the pain lanced through her again.

'Better we end it now, Khalim. Cleanly and completely. At least that way we'll be left with our memories, instead of destroying what we once had.'

Had he really imagined that she would agree to his outrageous suggestion? Could he honestly see Rose resigning herself to a lifetime of playing the understudy? And yet he did not want to let her go. Damn her! He knew that she still wanted him, just as much as he wanted her—so why could she not just agree to his proposition?

His mouth tightened, and he removed her hands from where they lay locked upon his shoulders.

'And that is your last word on the subject?'

She met the anger in his eyes and she turned away rather than face it. She did not want her last memory of Khalim to be one of smouldering rage. 'Yes,' she said.

'So be it,' he said, with chilling finality. 'Philip is waiting.'

She heard him leave the room and go to answer the door, heard him speaking in an undertone to Philip, and then suddenly he was back and she whirled round to find him looking remote and frozen, and she guessed that reality really was beginning to kick in. She wanted to go up and comfort him again, but there was something so forbidding about the icy set of his features that she didn't dare.

She wondered if her face showed that inside her heart was breaking. 'Goodbye, Khalim.'

He thought how detached she looked, as if nothing could touch her. And perhaps nothing could—for *he* certainly could not. She wanted no part of him, unless she could have everything of him. She wanted too much! 'You will continue to live here?' he questioned.

'How can I?' She meant—how could she possibly stay in a place which had been filled with his presence if he was no longer there? How could she bear to face the empty space on the bed beside her? Or consign herself to being without his warm body enfolding hers night after night?

'The deeds of the house are in your name,' he said. 'I bought it for you.'

'And why did you do that?' she demanded. 'As a kind of insurance policy?'

'You have a way of reducing everything down to the lowest possible denominator, don't you, Rose?' he stormed. 'It was supposed to be an act of generosity—nothing more sinister than that!'

But suddenly she felt cheap. So this really *was* the payoff, was it? An expensive house in Chelsea to compensate for the fact that her sheikh lover had left her!

'I don't want your charity, Khalim!'

His face grew cold. 'Then please accept it as my gift, for that was the only way it was intended. Goodbye, Rose.' His black eyes raked over her one last time, before he turned away and out of the room without a backward glance.

Rose waited until she had heard the front door slam shut behind them and then counted slowly to a hundred, before she allowed herself the comfort of tears.

CHAPTER THIRTEEN

'ROSE, are you *mad*?'

Rose calmly finished placing the last of her clothes into a suitcase, and clicked the locks into place before looking up at Sabrina—a particularly glowing-looking Sabrina, she thought, with a brief pang of envy. But that was what being newly married did for you, wasn't it?

'No, I am certainly not mad. Why should I be?'

'Because this house is beautiful, and if Khalim wants you to have it—'

'I can't live here without him, Sabrina!' Rose thought how strained her voice sounded. Well, at least it would match the strain on her face. 'Can't you understand that?'

'I guess so.' Sabrina sighed. 'Guy was worried that something like this might happen.'

'You mean that Khalim would inevitably leave me to go back to Maraban and find someone more suitable?'

'Well, yes.' Sabrina bit her lip. 'I wanted to warn you about his reputation, but Guy said—'

'No.' Rose shook her head to interrupt her friend. 'I don't want Khalim portrayed as some feelingless heartbreaker who used me and then dumped me. I went into this with my eyes open, Sabrina. I knew exactly what would happen, and now it has.' And the pain of his leaving was more intense than she had imagined in her worst nightmares.

Sabrina had come straight round soon after Khalim had left for the airport. 'Khalim has just rung me,' she announced to a red-eyed Rose when she opened the door to her. 'Oh, darling Rose—I'm so very sorry.'

'He told you about his father, I suppose?' Rose questioned dully.

'Yes.' Sabrina shut the front door behind her. 'He also told me to look after you. He's worried about you, you know.'

'I'm not an invalid, Sabrina,' said Rose stiffly.

But actually, maybe she *was* beginning to feel like an invalid.

In the two hours since Khalim had left for the airport, she had wandered around the flat like a robot, picking up all her possessions and placing them in neat piles, ready to go.

It was surprising really, just how much of a home they had made. In three months of living together, they had built up much more than she remembered. Lots of books. Vases. A coffee set. A beautiful backgammon set. Little things she had brought to their home. A lump formed in the back of her throat and she swallowed it down.

No point in thinking like that. No point at all.

'But where will you *go*?' asked Sabrina.

Rose looked at her with a calm, frozen face. 'I'll be fine. Don't forget—I've still been paying the mortgage on my flat, all the time I've been living here with Khalim.'

'But I thought you said that Lara had moved that ghastly boyfriend of hers in.'

'Yes, she has.' Rose gave a worried frown, before a little of her customary fire returned to reassure her that she hadn't become a *complete* walking piece of misery. 'And she can jolly well move him out again!'

'And you're really going to sell this place?'

'Yes, I am.'

'Don't you think it's a little soon to be making major decisions like that?'

Rose shook her head. In a world which now seemed to have all the security of quicksand, there was only one thing she knew for sure. 'I won't change my mind,' she said quietly. 'I just know I have to go.'

'So will you buy somewhere else with the proceeds, if it's just the fact that you can't bear to live here without Khalim?'

'It isn't. I just don't want to be beholden to him in any way.'

'Oh, Rose, he can *afford* it!'

'That's not the point! I *know* he can afford it! But it will make me feel like it's some kind of pay-off.'

'I'm sure it isn't.'

'So I'm going to give the money to charity instead!' she declared.

'Khalim wouldn't want you to do that. He'd want you to use it on yourself. Guy says he's genuinely concerned about you—'

'Well, he needn't be,' said Rose stubbornly, because concern made her stupid heart leap with excitement. He might be *concerned*, but he wasn't here, was he? And he never would be, either. 'He's always telling me how brave and how strong I am. I'll get over it.'

Maybe if she said it often enough, she just might convince herself.

She stared at Sabrina's worried face. 'Khalim asked you out once, didn't he, Sabrina?'

Sabrina's eyes widened. 'Who on earth told you that?'

Rose smiled. 'Khalim did. He said…' Her voice began to waver as she remembered the closeness they had shared the night he had made the admission. 'He said that he didn't want there to be any secrets between us…' Her eyes filled with tears and she turned a stricken face to Sabrina who instantly came over and put her arms around her.

'Oh, Rose,' she whispered. 'Poor, darling Rose.'

'Just tell me one thing, Sabrina!' sobbed Rose helplessly. 'Why the hell did he have to be a *prince*? Why couldn't he have just been a normal *man*?'

The death of Khalim's father was announced on the national news that evening, and Rose found herself watching the set obsessively, unable to turn the television off, even though her sanity pleaded with her to.

There was a short clip showing Khalim arriving at Dar-gar airport, with hordes of people clogging up the tarmac and paying homage to their new leader.

How stern he looked, in his pure white robes, she thought longingly. And how icily and perfectly remote. Looking at the footage of his arrival, it seemed hard to believe that just a few hours ago they had been making love in the room next door.

She swallowed, and as the news switched to other items she turned the set off.

She went home to her flat that same evening, to find the place almost unrecognisable and Giles snoring on the sofa.

Biting back her temper, she marched over and shook him by the shoulder.

'Whoa!' He opened bleary eyes and blinked at her. 'Whassa matter?' he slurred.

Rose took a steadying breath as she backed off from the stench of stale alcohol. 'Where's Lara?'

'She's away filming. What are you doing here?'

'I'm moving back here—in to *my* home. I know it's short notice, but would you be able to find somewhere else to live, please, Giles? And if it's at all possible I'd like you out tonight.'

Giles sat up and sneered. 'What's happened? Has he kicked you out? Has your pretty prince tired of you?'

'Khalim's father died this morning,' she said, in a voice which was threatening to break.

Giles narrowed his eyes. 'So he's in charge now, is he? Wow!'

It shamed her that he had not expressed one single sentiment of sorrow for Khalim's father—even for convention's sake.

'Just go, will you, Giles?' she said tiredly.

'Okay, okay—I'll go and stay with my brother.'

Once he had gone, she set to cleaning the flat, and at least it gave her something to do to occupy herself, so that by midnight, when everything was looking pretty much normal again, she was able to take a long bath and fall into bed.

But she couldn't sleep.

For too long she had been used to drifting off in the warm haven of Khalim's arms. Now she felt cold. And alone. She put on a baggy T-shirt for comfort, but there was still precious little warmth to be found.

She found a purchaser for the house almost immediately. That part of Chelsea had people just *queuing* up to buy homes there—and she was lucky enough to find a newly engaged merchant banker who was a first-time buyer.

'I want to complete the sale as quickly as possible, that's my only condition,' she told him and his horse-faced fiancée.

'Soon as you like,' he agreed smoothly, barely able to contain his glee as he examined the luxurious wealth of fixtures and fittings.

Rose tried to throw herself into her work, and when the money for the sale came through she went straight to the Maraban Embassy in Central London. It was difficult to keep a rein on her emotions as she spoke to the receptionist—a man whose glittering black eyes reminded her of Khalim, and made her feel such a deep sadness.

'Yes?' he asked.

Rose pulled the cheque out of her handbag, still finding it difficult to come to terms with just how much money the house had made. Khalim had been correct, she thought wryly—it *had* been a good investment.

'I'd like to make a donation to the Maraban Orphans' Fund,' she said.

The receptionist put his pen down and his look of surprise quickly became a smile of pleasure. 'How very kind,' he murmured. 'I will ask one of our attachés to come down and speak with you.'

'Can't I just leave the money, and go?'

He glanced down at the cheque, narrowed his eyes in shock and shook his head. 'I'm afraid that will not be possible. You are extremely generous, Miss…' he glanced down at the cheque again '…Thomas.'

Twenty minutes later, Rose was shaking hands with a courteous if somewhat bland attaché, who kept thanking her over and over for her generosity.

'You would like to sign the book of condolence before you leave?' he asked.

Rose hesitated. 'Yes, please,' she said quietly.

They left her alone in a room where a black-draped photograph of Khalim's father hung above a simple arrangement of lilies, alongside which a single candle burned. It was a photo which must have been taken when he was in his prime. How like his son he looked with those stern, handsome features and those fathomless black eyes, she thought.

Hot tears stung her eyes as she lifted the pen and stared at it as if seeking inspiration. What to write?

And then the words seemed to come pouring out all by themselves.

'You were a fine ruler,' she wrote, 'whose people loved and respected you. May you rest in peace, in the knowledge that your only son has inherited your strength and your wisdom to take Maraban into the future.'

Somehow she got out of there without bursting into tears, but at least there was a sense of a burden having been lifted. She'd cut her ties with Khalim, she realised—and, in so doing, had shown her own strength and wisdom. Now she must get on with rebuilding her life.

But this was easier said than done.

A job which had once enthralled her now became a number of hours in the day to be endured. I *must* snap out of it, she told herself fiercely—or I won't have a job as well as my man.

Yet, try as she might, she found herself gazing sightlessly out of the window time after time.

In the weeks which followed Khalim's departure, images

came back to burn themselves in her mind's eye—and to haunt her with their poignant perfection.

She remembered the first time she had shared a bathtub with him, and after the inevitable love-making they had washed each other's backs, giggling as bubbles frothed up and slid over the side and onto the floor.

He had looked at her with an expression of mock-horror. 'Now who is going to clean *that* up?'

'You are! You're the one who insisted on joining me in the bath!'

In that split-second of a moment Khalim had looked care-free—his rare and beautiful smile making her heart race. 'You'll have to make me, Rose!'

'I have my methods,' she had purred boastfully, her hands sliding underneath the water to capture him, and he had closed his eyes in helpless pleasure.

So what was she doing remembering *that*? Trying to torture herself? To remind herself of how unexpectedly *easy* it had been to adjust to a man like Khalim? And it had.

She hadn't expected to be able to sit enjoying such simple companionship with him in the evenings as they'd played backgammon or cooked a meal together. Oh, *why* had it been so easy? she asked herself in despair.

And then, two nights later, she had a visitor when she arrived back at the flat after work.

Philip Caprice was sitting in a long, dark limousine outside the flat and Rose's heart leapt when she saw the car, her eyes screwing up in an attempt to scan the smoky glass, in futile search for the one person she really wanted to see.

Philip must have seen her approaching, because by the time she came alongside the car he had got out and was standing waiting, a polite but slightly wary smile on his face.

'Hello, Rose,' he said.

She nodded in greeting. His eyes looked very green against his lightly tanned skin. Tanned by the glorious heat of the Maraban sun, she observed with a pang. 'Philip,' she gulped.

'May I come inside and talk to you?'

She wanted to say no, to ask him what was the point—but her curiosity got the better of her. And, besides, she wanted to hear news of Khalim.

'Yes, of course you can.'

'Thank you.'

Lara was still away filming and so the flat was empty and mercifully tidy and she found herself thinking about the time when she had turned up with Khalim to find total chaos. Remembered the rather fastidious look of horror which had darkened his handsome face, and the resulting decision for him to find them somewhere to live.

Just *stop* remembering, she told herself fiercely. Stop it!

'Would you like some coffee, Philip? Or tea, perhaps?'

He shook his dark head. 'Thank you, but no.'

He seemed, she thought, a trifle uncomfortable. What was the purpose of his visit? she wondered. 'What can I do for you, Philip?' she asked pleasantly.

'Khalim has sent me.'

She bit her lip. 'H-how is he?'

'He's sad, of course—but coping magnificently, just as you would expect.'

'Yes.' Of course he was. Swallowing down her pain, she said, 'So what is the purpose of your visit here today, Philip?'

Philip nodded thoughtfully, as if her reaction was not the one he would have anticipated. 'He asked me to bring you this.' He opened up his briefcase and withdrew a slim, dark leather box and handed it to her.

Rose stared down at it. 'What is it?'

'Why don't you open it, and see?'

Caution told her to give it straight back to him, but that old devil called curiosity seemed to be guiding her actions instead. With miraculously unshaking hands, she opened the clasp.

Inside was a necklace, although the word seemed oddly

inadequate for the magnificent piece of jewellery which dazzled at her from its navy-velveted backdrop.

A necklace of sapphires and diamonds which blazed with unmatchable brilliance, and, at the very centre of the piece, a single deeper blue sapphire, the size of a large walnut.

Rose lifted her eyes to his, her face pale and her voice now trembling. 'Wh-what is the p-purpose of this?'

'Isn't it obvious?'

'Not to me it isn't, no. Why is he sending his emissary with expensive baubles? To sweeten me up? Is that it? To induce me to fall in with his wishes?'

'He doesn't want it to be over, Rose.'

'Well, it *is* over,' she said stubbornly. 'It has to be. I thought I made that clear. I'm not prepared to become his part-time mistress, Philip—I told him that unequivocally. So perhaps you'd like to give this back to him, and tell him that pieces of jewellery, no matter how gorgeous, will not change my mind.' And she snapped back the clasp and handed it back to him.

Philip stared down at the proffered case for a long moment before he took it. 'You won't change your mind?' he asked slowly.

She shook her head, but with the pain again came the sense of liberation, and of dignity. 'I can't. Tell him that. And tell him not to contact me again—that's best for both our sakes.' She kept her voice steady. 'Tell him to make a happy life for himself in Maraban, and I will endeavour to do the same for myself in England.'

Philip nodded. 'He will not be pleased.'

'I didn't imagine for a moment that he would be. And please tell him not to mistake my resistance for enticement.' She gave a heavy sigh. 'I'm trying to be practical, Philip, for both our sakes.' And my heart is too fragile. If I stop it now, I will survive, she thought. And so will he. If I let it continue in the cloak-and-dagger way of being his foreign mistress, then I risk it breaking into a thousand pieces.

'Do you have any message for him?'

She longed to ask Philip to tell him that she loved him, and that she would never stop loving him—but wouldn't that give him the power to try and wear her down? And who knew how long she would be able to resist *that*?

She nodded. 'Just wish him luck, Philip. Tell him to make Maraban great.'

Philip looked as though he wanted to say something else, but clearly thought better of it. He dropped the case into his briefcase and gave a brief, courteous smile.

'That was never in any doubt,' he said. 'It is his personal happiness which is precarious.'

So he wanted it all. A wife in Maraban and a mistress in London. She remembered something that Khalim had once said to her, and shrugged. 'And that, I'm afraid, Philip—that goes with the territory.'

CHAPTER FOURTEEN

THERE were swathes of dark green holly leaves, their blood-coloured berries gleaming as Rose looped them through the bannister of the sweeping staircase which dominated the hall-way of her parents' farmhouse.

'There!' She stood back to admire her handiwork and turned to where her brother was standing holding all the pins and tacks. 'What do you think, Jamie?'

'Perfect,' smiled her brother.

'And you like the tree?'

He stared for a moment at the huge conifer which stood next to the hatstand. She had festooned it with silver and gold baubles and tied scarlet ribbons around the ends of all the branches. 'Perfect,' he said again, and narrowed his eyes thoughtfully at her. 'You seem happier these days, Rose.'

She hesitated for a moment. Did she? Then appearances could be very deceptive. Because even though most of the time she *did* feel, if not exactly happy, then certainly more contented than before—the pain of losing Khalim could still come back to haunt her and tear at her heart with an intensity which had the power to make her feel weak and shaking.

She shrugged. 'Well, it's been over a year now since...' Her voice tailed off. To say the words made it real, and so much of her wished that it were nothing but some cruel fantasy.

'Since lover-boy went back to Maraban?'

She frowned. 'There's no need to say it in quite that tone, Jamie.'

'What way is that? The disapproving way in which any brother would speak if their sister had had her heart broken by a man who should have known better?'

Rose sighed. 'I keep telling you—he didn't exactly have to kidnap me! I knew exactly what I was getting into, I just—'

'Expected that the end result might be different?' he prompted softly.

Well, no. Of course she hadn't, not really. She had *hoped*, of course she had—because hope was part of the human condition, even when deep down you knew that to hope was useless.

She shook her head. 'I gave up hoping a long time ago, Jamie. Let's leave it, shall we? What time are Mum and Dad getting back?'

'Their train gets in at three, and I said I'd go and collect them from the station. Though it beats me why anyone in their right mind should choose to go Christmas shopping in London, on Christmas *Eve*!'

Rose smiled. 'It's a family tradition, remember? And I like traditions! Now I think I'll go and hang some greenery round the fireplace. Want to help me?'

Jamie grinned. 'I think I'm all spent out where decorating activities are concerned! I might just go and put a light under that pot of soup. Going to have some with me, Rosie?'

'No, thanks. I had a late breakfast.'

'You are eating properly again now, aren't you?'

'I never stopped!'

'That's why when you turn sideways you could disappear?'

She forced a smile. 'I'm not *thin*, Jamie—just slimmer than I used to be.'

'Hmm. Well, Mum is planning to feed you up on Christmas pudding—be warned!'

'Can't wait!'

She went into the sitting room and sat down on the floor to begin tying together the greenery she had brought in from the garden.

Hard to believe that they would soon be into a new year,

but maybe the brand-new start would give her the impetus she needed to get on with her life. *Really* get on with her life.

She had made changes. Had switched from Headliners to another, smaller agency—where the different faces and different clients had forced her to concentrate on work, instead of dwelling on the darkly handsome face she missed with such an intensity.

And she had sold her flat in Notting Hill, too. She had bought somewhere slightly smaller and in a less fashionable area of London, which meant that she no longer needed to take in a lodger.

She didn't have to pretend to be feeling good in front of a flatmate now that she lived on her own. And if she felt like a quiet evening in, reading or watching television, then there was no one to nag her about going out and *meeting* people. She didn't want to meet people. Especially not men. She had known very early on that Khalim would be an impossible act to follow, and in that her instincts had not failed her.

Somewhere in the distance, she heard the chiming of the doorbell, and because she was up to her ears in stray bits of conifer she hoped that Jamie might answer it. She heard the door open, and then murmurings.

'Rose!'

She blinked at the rather urgent quality in Jamie's voice. 'What is it?'

'You have a visitor.'

She looked up to see Jamie framed in the doorway of the sitting room, his face white and tense, a look of something approaching anger hardening his mouth.

'What's the matter?' she asked.

'It's *him*!'

'What is?' she questioned stupidly.

'*Khalim!*' he whispered. 'He's here. Right now. Waiting in the hall.'

The world span out of control and she felt all the blood

drain from her face. 'What does he want?' she whispered back, in a voice which did not sound like her own.

'To see you, of course!' Jamie glowered. 'You don't *have* to see him, you know, Rose! I can send him away, if that's what you want.'

And wouldn't that be best?

She had done everything in her power to eradicate him from her memory in the intervening year since she had last seen him. She had been largely unsuccessful in this, it was true, but it hadn't been through a lack of trying. Wouldn't seeing him again just reopen all those old wounds, making the original injury even worse than before?

But how could she *not* see him—when her heart was banging fit to burst at the thought that he was here? Now.

She stood up and brushed some spray fronds of greenery from the front of her jeans. 'No, I'll see him, Jamie,' she said quietly. 'Will you send him in, please?'

In an effort to compose herself, she walked over to the window and looked out at the stark winter landscape which seemed to mirror the icy desolation of her emotional state.

She heard him enter the room. That unmistakable footfall.

'Rose?' came the deep and slightly stern entreaty from behind her.

Heart hammering, Rose forced herself to face him, and when she did her breath caught in her throat with longing.

He looked…

Oh, but he looked perfect—more perfect than any man had a right to look. And he was not wearing one of the immaculate suits he usually wore when he was in Europe—instead, he was dressed in the flowing, silken robes of Maraban. The ebony eyes were gleaming with some unspoken message and his face was as stern and as fierce as she had ever seen it.

Sabrina's heart turned over with love and longing as she stared into the unfathomable glitter of his eyes, but she prayed that her face didn't register her feelings.

Why was he here?

'Hello, Khalim,' she said, in a voice which she didn't quite recognise as her own.

He thought how pale her face was, so that the blue eyes seemed to dominate its heart-shaped frame with their unforgettable dazzle. And how fragile she looked, too—the jeans he remembered looking slightly loose on the waist, and around the swell of her bottom. 'Hello, Rose,' he said softly.

She drew a deep breath. 'How did you find me?'

He gave a brief, hard smile. It had been clear that she had not wanted him to find her. She had changed her job and changed her flat—no, the message to stay away had been quite clear. 'It was not difficult.' He shrugged.

Not for him, no—of course it wasn't. 'Did you get Philip to search for me?' she mocked.

'What did you expect me to do?' he retorted. 'Scour the pages of the telephone directory myself? Running a country takes up almost all of my waking hours, Rose.'

'Of course. I shouldn't have been so flippant.' Her voice trembled. 'H-how is Maraban?'

'Lonely,' he said with the brutal honesty which seemed to come so easily around her.

She quashed the foolish flare of hope which leapt in her heart. She had never allowed fantasy to get in the way of reality where he was concerned, and she wasn't about to start now. 'Oh? So no suitable bride been found for you yet?'

'No,' he agreed equably, because the waspish way she asked that question told him that maybe her message of wanting him to stay away had been ambivalent. That maybe she still cared. 'No wife.'

'But not through lack of trying, I imagine?'

He was not going to tell her lies, nor to play games with her. 'That's right.' He allowed his mind to briefly dwell on every available high-born Maraban woman who had been brought before his critical eye. And how every doe-eyed look of submission had only emphasised the equality he had shared with Rose.

'But none of them came up to your exacting standards, Khalim?'

'Not one.' He smiled. 'That's why I'm here today.'

She reminded herself of what his terms had been before he'd left, and they would not have changed—why should they when the circumstances were exactly the same as before?

'Would you mind making yourself a little clearer?'

He owed her this. The unadorned truth. The only words which would express the only thing which mattered.

'I love you, Rose.'

The words rang in her ears. Alien words. Secretly longed-for but inconceivable words...words from which she would never recover if they weren't true. She met the lancing black stare and her heart began to pound. Because it didn't matter what logic or common sense told her—Khalim would not use words like that if he didn't mean them. Why would he?

Khalim narrowed his eyes as he watched the wary assessment which had caused a frown to appear between the two delicate arches of her eyebrows. Had he imagined that she would fall straight into his arms the moment that those words were out of his mouth?

'Shall I say it again?' he questioned softly. 'That I love you, Rose. I have always loved you. I shall love you for the rest of my days, and maybe beyond that, too.'

She shook her head distractedly. It didn't matter—because fundamentally nothing had changed. 'I can't do it, Khalim,' she whispered. 'I just can't do it.'

Black brows knitted together. 'Do what?'

'I can't be your mistress—I just can't—because it will break my heart.' Maybe if she appealed to his innate sense of decency, he might go away and leave her alone. Stop tempting her into breaking every rule in the book. She sucked in a huge, shuddering breath. 'You see, I love you, too—I love you in a way I didn't think it was possible to love.'

'And that's a problem, is it?' he asked gently.

'Of course it's a problem! I can't say I'm not tempted to become your mistress—of course I am! I've ached and ached for you since you went back to Maraban, and just when I thought I might be getting over it—'

'*Are* you?' he questioned sternly. 'Getting over me?'

The truth was much more important than remembering not to pander to his ego. 'No, of course I'm not,' she admitted. And she didn't think she ever would. 'But what chance do I have if we become lovers again? I'll just get sucked in, deeper and deeper, and then sooner or later there *will* be a Maraban woman who you will want to make your wife—'

'Never!' he said flatly.

'You can't say that!'

'Oh, yes, I can,' he corrected resolutely. 'There is only one woman who I could ever imagine making my wife. One woman who I have every intention of making my wife, and that woman is you, Rose. It only ever *has* been you.'

She stared at him in disbelief, telling herself that she had not heard him properly. Words of love and commitment she had only ever listened to in her wildest dreams. And dreams didn't come true—everybody knew that. 'You can't mean that.'

He smiled then as he heard the loving tremble in her voice. 'Yes, I can, Rose. I have the agreement of my government to make you my bride just as soon as the wedding can be arranged.'

She longed to touch him, to run her fingertips with reverent wonder along the sculpted perfection of his face, but she was scared. 'But why the change of heart?'

He shook his head. 'No change of heart, my darling—that has remained constant since the first time I ever laid eyes on you. The difference is that my advisors have come to realise that a happy man makes a good ruler.' The stark, beautiful truth shone like ebony fire from his eyes. 'And I cannot ever be a happy man without you by my side. Come to me, Rose, come and kiss me, and make my world real once more.'

She didn't need to be asked twice—she was across the room and in his arms, and as he buried his lips in the flaxen satin of her hair she discovered that he was shaking as much as she was.

'Khalim,' she said brokenly.

'Sweet, sweet, beautiful Rose—my Rose, my only Rose,' he murmured against its scented sweetness, and she raised her face to his in wonder as she read the look of love on his face.

He bent his head to kiss her, and an intense feeling of emotion threatened to rock the very foundations of his world.

They were breathless when the kiss ended, and Rose lifted her hand up, traced the sensual outline of his lips with her finger.

'They don't mind? They honestly don't mind you taking a Western woman for your bride?'

His shrug was rueful. 'The more traditional element of the court were distinctly unimpressed, but the hand of my father guided events—even beyond his death.'

'I don't understand.'

'Do you remember he asked to meet you?'

'Yes, of course I do!'

'He had sensed my distraction since meeting you and wanted to know why. And when he met you, he understood perfectly.' He paused. 'Afterwards he commented on your similarity to my great-great-grandfather's true love.'

'Y-yes,' she said slowly as she waited for the rest of the story to unfold.

'And Malik was never the same man after she was sent away—'

'Is that Malik the Magnificent?' she asked tentatively.

Khalim narrowed his eyes. 'How on earth did you know that, Rose?'

'I read about it, of course—in the chapter about your ancestors.'

He smiled, thinking that she would make a wonderful

Princess of Maraban! 'His heart was not into ruling after that. He complied with convention and took a Marabanesh wife, but was left a bitter and empty shell of a man.' His eyes met hers with a candid light. 'My father did not want to see history repeating itself.'

'History or destiny?' she echoed softly, and her eyes lit up with a glorious sense of the inevitable. 'Or maybe even *pre*-destination, as though all this was somehow *supposed* to happen all along.'

'Predestination?' His deep voice lingered thoughtfully on the word, and he nodded. 'Yes. It exists. It's what drives us all. It's why I met you, Rose.'

The love from his eyes dazzled her, and she gazed up at him. 'What on earth can I say to something as beautiful as that?' she whispered.

He smiled. 'Say nothing, sweet Rose. Just kiss me instead.'

EPILOGUE

THE late afternoon air was warm and scented as Rose and Khalim alighted from the smoky-windowed car and made their way towards their apartments—situated in the grandest part of the palace. And where once she had been taken to see Khalim's father as he lay dying.

Rose was grateful to have met him, no matter that the visit had been brief. It pleased and warmed her to know that he had had the perception and the wisdom to override convention and to let their wedding take place.

And what a wedding!

The whole of Maraban had gone absolutely wild with excitement, happy that their leader should have found a woman to love at last, and proud of the pale, blonde beauty of his Rose.

Guy had been delighted to be best man, and Sabrina her maid of honour, and all of Rose's family had been flown out to Maraban in some style. They had feasted and celebrated for three enchanting days, crushing lavender and rose petals beneath their feet as they danced, and at the very end of the celebrations Rose and Khalim had ridden through Dar-gar on their Akhal-Teke horses. Rose's mount in a pure white—as white as the winter snows—and in such contrast to Khalim's Purr-Mahl.

For he had insisted that she learn to ride—had even insisted on teaching her himself. And what a hard taskmaster he had proved to be—not satisfied until she could gallop alongside him with a fearlessness which matched his own.

Never satisfied...and yet always satisfied.

It was the same in their marital bed on silken sheets which whispered and wrapped themselves around their entwined bodies. Would their passion for each other never abate? she sometimes asked herself in helpless wonder as she came back down to earth from some remote place of pleasure which Khalim had taken her to.

She hoped not.

He touched a light hand to her elbow as a golden shaft of sunlight turned her hair to pure spun gold. 'Tired?' he asked softly, thinking how all the people had warmed to her that afternoon. As they always warmed to her. For his Rose had a gentle understanding which made people instantly love her.

As he loved her, he thought fiercely—loved her more than he would have thought possible to love another person.

'Tired?' Rose smiled up at him dreamily. 'No, of course I'm not. It was a wonderful afternoon. Wasn't it?' she asked him, a touch anxiously.

'You know it was.' They had been to the opening of the newly refurbished Maraban Orphanage, now named after its princess. No announcement had ever been officially made, but word had got around on the grapevine of Rose's generous donation when she'd still been living in London, when she had believed her relationship with Khalim to be over.

'Such unselfishness,' his mother had cooed, totally in thrall with her daughter-in-law herself. As were his sisters. In fact, everyone. Well, almost everyone.

Khalim allowed a wistful smile to play at the corners of his mouth.

Except for Philip, of course. Philip had tendered his resignation a year after Rose had become Princess, even though both she and Khalim had asked him to reconsider.

But Philip had shaken his dark, handsome head, the green eyes enigmatic, giving little away.

'I cannot,' he had demurred.

'It isn't *me*, is it, Philip?' Rose had asked him.

He gave her a fond smile. 'Never you, Princess,' he had murmured. 'But I am part of the past, it is time for me to go. Your new emissary must be someone who will engage in your joint future. Think about it. You know that what I say is true.'

Yes, Khalim had known—Philip's insight had been one of the reasons he had made him his emissary. And even Rose had known that, too—though she was sad for a little time, because she herself had become fond of the cool Englishman and his connection with her old life.

The doors to their apartments were opened and they went inside, Khalim giving a swift shake of his dark head to the robed figure who looked enquiringly at him. He wanted to be alone with her.

Because Rose had seen very early on in her marriage that absolutely everyone wanted a piece of Khalim, and that unless she put her foot down their time together would be limited indeed. And so—to much outrage at first—she had insisted on having their own kitchen built inside their private apartments.

'I don't always want to be served food,' she had told Khalim stubbornly when he'd tried to oppose her plan. 'Sometimes I want to cook myself, for just the two of us, the way I used to when we lived together in London, remember?'

He'd smiled. 'How could I ever forget?'

'And, of course, for you to cook for *me*!' She had seen his look of outrage and slanted him a provocative smile. 'We don't want you forgetting how to fend for yourself, do we, my darling?'

'Oh, Rose,' he had moaned, helpless in the capture of that smile.

He watched her now as she moved with such elegant grace towards the kitchen, and followed her, wondering whether he should take her to bed now, or later. That was the trouble and also the joy of their relationship—he never stopped wanting her. But his powers of self-control had been sorely tested.

Today, her flaxen hair was complimented by the lavender silk of the gown she wore, and he looked at her with a slightly jealous pride. Too bad that they were now having to contend with hordes of foreign journalists eager to capture the beauty of the Marabanesh princess. His Rose was going international, while he wanted her all to himself! And yet deep in his heart he knew that she gave herself completely to him. And always would.

She turned to find him watching her and thought that right now was just the moment to make her gift to him. 'Khalim,' she said softly, in perfect Marabanese. 'Shall I make some mint tea for us to drink?' And she thought that she would never forget the look on his face as he stared at her with a kind of dawning wonder.

'Rose?'

She continued speaking in his native tongue. 'I've been having lessons,' she told him shyly. 'From Fatima. Whenever you've been dealing with affairs of state, I've been poring over my dictionary! And Fatima says I'm almost fluent and that I—'

But she couldn't say any more on the subject, because he had swiftly crossed the room, and had pulled her into his arms and was looking down at her with a fierce and tender love.

'Were the gods looking down on us the day I met you, Rose?' he demanded heatedly. 'And were they Jupiter and Venus?'

'I expect so,' she said demurely, because she knew just what he wanted when he looked at her like *that*. What *she* wanted, too, more than anything else.

She gave herself up to his kiss. Well, the mint tea could always wait.

The Mistress's Child

CHAPTER ONE

HE WALKED into the office and all her dreams and night-mares came true.

Lisi felt giddy. Sick. But maybe that was just the effect he was having on her heart-rate.

Up until that moment it had been a perfect day—her last afternoon at work before she finished for Christmas. There had been nothing bigger on her mind than the arrangements for Tim's birthday party the following day and wondering, along with everyone else, whether the threatened snow would fall.

She stared up into the cool, chiselled features and her fingers—which had been flying furiously over the key-board—froze into stillness. But so did the rest of her—heart, body and soul. For one long, timeless moment their eyes met and she wondered what on earth she could say to him, but just the sight of him was making speech impos-sible.

He was as devastating as he had always been, but his body looked leaner, harder—all tight, honed muscle which even the elegant winter coat couldn't disguise.

Instinct made her want to stand up and demand what he was doing there, to ask him how he had the nerve to show that heartbreaking face of his, but the stakes were much too high and she knew that she could not afford to give into instinct.

'Hello, Philip,' she said at last, astonished to hear how steady her voice sounded.

He should have been expecting it, but her effect on him took him completely off guard and the sound of her low, husky voice ripped through his defences. Damn her, he thought bitterly as he recalled her soft white thighs wrapped around his body as he had plunged deep, deep inside her, unable to stop himself even though every fibre of his being had tried. Damn her!

He felt the leap of blood, like a fountain to his senses, and it felt like being resurrected. Months which had moved into years of living in an emotional and physical wasteland and she had vanquished his icy indifference simply by the lilting way she said his name. His normally lush, sensual mouth was thin and unsmiling.

'Why, for a moment there I thought you didn't remember me, Lisi,' he mocked softly.

Not remember him? She would have to be dead not to have remembered him, even if she hadn't had the living proof to remind her every single day of her life.

She kept her face impassive, but in reality she was greedily registering every detail of that arrogantly beautiful face. Thinking of her son's face and searching for heartbreaking signs of similarity—but thank God there was none. His lightly tanned golden skin was so very different from her son's natural pallor, as were Philip's startling emerald eyes. They made the aquamarine hue of Tim's look so diluted in comparison.

And then her heart began to race and the inside of her mouth turned to sandpaper as painful questions began to buzz silently around her head. Why was he here?

Did he *know?*

The foundations of her world threatened to rock on their axis, but she kept her face as calm as his. He couldn't know. He couldn't possibly know!

'Not remember you? Of course I remember you,' she said, in as bland a voice as she could manage—she even tacked on a weak attempt at a smile as she met the emerald ice of his stare. 'I always remember—'

'All the men you've slept with?' he challenged, unable to resist the taunt, cruelly pleased by the sting of colour which brought roses to the whiteness of her skin.

She felt heat flaring across her cheeks, but that was her only outward reaction to his remark. How blatant, to say something as provocative as that, she thought indignantly—especially when you considered *his* track record. And all the while looking at her with that cold, studied insolence which did nothing to mar the sheer beauty of his face.

She bit back the temptation to remind him that there had been no sleep involved. He had not wanted to sleep with her—and for very good reason. She repressed a shudder as she was reminded of what a gullible fool she had been.

Far better to change the subject completely. To find out what he wanted and to see the back of him.

'I was about to say that I always remember clients—' She wished that she could bite the word back. It seemed so cold and unfeeling in view of what she had shared, until she reminded herself that they had shared nothing—except their bodies.

'Clients,' she continued valiantly, 'who have involved this company in as many deals as you once did. You brought us a lot of business, Mr Caprice. We sold a lot of properties through you.'

So she remembered his surname, too. Philip didn't know whether to be flattered or not, though he was certainly surprised. He suspected that he had been just one in a long line of men she had enticed into her bed—a woman who looked like that would have no trouble doing so. Did she have a photographic memory for *all* their names?

He studied her—taking all the time in the world to do so—and why not? Hadn't she haunted his memory with bitter-sweet recall? Given him the acrid taste of guilt in his mouth every time he'd thought of her in nearly four years?

Even though he had tried his hardest not to think of her. Tried and failed every time.

But Lisi Vaughan had been a fever in his blood for far too long now.

His eyes skimmed over her. Time had not made much of a mark—certainly not on her face, which was probably the most beautiful he had ever seen. A face completely devoid of make-up, which gave it an odd kind of purity which seemed so at odds with her innate sensuality.

The eyes he remembered because they were icy and aquamarine—unique. Slanting, siren's eyes, half shielded by a forest of thick, dark eyelashes, which made her look so minxy. The darkness of her lashes was echoed in her hair—deep, dark ebony—as black as the coals of hell itself and made even blacker by its dramatic contrast to the whiteness of her skin. She looked like a witch, he thought, a beautiful temptress of a witch with a body which few men would see outside paradise.

He knitted his eyebrows together almost imperceptibly. Not that her body was on display much today, but some things you couldn't disguise—even though she had done her level best with some plain black skirt and high-necked blouse which made her look almost *dowdy*.

No. On second thoughts—certainly not dowdy. Philip swallowed as she moved her head back, as if trying to escape his scrutiny, and the movement drew attention to the unforgettable swell of her breasts. Her waist was as tiny as ever, but her breasts were slightly fuller, he thought, and then was punished with the heavy jackknifing of desire in response.

Lisi could feel her heartbeat growing thready and erratic. She wished he wouldn't look at her that way. It reminded her of too much she would rather forget. Of tangled limbs and the sheen of sweat, the sweet, fleeting pleasure of fulfilment followed by the shattering pain of rejection. He had no *right* to look at her that way.

She quashed down the desire to tell him to get out, and forced a pleasantry out instead. He was not the kind of man to be pushed. If she wanted him out of there—and she most certainly did—then he must come to the conclusion that it had been his idea to leave and not hers.

Keep it cool and keep it professional, she told herself. 'Now. How can I help you?'

He gave her a grim smile, not trusting himself to answer for a moment, and then he lifted his eyebrows in mocking question. 'What a sweetly expressed offer,' he murmured.

'Why, thank you,' she said demurely.

'Do you say that to all the men?'

'Most of them are grown-up enough not to read anything into it.' She matched his remark with a dry tone of her own and then fixed her eyes on his unwaveringly, trying not to be distracted by that dazzling green gaze. 'So. Are you interested in a property for sale, Mr Caprice?'

Her unemotional attitude was having precisely the wrong effect on him. 'Oh, what's with all this "Mr" stuff?' Again he felt the sting of life to his senses, but ruthlessly he subdued them and gave a short laugh instead. 'Come on, Lisi,' he purred. 'I think we can dispense with the formalities, don't you? Surely we are intimate enough with each other to use first names?'

'*Were* intimate,' she corrected, and the heat in her face intensified as she was forced to acknowledge it aloud. 'Past tense. Remember?'

How could he possibly forget? And wasn't that why he had come here today—to change the past back to present? To rid himself of her pervasive and unforgettable sensual legacy. Wouldn't a whole night lost in the scented curves of her siren's body mean that he would be free of the guilt and the longing for ever? Sensations which had somehow chained him to her, and made him unable to move on.

He looked around the office, where the Christmas decorations were glittering silver and gold. In the corner stood a small artificial tree which was decked with shining crimson-red baubles and tiny white fairy lights.

He found Christmas almost unbearable—he had forgotten its poignant lure while he had been away. You could tell yourself that it was corny. Commercial. That all its true values were forgotten these days—but it still got to you every time.

And this was his first Christmas back in England since working in Maraban, where of course they had not celebrated the feast at all. He had not even had to think about it.

He was slowly beginning to realise that living in the Middle East had protected him from all the things he did not want to think about. And Christmas brought with it all kinds of things he would rather not think about. Feelings, mostly. Feelings of remorse. The pain of loss and the pain of wanting. Or, rather, of not wanting. For too long now, his body had felt as unresponding as a block of ice until he had walked in here today and seen her, and now his groin was on fire with need. Damn her, he thought again. Damn her!

He gritted his teeth, his gaze moving to her hand. She wore no wedding ring, nor any pale sign that one might have been recently removed, either. But women these days lived with men at the drop of a hat and he needed to find out if she was involved with someone. But even if she *did* have another man—would that honestly prevent him from doing what he intended to do?

He sat down in the chair opposite her desk, spreading out his long legs and not missing the thinning of her mouth as she watched him do so. He coolly crossed one leg over the other and felt a jerk of triumph as he saw her eyes darken. She wants me, he thought and his heart thundered in his chest. She still wants me.

'I must say that I'm surprised to see you still working here,' he observed, looking around the office of the small estate agency.

Lisi stiffened, warning herself not to get defensive. It was none of his business. She owed him nothing, least of all the truth.

'I just happen to like selling houses,' she said.

'I guess you do.' It had been another aspect of her character which he had been unable to fault—her unerring ability to match the right property to the right client. It had been what had brought him back to this small English village time after time as he'd sought valuable property for a clutch of wealthy buyers. In the beginning he had always dealt with Jonathon, the owner and senior negotiator, but after a while Lisi had taken over. Beautiful Lisi, with her ready smile and soft, sympathetic manner.

Part of him had not expected to find her here. He had imagined that she would be running her own place by now—and it was more than a little disconcerting to see her at the same desk, in the same office. As if time had stood still, and she with it. He gave her a questioning look. 'Most people would have moved on by now—to bigger and brighter things.'

And leave her safety net? Her cushion?

Her job had been the one familiar constant in those dark, far-off days when she had wondered just how she was going to cope—how could she ever have left it? 'Not me,' she said staunchly.

'Why ever not?' he asked quietly, bemused—because she had not only been good at her job, she had been ambitious, too.

She didn't break the gaze, even though her stomach was

churning over with anxiety, as if he somehow knew her secret and was just biding his time before he confronted her with it. Distract him, she thought. 'Why on earth should my job prospects interest you?'

'Call it curiosity,' he told her softly. 'Ex-lovers always interest me.'

Lisi repressed a shudder. She didn't feel like his ex-lover—she felt like a woman who had shared his bed under false pretences before he had disappeared dramatically from her life. But she didn't want to analyse *that*—not now and not with him here. Instead she took his question at face value.

'I love my job,' she said staunchly. 'It's convenient and it's local—and there's no reason why I should travel miles to find something which is already on my doorstep, is there?'

'I guess not.' But he couldn't help wondering why she had settled for such steady small-town life when she was still so young and beautiful. His eyes were drawn irresistibly to the lush lines of her mouth, knowing that he would never be satisfied until he got her out of his system one last time.

For good.

He gave a conventional smile as he forced himself to make conventional conversation. 'And of course Langley is a very pretty little village.'

Lisi was growing uncomfortable. She wished he would go. Just his proximity was making the little hairs on the back of her neck stand up like soldiers and she could feel the prickle of heat to her breasts. She remembered the lightning feel of his mouth as it caressed all the secret places of her body and thought how sad it was that no other man had ever supplanted him in her memory.

She cleared her throat. The last thing she wanted was to antagonise him and to arouse his suspicions, but she could not tolerate much more of him sitting across the desk from her while she remembered his love-making, the unmistakable glint in his eyes telling her that *he* was remembering, too.

'You still haven't told me how I can help you,' she asked quietly.

Philip narrowed his eyes. He didn't know what he had expected from her today. More anger, he guessed. Yes. Much more. And more indignation, too. Lisi looking down her beautiful nose at him for daring to reappear without warning and after so long. Particularly after the last words he had ever said to her.

Yet there was an unexpected wariness and a watchfulness about her rather than the out-and-out anger he might have expected, and he wondered what was the cause of it. Something was not as it should be.

He ran a long, reflective finger along the faint shadow which darkened his jaw. 'You mean am I here today on business? Or pleasure?'

She gave a thin smile. 'I hope it's the former! Because I don't think that the atmosphere between us could be described as pleasure—not by any stretch of the imagination.'

Oh, but how wrong she was! You didn't have to like a woman to want her. He knew that. Liking could die, but lust seemed to have a much longer shelf-life. 'Then maybe we should try and put that to rights.'

'By placing as much distance as possible between us, you mean?'

'Not exactly.' He leaned back in the chair and narrowed his eyes in provocative assessment. 'Why don't I take you for a drink after work instead?'

His audacity left her reeling, and yet there had been weeks and months when she had prayed for such a proposition, when she'd tried to tell herself that what had happened between them had all been one big misunderstanding and that there must be a perfectly reasonable explanation for his behaviour.

But those hopes had soon dwindled—along with the growing realisation that Philip Caprice had changed her life irrevocably. And how, she reminded herself. He had brought with him trouble and upheaval, and if she wasn't very, very careful—he could do the same all over again. And this time she had much more to lose.

'A drink? I don't think so. Not a very good idea,' she told him in a trembling voice and then paused for effect— to try and hurt him as much as he had once hurt her. 'I can't imagine that your wife would like it very much. Or has she grown used to your infidelities by now?'

He stilled as if she had struck him, though he had been expecting this accusation from the moment he'd walked in. He was surprised that she had taken so long to get around to it. 'My wife wouldn't know,' he said tonelessly.

'Oh, so it all became too much for her, did it?' Lisi sucked in a breath which threatened to choke her. 'Did she divorce you when she found out about me, Philip? Or were there others? There must have been, I guess—I'm not flattering myself that I was something special.'

He felt the pain of remorse. 'There was no divorce.' His eyes were very green—colder than ice and as unforgiving as flint. 'She—' He seemed to get ready to spit the next words out. 'She—died.'

Lisi registered the bizarre and unbelievable statement and flinched as she saw the brief bleakness which had flared up in his eyes.

Died? His wife had *died*? But how? And why? And when? Not that she could ask him. Not now. And just what could she say in a situation like this? Offer condolences for a woman she had unwittingly deceived? She swallowed down her awkwardness. 'I'm sorry—'

He shook his head. 'No, you're not. Don't pretend. You didn't know her.'

'Of course I didn't know her! I didn't even know *of* her, did I, Philip? Because if I had…if I had—' She chewed frantically on her lip.

'What?' he interjected softly. 'Are you trying to say that you wouldn't have gone to bed with me if you'd known she existed?'

'No,' she whispered. 'Of course I wouldn't.'

'Are you so sure, Lisi?'

She bent her head to gaze unseeingly at all the property details she had been typing up. Of course she wasn't sure. She wasn't sure of anything other than the fact that Philip Caprice had exercised some strange power over her—the power to transform her into the kind of wild, sensual creature she hardly recognised, and certainly didn't like.

'Just go away,' she said, her voice very low. 'Please, Philip. There's nothing left to say, and, even if there was, we can't have this conversation here.'

'I know we can't.' He leaned forward and the movement caused his trousers to ride and flatten over the strong, powerful shafts of his thighs and he heard her draw in a tiny breath. 'So let's have that drink later and catch up on old times. Aren't you interested to compare how the world has been treating us?'

Something in his words didn't ring true and again she felt a frisson of apprehension. Why would Philip suddenly reappear and want to *catch up on old times*?

'I don't think so.'

'Oh, come on, Lisi—what have you got to lose?'

Her freedom? Her sanity? Her *heart*? She shook her head. 'I'm busy after work,' she said, despising herself for being tempted all the same.

But there was something in her body language which told a conflicting story, something which put his senses on full alert—and, besides, he wasn't going away from here until he got what he had come for. 'How about tomorrow night then?'

'I'm busy.'

'You mean you have a date?'

Lisi stared at a face which held the arrogant expression of a man who was not used to being turned down, and came to a decision. She had thought that playing it polite might do the trick, that he might just take the hint and go away again. But she had been wrong. And the longer he stayed here…

Politeness abandoned now, she rose to her feet. 'I don't know how you have the cheek to ask that! My personal life is really none of your business, Philip.'

The fire in her eyes heated his blood, and there was answering fire from his as he echoed her movement and stood up to tower over her, thinking how small and how fragile she looked against his robust height.

'Like I said,' he murmured, 'I'm just curious about ex-lovers.'

Her heart was pounding with rage and fury and with something else, too—something far more threatening—something too closely linked with the overwhelming desire she had once felt for him. 'I don't think that the extent of our little *liaison* really warrants such a flattering description as "ex-lover", do you?'

He wasn't doing much thinking at all. Not now. He was entranced by the rise and fall of her heavy breasts beneath the thin white shirt and he felt an explosion of need and lust which made him grow exquisitely hard, and he thanked God that the heavy overcoat he wore concealed that fact.

'If the term offends, then what would you rather I called you, Lisi?' he asked steadily.

'I'd rather you didn't call me anything! In fact, I'd rather you turned straight around and went out the way you came in! What is the point of you being here? Do you honestly think you can just waltz back in here after all this time, and pick up where we left off?'

'Is that what you'd like, then?' he asked softly. 'To pick up where we left off?'

Yes! More than anything else in the world!

No! The very *last* thing she wanted!

Lisi stared distractedly at the hard, angular planes of his face and—not for the first time—wished that she had more than one beautiful yet unsatisfactory night to remember this man by. And then reminded herself that she had a whole lot more besides.

Imagine the repercussions if he were to find out!

She gave a humourless laugh. 'I outgrew my masochistic phase a long time ago!' She looked down deliberately at her watch. 'And now, if you'll excuse me, I really do have work to do!'

He remembered her as uncomplicated and easygoing, but now he heard the sound of unmistakable frost in her voice and he found himself overwhelmed by the urge to kiss the warmth back into it. And it was so long since he had felt the potency of pure desire that he found himself captive to his body's authority. Compelled to act by hunger and heat instead of reason—but then, that was nothing new, not with her.

A pulse began to beat at his temple. 'You don't look too busy to me.'

Like an onlooker in a play, Lisi stared with disbelief as she saw that he was moving around to her side of the desk, with a look on his face which told its own story.

'Philip?' she questioned hoarsely as he bent towards her.

'Answer me one thing and one thing only,' he demanded.

His voice was one of such stark command that Lisi heard herself framing the word, 'What?'

'Is there a man in your life?' he murmured. 'A husband or a fiancé or some long-time lover?'

This truth was easy to tell, but then perhaps that was because she was compelled to by the irresistible gleam of his eyes. She shook her head. 'No. No one.'

He looked down at her for one brief, hard moment and knew a moment of sheer, wild exultancy before he pulled her into his arms with a shudder as he felt the soft warmth of a woman in his arms again.

The blood roared in her ears. She wanted to push him away and yet she was powerless to move, so tantalising was his touch. Suddenly she knew just how a butterfly must feel shortly before it was impaled against a piece of card. Except that a butterfly would receive nothing but pain— while Philip could give her untold pleasure.

'What the hell do you think you're doing?' she breathed as she felt the delicious pressure of his fingers against her skin through the shirt she wore.

'You know what I'm doing.' Doing what he had been wanting to do ever since he had walked back in here again today. Doing what had haunted him for far too long now.

'You need kissing, Lisi,' he ground out and pulled her even closer. 'You know you do. You want me to. You always did. Didn't you?'

His arrogance took away what little of her breath was left, because just the sensation of feeling herself in the warm circle of his arms again was enough to make her feel as weak as a kitten.

'Get out of here! We're standing in the middle of my bloody *office*—' she spluttered, but her protest was cut short by the ringing of the doorbell and Marian Reece, her boss and the owner of Homefinders, walked in, her smile of welcome instantly replaced by one of slightly irritated bemusement as she took in the scene in front of her.

'Hello, Lisi,' she said steadily, looking from one to the other. 'I'm sorry—am I interrupting something?'

Hearing the unmistakable reproof in her boss's voice, Lisi sprang out of Philip's arms as if she had been scalded, thinking how close he had been to kissing her. Would she have let him? Surely not. But if she had…?

Her heart was crashing against her ribcage, but she struggled to retain her breath and to appear the kind of unflappable employee she usually was. 'H-hello, Marian. This is Philip Caprice. We were, um, we were just—'

'Just renewing our acquaintance,' interjected Philip smoothly and held his hand out to Marian, while smiling the kind of smile which few women would have the strength to resist.

And Marian Reece was not among them.

Lisi had known the forty-five-year-old since she had bought out the estate agency two years ago. She liked Marian, even though the older woman led a life which was streets apart from her own.

But then Marian was a successful businesswoman while Lisi was a struggling single mother.

'Lisi and I are old…friends,' said Philip deliberately. 'We go way back.'

'Indeed?' said Marian rather tightly. 'Well, call me a little old-fashioned—but mightn't this kind of fond greeting be better reserved for *out* of office hours?'

Fond? Inside, Lisi almost choked on the word. 'Yes, of course. And Philip was just leaving, weren't you, Philip?'

'Unfortunately, yes—I have some business to see to.' He glittered her a look which renewed the racing in her heart. 'But I'll be back tomorrow.'

Lisi thought it sounded more like a threat than a promise. 'Back?' she questioned weakly. 'Tomorrow?'

'Of course. You haven't forgotten that you're going to sell me a house, have you, Lisi?'

Lisi blinked at him in confusion. Had she had missed something along the way? 'A house?' He had mentioned *nothing* about a house!

'That's why I'm here,' he said gently. 'I'm looking for a weekend cottage—or something on those lines.'

Was she being offered a lifeline? In the old days he had done deals for rich contemporaries of his from university— they had valued his taste and his discretion.

'You mean you're buying for someone else?' Lisi stared up at him hopefully.

Her obvious resistance only increased his desire for her—although maybe she knew that. Maybe that was precisely why she was batting those aquamarine eyes at him like that and unconsciously thrusting the narrow curves of her hips forward. 'Sorry to disappoint you, sweetheart—but I'm looking for a country home for myself.'

Lisi's world threatened to explode in a cloud of black dust. 'Around *here*?' she questioned hoarsely.

'Sure. Why not? I know the area. It's very beautiful— and just about commutable from London.' His eyes mocked her. 'Sounds just about perfect to me.'

'Does it?' asked Lisi dully.

'Yes, of course we'll be delighted to find something for you, Mr Caprice,' said Marian crisply. 'I can look for you myself, if you prefer.'

He shook his head. 'Oh, no,' he contradicted softly. 'I'm quite happy to deal with Lisi.'

Well, I'm not happy to deal with *you*, she thought hysterically, but by then it was too late. He was charm personified to Marian as he said goodbye, and then he took Lisi's hand in his and held it for just a little longer than was necessary while he held her gaze.

'Goodbye, Lisi. Until tomorrow.'

'Goodbye, Philip.' She swallowed, while inside her heart raced with fear and foreboding.

She stood in silence with Marian as they watched him leave and Lisi's hands were shaking uncontrollably as the door clanged shut behind him.

Marian turned to look at her and her eyes were unexpectedly soft with sympathy. 'So when are you going to tell him, Lisi?' she asked softly.

Time froze. Lisi froze. 'Tell him what?'

'The truth, of course.' She placed a perfectly manicured hand on Lisi's shaking arm. 'He's the father of your child, isn't he?'

CHAPTER TWO

LISI stared at Marian. 'You can't know that!' she babbled, and now her knees really *were* threatening to give way. 'Tim looks nothing like him!'

'Sit down, dear, before you fall down.' Marian gently pushed her back down onto her chair and went and poured a glass of water from the cooler, then handed it to her. 'Now drink this—you've gone even paler than usual.'

Lisi sucked the chilled liquid into her parched mouth and then shakily manoeuvred it to a corner of her desk before raising her eyes beseechingly to her boss. 'He doesn't look anything like Philip,' she repeated stubbornly.

'Lisi,' said Marian patiently. 'Tim is your living image— but that doesn't mean that he hasn't inherited any of his father's characteristics. Sometimes a mother can blind herself to what she doesn't want to see. Sometimes it's easier for an outsider to see the true picture. I knew immediately that Philip was Tim's father.'

'But how?' Lisi demanded brokenly.

Marian sighed. 'Well, Tim is an unusually tall boy for his age—we've always said that. He has his father's strength and stature—and there's a certain look of him in the shape of his face, too.'

A chasm of frightening dimensions was beginning to open up in front of Lisi's feet. 'A-anything else?' she demanded hoarsely.

Marian shrugged awkwardly. 'Well, I've never seen you behave like that with a man before—'

'Because he was hugging me in the office, you mean?'

'*Hugging* you?' Marian raised her eyes to heaven.

22

'That's a new way to describe it! He looked more like he wanted to eat you up for breakfast, lunch and tea—and vice versa. Like no one else existed in the universe other than him.'

And he had always had that effect on her—even though she could have been nominated for an Oscar, so hard had she always tried to hide it in the past. Philip could do and behave exactly as he pleased and Lisi would always be there with a smile for him. No questions, Lisi. Weak Lisi. Foolish Lisi.

Well, not any longer!

'It must have been a very passionate relationship,' observed Marian.

If only she knew!

'The question is, what are you going to tell him?'

Lisi shook her head. 'I'm not. I'm not going to tell him.'

Marian screwed her eyes up. 'Oh, Lisi—do you honestly think that's a good idea?'

Lisi shook her head. 'I know it isn't ideal, but it's the only thing I can do.'

'But why, dear? Why not tell him? Don't you think he has the right to know that he has a beautiful son?'

'The right?' Lisi looked at her boss and knew that she could not tell her whole story—but part of the story would surely make her point for her. And illustrate as well as anything just how little she had meant to Philip.

'Marian—he walked out on me. He made it clear that he thought our night together was a big mistake, and that he wanted nothing more to do with me.'

Marian frowned. 'One night? That's all it was? Just one night?'

Lisi nodded. 'That's right.' She saw Marian's rather shocked face. 'Oh, it wasn't the *classic* one-night stand—believe me.' It hadn't even been meant to happen. 'I...I used to see him every couple of months or so,' she continued painfully. 'We had grown to like one another, though I realise now that I never really knew him, or anything about him. But the ''affair'' wasn't really an affair, as such.' In fact, it hadn't lasted beyond midnight.

'But isn't it time he found out the truth—whatever has happened between you? I have children of my own, Lisi, and children *need* a father wherever possible. They need to know their roots and where they come from.'

Lisi sighed. How could she possibly explain this without sounding scheming and cold-hearted? 'Maybe I'll tell him if he shows any sign of wanting to *be* a father, but if I just announce it without careful consideration—can't you just imagine the consequences? Philip demanding contact. Philip turning up to take Tim out...' Philip taking Tim's affection...while feeling nothing for her but lust at best, and contempt at worst. 'Tim doesn't even *know* about Philip!'

'But surely other people round here must know he's the father? *Someone* must know?'

Lisi shook her head. Her night with Philip had gone unnoticed and unremarked upon, and that was how she had kept it. No one knew the truth except for her mother, and that had been a death-bed secret. Even her best friend Rachel thought that her refusal to divulge the identity of Tim's father was down to some fierce kind of pride at having been deserted, but it went much deeper than that.

Lisi had accepted that Philip could and had just walked out of *her* life—but she had vowed that he would never play emotional ping-pong with that of her son. A child was a commitment you made for life, not something to be picked up and put down at will—especially if the father of that child was married.

Except now that his wife was dead. So didn't that change things?

Lisi shook her head. 'Nobody knows. Not a living soul.' She stared at Marian. 'Except for you, of course.'

'I won't tell him, if that's what you're worried about, Lisi,' said Marian awkwardly. 'But what if he finds out anyway?'

'He can't! He won't!'

'He's planning on buying a house here. It's a small village. What if he starts putting two and two together and coming up with the right answer? Surely he'll be able to work out for himself that he's the father?'

Lisi shook her head. Why should he? It was a long time ago. Months blurred into years and women blurred into other women, until each was indistinguishable from the last. 'Maybe he won't find a house to suit him?' she suggested optimistically, but Marian shook her head with a steely determination which Lisi recognised as the nine-carat businesswoman inside her.

'Oh, no, Lisi—don't even think of going down that road. This is strictly business. And if a client—any client—wants to buy a house from this agency, then we find one for him to buy. Beginning and end of story. I simply can't allow you to prejudice any sale because of some past quarrel with your child's father—which in my opinion, needs some kind of resolution before Tim gets much older.'

'An outsider doesn't know how it feels,' said Lisi miserably.

'Maybe that's best. An outsider can tell you what she thinks you *need* rather than what you think you *want*.' Marian's face softened again. 'Listen, dear,' she said gently, 'why don't you take the rest of the afternoon off? You look much too shaken to do any more work. Peter will be back from his viewing shortly—and it's always quiet at this time of the year. Think about what I've said. Sleep on it. It may be better in the long run if you just come clean and tell Philip the truth about Tim.'

Better for whom? wondered Lisi as she took off her work shoes and changed into the wellington boots she always wore to work when the weather was as inclement as it was today. It certainly wouldn't be better for *her*.

She felt disorientated and at a loss, and not just because of Philip's unexpected reappearance. Tim didn't finish nursery until four, which meant that she had nearly two hours going spare and now she wasn't quite sure what to do with them. How ironic. All the times when she had longed for a little space on her own, when the merry-go-round of work and single motherhood had threatened to drag her down—and here she was with time on her hands and wishing that she had something to fill it.

She didn't want to go home, because if she did then she would feel guilty for not putting any washing into the machine, or preparing supper for Tim, or any of the other eight million tasks which always needed to be done. And mundane tasks would free up her mind, forcing her to confront the disturbing thoughts which were buzzing around inside her head.

Instead, she turned up her coat collar against the chill breeze, and headed up the main village street, past the duck pond.

The light was already beginning to die from the sky and the contrasting brightness of the fairy lights and glittering Christmas trees which decorated every shop window made the place look like an old-fashioned picture postcard. How their gaiety mocked her.

The breeze stung her cheeks, and now and again, tiny little flakes of snow fluttered down from the sky to melt on her face like icy tears.

The weathermen had been promising a white Christmas, and, up until today, it had been one of Lisi's main preoccupations—whether her son would see his first snow at the most special time of year for a child.

But thoughts of a white Christmas had been eclipsed by thoughts of Philip, and now they were threatening to engulf her, making her realise just why she had put him in a slot in her memory-bank marked 'Closed'. She had done that for reasons of practicality and preservation—but seeing him today had made it easy to remember just why no one had ever come close to replacing him in her affections.

And now he might be here to stay.

She climbed over a stile and slid down onto wet grass, glad for the protection of her heavy boots as she set out over the field, but she had not walked more than a few metres before she realised that she was being followed.

Lisi knew the village like the back of her hand. She had lived there all her life and had never felt a moment's fear or apprehension.

But she did now.

Yet it was not the heartstopping and random fear that a stranger had materialised out of nowhere and might be about to pounce on her, because some sixth sense warned her to the fact that the person following her was no stranger. She could almost sense the presence of the man who was behind her.

She stopped dead in her tracks and slowly turned around to find Philip standing there, his unsmiling face shadowed in the fast-fading light of dusk. Out here in the open countryside he seemed even more formidable, his powerful frame silhouetted so darkly against the pale apricot of the sky, and Lisi felt the sudden warm rush of desire.

And she didn't want to! Not with him. Not with this beautiful, secretive and ultimately deceitful man who had given her a child and yet would never be a father to that child.

She had overplayed the bland, polite card in the office today and he had not taken heed of her wish to be rid of him. The time for politeness was now past.

'Do you always go creeping up on people in the twilight, Philip?' she accused.

He gave a faint smile. 'Sometimes. My last employment meant that I had to employ qualities of stealth, even cunning.'

She resisted the urge to suggest that the latter quality would come easily to him, intrigued to learn of what he had been doing for the past four years. 'And what kind of employment was that?'

He didn't answer immediately. He wasn't sure how much of his past he wanted to share with her. What if anything he wanted to share with her, other than the very obvious. And his years as emissary to a Middle Eastern prince could not be explained in a couple of sentences in the middle of a field on a blisteringly cold winter's afternoon. 'Maybe I'll tell you about it some time,' he said softly.

So he wasn't going to fill in any gaps. He would remain as unknowable as he ever had been. She looked at him in exasperation. 'Why are you really here, Philip? What brought you back to Langley after so long?'

An unanswerable question. How could he possibly define what his intentions had been, when nothing was ever as easy as you thought it was going to be? *Something* had compelled him to return and lay a increasingly troublesome ghost to rest, and yet the reality was proving far more complex than that.

He had been dreaming of her lately. Images which had come out of nowhere to invade his troubled nights. Not pin-point, sharply accurate and erotic dreams of a body which had captivated him and kept him prisoner all this time. No, the dreams had been more about the elusive memory of some far-distant sweetness he had experienced in her arms.

Part of him had wondered if seeing her again would make the hunger left by the dream disappear without trace—like the pricking of a bubble with a pin—but it had not happened like that.

The other suspicion he had nurtured—that her beauty and charm would be as freshly intact as before—had sprung into blinding and glorious Technicolor instead. His desire for her burned just as strongly as before—maybe even more so—because nobody since Lisi had managed to tempt him away from his guilt and into their bed.

Not that there hadn't been offers, of course, or invitations—some subtle, some not. There had been many—particularly when he had been working for the prince—and some of those only a fool would have turned down. Was that what he was, then—a fool?

Or was it that one night with her had simply not been enough? Like a starving man only being offered a morsel when the table was tempting him with a banquet?

He looked into her eyes—their bright, clear aquamarine shaded a deeper blue by the half-light of approaching dusk. Her face was still pale—pale as the first faint crescent of the moon which was beginning its nightly rise into the heavens. Her lips looked darker, too. Mulberry-coloured—berry-sweet and succulent and juicy—what wouldn't he give to possess those lips again?

'Maybe I wanted to see you again,' he murmured.

It sounded too much like the kind of declaration which a woman dreamed a man would make to her, but there was no corresponding gentling of his tone when he said it. The deep-timbred voice gave as little away as the green, shuttered eyes did.

'Why?' She forced herself to say it. 'To sleep with me again?'

Philip's mouth hardened. He wasn't going to lie. 'I think you know the answer to that.'

She let out a cold, painful breath as the last of her hopes crumbled. It was as she had suspected. The warm, giving

Philip whose bed she had shared—that man did not exist. It had all been an act. He was merely a seductive but illusionary figure who had let his defences down enough to have sex with her, and then had retreated to his real world—a world which had excluded her because he'd had a wife.

Not just cruel, but arrogant, too!

'And you think…' She sucked in a deep breath. 'Do you really think that I've been sitting around, just waiting for you to come back and make such a—' she almost choked on the word '—*charming* declaration as that one?'

'But I'm not telling you any lies, am I, Lisi?'

She shook her head violently, and some of the thick, dark hair escaped from the velvet ribbon which had held it captive. 'No,' she agreed. 'Lies aren't your thing, are they? You lie by omission rather than fact! Like you omitted to tell me that you were married when you seduced me!'

'*Seduced* you?' He gave a short laugh and his breath clouded the air like smoke. 'You make it sound as though we were both starring in some kind of Victorian melodrama! There was no wicked master seducing some sweet little innocent who knew no better, was there, Lisi? Quite the contrary, in fact. You were the one who stripped naked in my bed. You knew exactly what you wanted and what you were doing. So please don't play the innocent. That night you kept me delightfully and memorably entertained—something which is simply not compatible with someone who isn't…' he narrowed his eyes into hard, condemnatory slits '…*experienced.*'

Lisi swallowed. He was insulting her, she knew that—and yet it was like no insult she had ever heard. The disparaging tone which had deepened his voice did not have her itching to slap the palm of her hand against that smooth, golden cheek the way it should have done.

Instead, it seemed to have set off a chain reaction which

began with the quickened pace of her heart and ended with the honey-slick throb of a longing so pure and so overwhelming that she could have sunk down into the thick, wet clods of earth and held her arms open to him.

But she had played the fool with Philip Caprice once before, and once was too often.

She raised her eyebrows. 'You know, you really ought to make your mind up how you feel about me. On the one hand you seem to despise me for my so-called experience—while on the other you seem unable to forget what happened.'

'Can you?' he demanded as he felt the heavy pull of need deep in his groin. 'Can you forget it, Lisi?'

Of course she couldn't! But then, unlike Philip, she had a very tangible memory of that night.

Tim.

She thought of Marian's words—wise, kindly experienced Marian who had urged her to tell him, who had emphasised how much a child needed a father. But what if this particular man had no desire to be a father? What if she told him and ruined both her and Tim's lives unnecessarily? What if Philip had *children of his own*?

Was now the time to ask him? In a field on a cold December night where stars were now beginning to appear as faint blurry dots in the skies?

She steeled herself. 'What happened to your wife, Philip?'

She took him off guard with her question, though perhaps that was because these days he had schooled himself not to remember Carla more than was absolutely necessary. The living had to let go—he knew that—just as he knew how hard it could be.

He used the same words as the press had done at the time. 'She was involved in a pile-up on the motorway.'

She nodded, painfully aware of how much the bereaved

resented other people's silence on the subject. She remembered when her mother had died, and people had seemed to cross the road to avoid her. 'Was it...was it instant?'

'*No.*' The word came out more harshly than he had intended, but he did not want to discuss Carla, not now. God forgive him, but he wanted to lose the pain of death in the sweet, soft folds of living flesh. 'Can't we go somewhere warmer, if we're going to talk?'

She shook her head. Tim would be out of nursery soon enough and she had no desire to take Philip home and have him see her little house with all its childish paraphernalia, which might just alert his suspicions.

And where else to go to talk in Langley on one of the shortest days of the year—the pub would have shut by now. There was always the hotel, of course, she reminded herself, and a shiver of memory ran down her spine.

'I don't think there's any point in talking. What is there left to say?'

He watched the movement of her lips as she spoke, saw the tiny moist tip of her tongue as it briefly eased its way between her perfect white teeth, and a wave of lust turned his mouth to dust. 'Maybe you're right,' he agreed softly. 'How can we possibly talk when this crazy attraction is always going to be between us? You still want me, Lisi— it's written all over your face,' and he reached out and pulled her into his arms.

'D-don't,' she protested, but it was a weak and meaningless entreaty and she might as well not have spoken for all the notice he took of it.

He cupped her face in the palm of his hand and turned it up so that she was looking at him, all eyes and lips and pale skin, and his voice grew soft, just as once it had before. 'Why, you're cold, Lisi,' he murmured.

It was the concern which lulled her into staying in his arms—that and the masculine heat and the musky, virile scent of him. Helplessly, she stared up at him, knowing that he was about to kiss her, even before he began to lower his mouth towards hers.

The first warm touch of him was like clicking on a switch marked 'Responsive'. 'Philip,' she moaned softly, without realising that she was doing so, nor that her arms had snaked up around his neck to capture him.

The way she said his name incited him, and he whispered hers back as if it were some kind of incantation. 'Lisi.' Her mouth was a honey-trap—warm and soft and immeasurably sweet. He felt the moistness of her tongue and the halting quality of her breath as it mingled with his. Even through the thickness of his greatcoat, he could feel the flowering of her breasts as they jutted against him and he felt consumed with the need to feel them naked once more, next to his body and tickling both hard and soft against his chest. 'Oh, Lisi,' he groaned.

All she could think of was that this was not just the man she had found more overwhelmingly attractive than any other man she had ever met—this man was also the biological father of her child, and in a way she was chained to him for ever.

Just for a minute she could pretend that they had been like any other couple who had created a child together. They could kiss in a field and she could lace her fingers luxuriously through the thick abundance of his hair, and feel the quickening of his body against hers and then…and then…

Then what?

The logical conclusion to what they were starting clamoured into her consciousness like a bucket of ice-cold water being torrented over her and Lisi pulled herself out of his arms, her eyes wide and darkened, her breath coming in short, laboured little gasps.

'You thought it would be that simple, did you, Philip? One kiss and I would capitulate?'

The ache of her absence made his words cruel. He raised his eyebrows in laconic mockery. 'You weren't a million miles away from capitulation, were you?'

She drew her coat around her tightly and the reality of the winter afternoon made her aware that she was chilled almost to the bone. 'I may have had a moment's weakness,' she hissed, 'but I can assure you that I have, or *had*, absolutely no intention of letting you take me in some damp and desolate field as if I were just some girl you'd picked up at a party and thought you'd try your luck with!'

'Luck?' he said bleakly, stung by the irony of the word. Maybe it was time he told her. Maybe he owed her that much. For what kind of bastard could have walked out on a woman like Lisi with only the baldest of explanations— designed not just to hurt her but to expurgate his own guilt? 'I really do think we need to have that talk, Lisi—but not now, and not here—'

'I don't think talking is what you *really* have in mind, do you?' she enquired archly. 'So please don't dress up something as simple as longing by trying to give it a respectable name!'

'Something as simple as longing?' he echoed wryly. 'You think that longing is ever in any way simple?'

'It can be for some people!' she declared hotly. 'Boy meets girl! Boy falls in love with girl!'

'Boy and girl live happily ever after?' he questioned sardonically. 'I'm a little too old to believe in fairy tales any more, Lisi, aren't you?'

His scent was still like sweet perfume which clung to her skin, and she drew away from him, frightened by the depth of how much she still wanted him. 'I'm going home now,' she said shakily, and fought down the desire to do the impossible. 'And I'm not taking you with me.'

He nodded, seeing that she was fighting some kind of inner battle, perversely pleased that she was not going to give into what he was certain she wanted. Maybe it had all happened too quickly last time. Maybe this time he should take it real slow. 'I'll walk with you.'

Her heart missed a beat. 'No, you won't!' She didn't want him to see where she lived, or catch a glimpse of her as she left the tiny cottage to go and collect Tim. And then what? For him to observe the angel-child who was her son and to start using that clever mind of his to work out that Tim was *his* son as well?

It was too enormous a decision to make on too little information, and who knew what Philip Caprice really wanted, and why he was here? She wasn't going to take the chance. Not yet.

'I'm not letting you walk home alone,' he said imperturbably.

Was it her imagination, or had he grown more than a little *autocratic* in the intervening years? 'Philip—this is the twenty-first century, for goodness' sake! How do you think I've managed to get by all these years, without you leaping out of the shadows ready and willing to play the Knight in Shining Armour? Langley is safe enough for a woman to walk home alone—why else do you think I've stayed here this long?'

He gave her a steady look. 'I don't know, Lisi. That's what makes it so perplexing. It doesn't add up at all.'

Her breath caught like dust in her throat. 'Wh-what doesn't?'

'You. Sitting like Miss Havisham at the same desk in the same office in the same estate agency. What kind of a life is that? What's your game plan, Lisi—are you going to stay there until you're old and grey and let life and men just pass you by?'

She caught a sudden vivid image of herself painted by

his wounding words. A little old woman, stooped and bent—her long hair grown grey, her skin mottled and tired from the day-in, day-out struggle of being a single mother, where money was tight. And Tim long gone. She drew in a deep sigh which was much too close to a sob, but she held the sob at bay.

'I don't have to stay here and be insulted by you,' she told him quietly. 'Why don't you just go away, Philip? Go back to where you came from and leave me alone!'

He gave a wry smile. If only it were as easy as that. He didn't try to stop her as she turned away from him and ran back over the field, the heavy mud and the heavy boots making her progress slow and cumbersome.

But she leapt over the stile like a gazelle and he stood watching the last sight of her—her hair almost completely free of its confinement now, and it danced like crazy black snakes which gleamed in the light of the moon—while his heart pounded like a piston in his chest.

CHAPTER THREE

LISI ran and ran without turning back, as if he were chasing her heels—and wasn't there part of her which wished that he were?

But once she was safely out onto the village street and she realised that Philip was not intent on pursuing her, she slowed her pace down to a fast walk. She didn't want to alarm anyone by looking as though the hounds of hell were snapping at her heels.

Her cottage was tucked up a little incline, three streets away from the shops, and she fumbled her key into the brightly painted blue front door, closing it firmly behind her, safe at last.

The place was small, but it was cosy and it was home and it suited the two of them just fine. Lisi had bought it once her mother's big house had been sold—a big, rambling old place which would have cost a fortune to run and maintain.

She drew the curtains and went round the room switching on the lamps and creating a warm, homely glow. Later, once she had collected Tim, she would light the fire and they would toast crumpets and play together—her son completely oblivious of the knowledge of whom she had just seen.

While down in the village his father would spend the evening doing God only knew what while she kept her momentous secret to herself.

Lisi shook her head. She felt like pouring herself a large drink and then another, but she wasn't going to start doing *that*. Instead she put on an extra sweater and made herself a cup of tea, then curled up on the sofa with her fingers curled around the steaming mug.

She looked at Tim's advent calendar which hung next to the fireplace. Only seven days lay unopened. Seven days until Christmas and only one until his birthday tomorrow.

Had fate made Philip turn up at the time of such a milestone in Tim's life? Or a cruel and bitter irony?

She remembered the birth as difficult—partly because she had gone through it all on her own. Lisi's fingers tightened around the mug. Just thinking about the long and painful labour cut through her carefully built defences, and the memories of Philip which she had kept at bay for so long came flooding out, as if her mind had just burst its banks, like a river.

It had started innocently enough—though afterwards she thought about whether there was ever complete innocence between a man and a woman. When and how did simple friendship become transmuted into lust?

The first few times he saw her he completely ignored her, his cool green eyes flicking over her with a disappointing lack of interest.

She knew exactly who he was, of course—everyone in the office did. Rich, clever, enigmatic Philip Caprice who owned a huge estate agency in North London.

He was something of a scout, too—because people seeking discretion and a home in the country flocked to him to find them the perfect place. Rich—fabulously rich—clients who had no desire for the world and his wife to know which property they were in the process of buying. According to Jonathon, he handled house sales for film stars and moguls and just plain old-fashioned aristocracy.

He always dealt with Jonathon. In fact, Lisi was the office junior, only six months into the job, and eager to learn. Jonathon had let her handle a couple of accounts—but terraced cottages and houses on the new estate on the outskirts of Langley were not in Philip Caprice's league!

And then he walked in one lunchtime, on the day after her twenty-second birthday. She had been left on her own in the office for the first time. Jonathon was at lunch and Saul Miller, her other colleague, was out valuing a property which was coming onto the market shortly.

The phones were quiet and all her work up to date and Lisi felt contented with life. She was wearing her birthday sweater—a dream of a garment in soft blue cashmere which her mother had bought—and her hair was tied back in a ribbon of exactly the same shade.

On her desk were the remains of her birthday cake and she was just wondering whether to throw it away or stick a piece of cling-film round it and put it in the fridge. Jonathon seemed to have hollow legs, and it *did* seem a shame to waste it.

The door to the office clanged and in came Philip and her heart gave its customary leap. His hair was thick and nut-brown, ruffled by the breeze, and he wore an exquisitely cut suit which immediately marked him out as a Londoner.

For a moment, words deserted her. He seemed to dwarf the room with his presence—it was a little like having a Hollywood film star walk into a small-town estate agency!

She swallowed. 'Good morning, Mr Caprice.'

He gave a curt nod. 'Jonathon not around?'

'He's not back yet. He, er—' she glanced down nervously at her watch, and then lifted her eyes to him '—he shouldn't be long. You're—er—you're a bit earlier than expected.'

'The roads were clear,' he said shortly. 'I'll wait. No problem.'

He didn't look as though he meant it and Lisi thought that his face looked bleak, as if he had had a long, hard morning—no, make that a long, hard month. There was a restless, edgy quality about him, as if he hadn't slept properly for a long time. She said the first, impulsive thing which came into her head and pointed to her desk. 'Would you like some birthday cake?'

He narrowed his eyes as if she had just offered him something vaguely obscene. 'Birthday cake?' He frowned. 'Whose? Yours?'

Lisi nodded. 'That's right. It's really quite nice—a bit sickly, perhaps, but birthday cakes *should* be sickly, I always think, don't you?' She was aware that she was babbling but something in the slightly askance question in his eyes made her babble on. 'Won't you have some?'

There was something sweet and guileless about her eager chatter which completely disarmed him. Nor was he completely oblivious to the slenderly curved figure and the white skin and black hair which made her look like some kind of home-spun Snow White. But with the ease of practice he dismissed her physical attractions and stared at the cake instead.

Lisi could see him wavering. She remembered how much her father had loved cake when he'd been alive. What did her mother always say? 'Show me a man who says he doesn't like cake, and I'll show you a liar!'

'Oh, go on!' she urged softly. 'Have some—I was only going to throw it away!'

'Now there's an offer I can't refuse!' He laughed, and he realised how alien his own laughter sounded to his ears. When had he last laughed so uninhibitedly? He couldn't remember. 'Sure,' he said, because he hadn't eaten much since yesterday. 'Why not?'

She was aware of his green eyes on her as she cut him a hefty portion and piled it onto one of the paper plates she had brought in with her. 'The last of Minnie Mouse.' She smiled, as she handed it to him. 'See? You've got her spotty skirt!'

'So I see,' he murmured. 'Aren't you a little old for Minnie Mouse?'

'Twenty-two,' she said, in answer to a question he hadn't asked, and when he frowned rather repressively she added inconsequentially, 'I *love* Disney characters—I always have!'

He took the plate from her and sat down in the chair opposite her desk, and bit into the cake. She had been right. Too sweet. Too sickly. Bloody delicious. He tried and failed to remember the last time he had eaten birthday cake. Or celebrated a birthday. Or celebrated anything. But there hadn't been a whole lot to celebrate lately, had there?

Lisi watched him, pleased to see him eating it with such obvious appetite. She thought how fined-down his face seemed, and wondered when was the last time he had eaten properly. She struggled against the instinct to offer to take him home and to have her mother cook a decent meal of meat and two veg with a vast portion of apple pie after-wards.

What was she *thinking* of? The man was a client! And a very well-heeled client, too—not the kind of man who would thank her for trying to mother him!

She licked her lips unconsciously as she looked at his long fingers breaking off another piece. Maybe mothering was the wrong word to use. There were probably a lot more satisfying things a woman would feel like doing to Philip Caprice than mothering, she realised, shocked by her way-ward thoughts.

She watched him finish every crumb on his plate and decided to show him how efficient she could be. 'Right then, Mr Caprice—let me find these properties for you to have a look at—Jonathon has sorted them all out for you.'

She bent her head as she began flicking through an old-fashioned filing box, and Philip felt an uncomfortable and unwanted fluttering of awareness as he looked at the ebony sheen of her hair and the long, elegant line of her neck.

Out of necessity, he had schooled himself not to be tempted by women, and certainly not women who were such a devastating combination of the innocent and the sensual, but for once he felt his resolve waver.

'Here we are.' Lisi found the last of what she was looking for, and held them out to him.

He noticed the way that the tip of her tongue protruded from between her teeth when she was concentrating. Tiny and pink. Shiny. He swallowed. 'Thanks.' He leaned across the desk and took the sheaf of house details from her.

'Jonathon should be back any minute, unless—' she gave him her most hopeful smile '—you'd like *me* to show you round?' She would have to leave the office unattended for a while, but Jonathon would be back from lunch any minute. She saw him frown and hoped that hadn't sounded like some sort of come-on. She blushed. 'I know I'm relatively inexperienced, but I'd be more than happy to.'

She seemed sweet and uncomplicated, and he couldn't deny that he wasn't tempted, but he steeled his heart against temptation.

'Listen, Jonathon knows me pretty well. He knows the kind of thing I like.' He saw her face fall, as if he'd struck her a blow, and he felt the sweet remains of the birthday cake in his mouth and sighed. 'Maybe next time, perhaps?'

This cheered Lisi up considerably, and later, when Jonathon had come back from the viewings and Philip had gone, she began to quiz him in a very casual way.

'He seems nice,' she offered.

Jonathon was busy writing up the offer which Philip Caprice had just made on some sprawling mid-Victorian mansion. 'Nice? Huh! Ruthless would be a better description! He's just got himself a terrific property at a knock-down price—beats me how he does it!'

'Maybe he's just a good businessman?' suggested Lisi serenely.

Jonathon scowled. 'Meaning I'm not, I suppose?'

'No, of course not—that wasn't what I meant at all!' Lisi glanced over his shoulder. 'Anyway—that isn't far off the asking price, is it?'

'True.' Jonathon sighed. 'If only he hadn't managed to wheedle out of the owner that they were desperate for a quick sale we might have held out for the full price.'

'I thought we were supposed to tell the vendor to keep out of negotiations with the purchaser, wherever possible?'

'I did,' said Jonathon glumly, then added, 'Only it was a *woman*. She took one look at him and decided to give him a gushingly guided tour of the place—only unfortunately it backfired. After that, he had her eating out of his hand and she's several thousand pounds out of pocket as a result.'

So was that ruthless, or just good business-sense? Whatever it was, it wasn't really surprising—Lisi thought that he could probably have *any* woman eating out of his hand.

'What's he like?' she asked. 'As a person?'

'Who knows?' Jonathon shrugged. 'He keeps his cards very close to his chest. I've dealt with him on and off for ages and I know next to nothing about him—'

Other than the very obvious attributes of being rich and gorgeous and irresistible to women, thought Lisi and put him out of her mind.

Until next time he came in.

Jonathon had gone to do some photocopying in the back room, and Lisi looked up to see the strikingly tall figure standing in the doorway and her heart gave a queer lurch. She frowned, shocked by the deep lines of strain which were etched onto his face.

Now there, she thought, is a man who is driving himself much too hard.

Philip glanced across the room to see the Birthday Girl sitting at her desk and smiling at him, and realised that he didn't even know her name.

'Hello, Mr Caprice!' she said cheerfully.

Reluctantly he smiled back—but there was something about her which made him *want* to smile. 'I think the trade-off for your delicious cake was that we should be on first-name terms, don't you? Except that I don't know yours.'

'It's Lisi—short for Elisabeth. Lisi Vaughan.'

Pretty name, he thought, and the question seemed to come out of nowhere. 'So are you going to show me around today, Lisi Vaughan?'

Lisi gulped, her heart banging excitedly in her chest. 'Are you sure you want me to?'

'Only if you're confident you can.'

She knew that confidence was the name of the game—particularly in selling—and why on earth should her confidence desert her just because she was about to accompany the most delicious man she had ever seen? She gave him her most assured smile. 'Oh, yes. I'm confident! That's if Jonathon doesn't mind.'

'I'll make sure he doesn't,' he said easily.

Jonathon knew better than to argue with his most prestigious client. 'Sure,' he agreed. 'Let's throw her in at the deep end!'

The viewing was unsuccessful—at least from a buying point of view. Philip tore the places to pieces in his car as he drove her back to the office afterwards.

'Overpriced!' he scorned. 'I don't know how people can ask that much—not when you consider how run-down the property is! And when you look what they've done to the garden—that garage they've built is nothing short of monstrous!'

'You didn't like it, then?' asked Lisi meekly.

He swiftly turned his head and, seeing her expression, laughed. 'Oh, very perceptive,' he murmured sardonically. 'You were good, Lisi,' he added unexpectedly.

'Was I?'

'Very good.' She had diplomatically left the monstrous garage until last and drawn his attention to all the good points in the house, but not in an in-your-face kind of way. She was chatty, but not intrusive, beautiful yet not flirtatious. In other words, she was a little like a glass of water—refreshing, but without any pernicious undertaste.

He sighed. Most of the women he met these days were nurses, and then only in a grimly professional capacity. Not that he wanted to meet women, of course he didn't—not with Carla lying so…so…

He flinched and changed gear more aggressively than he had intended to.

'It's a shame there's nothing else you're interested in,' Lisi was saying. 'I'll keep an eye out for your dream house!'

He threw her a rather mocking look. 'Do you think there is such a thing?'

Lisi thought of her mother's house and gave a slow smile. 'Oh, yes,' she said in a soft voice, and smiled. 'Very, very definitely.'

He smiled back, but the smile died on his lips as he forced himself to look away from the slender outline of her legs, relieved when Langley High Street came into view and he was able to draw up outside her office.

'Thanks very much,' she said as she began to push open the door. 'I enjoyed that!'

'No, thank *you*,' he said gravely, but as soon as she had slammed the door closed behind her, he made the car pull away. He didn't want to watch her confident young stride as she walked to the office, or the way her firm young breasts pushed against her soft, clinging sweater.

Lisi saw Philip seven, maybe eight times after that—on a purely professional basis. Sometimes Jonathon would accompany him on the viewings, but mostly it was her. For some reason she grew to know his tastes better than Jonathon. Often she would mentally reject a house once she had skimmed through the details, then phone him and suggest that he might like to see it.

'Do *you* like it?' he would demand.

She hesitated.

'*Do* you, Lisi?'

'I don't think it's quite what you're looking for.'

'Then I won't waste my time coming to see it.'

Leaving her wondering why she had been so foolish! Why hadn't she said that it was the most gorgeous place she had ever set eyes on?

Because then he wouldn't trust her judgement, and the fact that a man like Philip *did* meant more to her than it should have done.

She adored him, despite his emotional distance, but she kept it hidden from everyone—from Jonathon, from Saul Miller, even from her mother. And, especially, from Philip himself. Maybe she was aware that to fall for Philip Caprice would be batting right out of her league. And besides, it would be strictly unprofessional.

But she looked forward to his visits and they became the highlight of her life. Casually, she used to scour the diary to see when he was coming next, and—although she didn't make it look *too* obvious—she always felt her best on those days. Her hair always newly washed, and a subtle touching of fragrance behind her ears and at her wrists.

And then one glorious spring afternoon Philip walked into the office without his customary, flinty expression. He had loosened his tie and he seemed *lighter* in his mood, Lisi thought, though she wouldn't have dreamed of asking him why. That was not the way their relationship worked. They talked houses. Interest rates. Business trends.

'Hello, Philip.' She smiled.

He looked into her aquamarine eyes and smiled back. Carla had moved her fingers last night. The doctors were cautious, but quietly optimistic, and for the first time since the accident Philip had slept the night without waking. This morning he had awoken without the habitual tight knot of tension in his stomach. 'Hello, Lisi.' He smiled back. 'So what have you got for me?'

'I think you'll like it,' she said demurely.

The house she had rung him about was about as perfect as it was possible for a house to be. She had never heard Philip sound quite so enthusiastic, and the offer he made was accepted immediately. A rather more generous offer than usual, she noted, and briefly wondered what had made his mood quite so expansive.

It was getting on for six o'clock by the time he drove her back into Langley, and all the way along the lanes the hedges and trees were laced with the tender green buds of spring. He sighed. Spring. The time of new beginnings. He prayed that the signs were not misleading, and that there would be a new beginning for Carla.

Lisi heard the sigh, saw where he was looking. 'It's beautiful around this time of year, isn't it?'

He glanced across at her as she put her notebook back into her bag and snapped it shut.

He liked her. She worked hard and she didn't ask any questions. With Lisi he could relax, and he tried to think back to the last time he had done that. Really relaxed. 'I feel like celebrating,' he said.

'Well, then—why don't we? A quick drink won't hurt.' Her heart missed a beat while she waited to hear what he would say.

'Okay.' He changed down a gear. 'Where shall we go?'

'There's the pub or the hotel—either are good.'

'Yeah,' he said thoughtfully. 'I'm driving on to Somerset tomorrow, so I'm staying at the hotel.' Maybe they'd better go to the pub.

'I'll just have to ring my mother and tell her I'm going to be a little late.'

He raised his eyebrows, surprised. 'You live with your mother?'

Lisi smiled at his expression. How little of her he knew! 'Yes, I do.'

'Unusual, at your age.'

'I suppose so—but we get on very well.' No need to tell him that on her salary there was no way she could afford a place of her own, even if she had wanted to.

They went to the pub and settled down with their wine, but away from the usual professional boundaries which defined their relationship, Lisi found herself gulping hers down more quickly than usual.

He saw her empty glass and one elegant eyebrow was elevated. 'Another?'

'Please.' She nodded automatically, her eyes drinking in his tall, lean frame as he went up to buy her another drink.

She told him little anecdotes about village life, and when he smiled that slow, sexy smile she felt as though she had won first prize in a competition.

'You must let me buy *you* a drink now!' she offered, wishing that the evening could just go on and on.

He shook his dark, ruffled head. 'I'm fine. Really.'

'No, honestly—I insist! Just the one.' She smiled up at him. 'Equal rights for women, and all that!'

He laughed, thinking, Why not? 'Okay, Lisi,' he said gently. 'Just the one.'

In the cosy warmth of the bar, Lisi chatted away, and Philip was thinking that maybe it was getting just a little *too* cosy. He glanced at his watch. 'I guess it's about time we made a move,' he said, when he noticed that her cheeks had gone very pink and that she kept blinking her beautiful aquamarine eyes. 'Are you okay?' he frowned.

She nodded, even though the room was beginning to blur a little. 'I'm fine,' she gulped. But with a quick a glance at her watch she realised she'd drunk in record quick time. 'I'm just a bit whoozy. I guess I'm not used to drinking.'

'Have you eaten?' he demanded.

'No.'

His mouth tightened. A great influence he was turning out to be. And now she had acquired a deathly kind of pallor. He couldn't possibly send her home to her mother if she was half-cut, could he?

'Come on,' he said decisively, standing up and holding out his hand to her. 'You need something to soak up that alcohol.'

She clutched onto his hand gratefully and allowed him to lead her out of the pub. Outside the fresh air hit her like a sledgehammer, and she swayed against him and giggled.

Philip shot her a swift, assessing look. She needed food and then he needed *out*. What he did not need was some beautiful young woman brushing the delectable curves of her body so close to his.

But by the time they reached his hotel, Lisi had gone very pale indeed and Philip realised that he was trapped. He couldn't send her home like this, but neither could he see her managing to sit through a meal in a stuffy restaurant.

'You need to lie down,' he said grimly.

It sounded like heaven. 'Oh, yes, please,' she murmured indistinctly.

'Wait here while I get my keys,' he told her shortly, relieved to see that the foyer was completely empty, apart from the receptionist. And receptionists were trained to turn a blind eye, weren't they?

Lisi followed him up the stairs and walked with exaggerated care. She wasn't drunk, she told herself. Just feeling no pain!

Grimly, he pushed open the door, wondering just how he had managed to get himself into a situation which could look to the outside world as though he were intent on *seduction*. While nothing could be further than the truth. But he averted his eyes as she flopped down onto the bed like a puppet which had just had its strings cut.

'Kick your shoes off,' he growled.

The alcohol had loosened her inhibitions, and she giggled again as she obeyed his terse command, sneaking a look at him from between her slitted eyes and thinking how utterly gorgeous he looked. She wriggled and stretched her arms above her head with a blissful sigh.

The sight of her lying with such abandon on the scarlet silk coverlet was too much to bear. 'Go to sleep now,' he told her tightly. 'I'll wake you in a couple of hours and give you some food, then send you home.'

He made her sound like an abandoned puppy! thought Lisi. But her indignation faded into the distance as delicious sleep claimed her.

Philip sat moodily at the bar, sipping at a coffee and wondering whether he should ring the hospital. Maybe later. After Lisi had gone. And he *wanted* her gone!

But his body was telling him other things. Tormenting him with tantalising reminders of making love to a woman. He shifted uncomfortably on the bar stool, and would have taken the longest and coldest shower in the world had it not been for the fact that his room was occupied by the cause of his torment.

He waited a couple of hours and then ordered a plate of steak and chips to take upstairs to her. 'And a pot of strong coffee,' he added grimly. But it was with a heavy heart and an aching body as he slowly carried them into his room, and his breath froze in the back of his throat.

Because she was naked.

Naked in his bed.

Her arms were flung above her head, and part of the scarlet silk coverlet had slipped down to reveal one pert and perfect breast—pale and luscious and centred by a tiny thrusting peak of rose. Her long legs were accentuated by the coverlet which moulded itself against them and her clothes were in an untidy heap on the floor beside the bed, with a wispy thong lying uppermost.

Sweet heaven! Philip very nearly dropped the tray.

His heart was pounding fit to deafen him and he could feel the immediate jerk of a powerful erection as he shakily put the tray down on a small table.

He strode over to the bed, trying to use his anger to dampen down the overpowering need to join with her in the most fundamental way possible.

He reached his hand down to shake her by the shoulder but something happened along the way. His fingers irresistibly reached for her breast and he was appalled to find them stroking little circles, but unable to stop himself from finding the bud of her nipple and feeling it harden beneath his touch.

'Oh!' she breathed.

Eyes closed, still in the mists of sleep, Lisi writhed with pleasure beneath the bedclothes and the unconsciously sexy action nearly made him lose his mind. The blood roared in his head, his composure utterly shattered by the sight of a naked woman, warm and responsive and waiting in his bed.

With an unbearable effort, he tore his hand away from her nipple and moved it up to the soft silk of her shoulder, intending to shake her. But instead of shaking her, again he found his fingers kneading rhythmically against her cool flesh, urged on by the clamouring demands of his body.

'Wake up,' he ordered, in a low, furious voice. 'Wake up, Lisi!'

Lisi's eyes snapped open and she stared with disbelief into the dark, angry eyes of Philip. It took a second or two to get her bearings.

A strange bed.

A hotel room.

One drink too many.

'Oh, hell!' She sat bolt upright in bed and heard him utter something agonised beneath his breath, and she realised that she was wearing nothing at all and that Philip was staring at her bare breasts with a wild kind of furious hunger in his eyes.

'Put something on!' he snapped.

She was still befuddled by sleep. 'Where are my clothes?'

'How should I know where your bloody clothes are?' he roared. 'It wasn't me who took them off!'

Lisi blushed as vague memories came back to her. Feeling too hot and tossing her clothes to the ground with abandon. She had! Acutely aware of her nakedness and of the sound of Philip's quickened breath, she leaned over the side of the bed to hunt for them, and the movement made her breasts jiggle unfettered.

Suddenly Philip lost it completely. He moved towards her, tumbling onto the bed next to her and pulling her roughly into his arms to kiss her before he had the time or the inclination to think about the wisdom of his actions.

And once he had kissed her that was the beginning of the end—his starved senses and hungry body made sure of that.

The thong fell uselessly from her hand and there was a split second of doubt in Lisi's mind but that doubt fled the moment that he kissed her.

His mouth plundered hers as if it were the richest treasure

he had ever encountered and her lips parted for him immediately, moist and sweet and tasting faintly of wine.

Lisi's heart was beating so hard she thought that it might burst. This was every wish she'd ever had, every sweet dream come true. Philip. Here. In her arms. Her hands went up to his shoulders and felt the silk of his shirt beneath her fingertips. She was wearing nothing and he was covered up with all these clothes—it wasn't fair!

He lifted his head from hers and she could see that his eyes looked almost ebony in the lamplit room. 'Do you want to undress me, Lisi?' he asked unsteadily, because he couldn't trust himself to do it with any degree of finesse. Not when her breasts were peaking towards him like that and he longed to take one into his mouth and suckle her.

'Yes,' she murmured throatily, made bold by that look of raw need on his gorgeous face. Deftly, she began to unbutton his shirt, springing open the tiny buttons to reveal a golden-skinned torso sprinkled with a smattering of dark hair. She indolently ran the flat of her hand over the soft whorls, feeling him shudder beneath her as she did so, loving the power of having this big, handsome man respond so passionately to her.

He kissed her again. And again. Until she was mindless with longing—willingly pinned to the bed by his muscular frame and praying for him to make love to her properly.

Logic and reason had vanished from his mind—obliterated by the wet lick of her tongue as it flicked against his. If he didn't have her soon, he would explode. 'Undress me,' he commanded huskily. 'Undress me *now*, Lisi!'

She slid the shirt over his shoulders, anointing the flesh which she laid bare with soft little kisses which made him moan with pleasure beneath her mouth.

His belt came off easily, but her fingers faltered slightly when she was unzipping his trousers as she felt the formidable hardness of him brush against her palm.

'Don't touch me,' he pleaded. 'Not there. Not yet.'

He couldn't wait to be free of his clothes and yet he could hardly bear to watch the erotic vision she made as she pushed the covers off and sank down on her knees astride him, easing the trousers down slowly over the long, powerful shaft of his thighs. She eased them over his knees and further still, her hands brushing against the soft swell of his ankles and lingering there.

'Hurry up,' he pleaded.

Lisi skimmed one of his socks off—immensely flattered by his eagerness and yet slightly taken aback by it. Instinctively, she had known that he would be a passionate man, but she had expected him to exercise restraint as well. And steely control. Those were the qualities which seemed to fit more with the Philip Caprice she knew.

But it seemed that she had been completely wrong. She freed his foot from the second sock.

And then at last he was naked, too.

And aroused.

Very, very aroused.

Lisi swallowed. Surely he couldn't possibly… Surely she couldn't possibly… But then she bucked beneath his fingers as he slithered his middle finger along where she was so hot and slick and hungry. 'Oh!' she moaned in ecstasy.

He smiled, but it was a smile laced with a daunting kind of promise and Lisi felt the briefest shiver of apprehension as she saw the new and urgent tension which had entered his body.

'I want you,' he whispered.

'And I want you, too.'

'Now?' he teased. 'Or shall I play with you a little first?'

His provocative words made her melt even more. She had never been turned on so quickly, nor so thoroughly. There was no need for prolonged foreplay; she was ready.

And very, very willing. She put her arms around his neck and looked up at him with open invitation in her eyes.

'Let's play together,' she whispered back.

He groaned as he moved over her. It was like a dream—the most erotic dream he had ever encountered. He moved on top of her and could feel her shudder as he pressed right up against her burning heat. He delayed it for as long as he could—probably about a second—before powerfully thrusting into her and a deep, helpless cry was torn from his throat.

Lisi gasped aloud as she felt him fill her, but she wanted him deeper still, as deep as it was possible to go. She moved without thinking, lifting her legs right up so that her ankles were locked tightly around his neck, and he raised his head in a kind of dazed wonderment as he looked down at her.

'God, Lisi,' he groaned, and then thrust into her so deeply that she gasped again.

Through the stealthy lure of approaching orgasm, Philip heard warning bells ringing in his head, and he realised what he had never before failed to remember.

'Oh, God,' he groaned. 'Protection! Lisi, I never thought—' With a monumental effort he began to pull out, but Lisi only clenched her muscles, and gripped him even tighter and he shuddered. 'D-don't,' he commanded unsteadily.

'It's o-okay,' she gasped, because she had thought that she would die if he stopped what he was doing. 'It's safe.'

'You sure?'

She nodded. Of course she was sure. 'Make me come,' she begged, astonished by her lack of inhibition, but then something about Philip was making her feel this free. Freer than she had ever been in a man's arms.

'With pleasure,' he ground out, and moved inside her. He held back his own needs while he thrust into her over and over again, his mouth suckling at her breast, while his finger flicked tantalisingly over the tight, hot little core of her. And he whispered things to her, words so erotic, they were almost shocking.

Lisi was nearly crying with the pleasure—almost overloaded with it—and then the crying became a shudder and she was calling out his name and telling him that he was the most perfect lover in the world as waves upon waves took her soaring.

He let himself go, sweat sheening his chest as it slicked against her breasts, and when it happened it was stronger and more intense than any other orgasm he had ever experienced, so that even in the midst of pleasure, he felt the first shimmerings of guilt.

She felt him shuddering inside her for so long that she thought he would never stop. She wished that he wouldn't. Just go on filling her with his seed all night long. And only when he was completely spent did she let her legs drift down to lie on either side of him. With a satiated little smile, she lifted her head to kiss him but he turned away, as if her mouth contained poison, then rolled away from her completely, so that he was right on the other side of the bed.

Lisi's heart pounded.

Perhaps he was just tired. He always seemed to *look* tired. She would let him sleep and then he would reach for her again in the night, and…

She heard the sound of movement and saw that he was getting off the bed and reaching for his clothes.

Her heart pounded again. He couldn't be *leaving*! He couldn't! She swallowed down what was surely an irrational fear. He was obviously going to the bathroom—but he didn't need to put his clothes on to do that, surely? 'Philip?'

He finished buttoning up his shirt before he turned

around and when he did his face was as cold and as expressionless as flint. He raised his eyebrows. 'What?'

'You're not going?'

He was sickened with disgust at his lack of control, and his mouth tightened. 'Yes.'

She stared at him without understanding. 'But why?' she asked, in a mystified voice. 'Why are you leaving now?'

It hurt to say it, probably more than it hurt her to hear it. 'Because I'm married,' he said, in a hard, cold voice.

He grabbed his jacket and his unopened overnight bag and walked out without a backward glance.

And Lisi didn't see him again.

CHAPTER FOUR

PHILIP spent a sleepless night, tossing and turning, his thoughts full of Lisi and the effect of seeing her again.

He hadn't thought beyond his trip to Langley. He had just found himself on the road here, driven on by a burning need to tie up the loose ends of a regrettable liaison—so that he could put it behind him, once and for all.

But he had not reckoned on how he would feel if he saw her again. Part of him had thought that she might have moved on. Or settled down. Married some upstanding local and be well on the way to producing a brood of children. To his astonishment, she was still single.

And just the sight of her had been like a touch-paper to his senses. He still wanted her—wanted her more than he felt comfortable with, and, to judge from her response to his kiss, she wasn't exactly immune to him, either.

He owed her the truth, he realised. There would be no sense of closure for either of them until he had done that. *She* might have instigated what had happened, but he had gone into it more than willingly. She needed to know why he had feasted on her body and then just left her lying there without a second glance.

He glanced at his watch, but it was still early. He showered and dressed and drank some coffee before switching on his computer to check his e-mails. But he stared blankly at the untouched messages in his inbox and turned his head instead to study the forbidding grey of the winter sky.

Just as soon as the office opened he would go and see her. And tell her.

Marian Reece glanced up as the bell on the office door

rang and in walked the tall, expensively dressed man who had been talking so intently with Lisi the day before.

She smiled. 'Good morning! Mr Caprice, isn't it?'

Philip nodded and forced an answering smile. 'That's right. Philip Caprice.' He glanced around the office. 'Is Lisi around?'

Marian shook her head. 'Oh, no! She's finished now. For the Christmas holidays. She—' She seemed to change her mind about her next words. Instead, she said, 'But I'm sure that I can help you.'

He looked at her blankly. 'Help me?'

Marian studied him in bemusement. 'Well, you *did* say that you were interested in buying a house in this area!'

He narrowed his eyes. Did he? Wasn't the truth rather more complex than that? He had been doing business in the area, and something—the dreams, perhaps?—had prompted him to call in and see if Lisi Vaughan was still around. And she was—though wasn't there a part of him which wished she weren't? That had hoped she would have been long gone and then he could consign her to bitter-sweet memory? But at least the suggestion of house-hunting would legitimise his being here. 'That's right,' he said evenly. 'If you could let me have a few details to glance through.'

'Of course.' She gave a coy smile. 'I'll need to know your price range, though.'

He mentioned a sum that made her pupils dilate and she immediately reached for a sheaf of papers which stood neatly stacked on a corner of her desk. 'I *thought* you'd be looking at the top end of the market,' she said triumphantly, and handed them to him.

Philip glanced down at them without interest.

'The most attractive property we have on our books is The Old Rectory,' said Marian, straightening up and looking at him expectantly, but his gaze remained noncommittal. 'It's a beautiful old house, with a wealth of architectural detail—although it does require considerable updating, of course—'

'Why hasn't it sold already?' he cut in.

Marian blinked. 'Sorry?'

'If it's so beautiful, then why hasn't it been snatched up?'

Marian gave a little cough and lowered her voice. 'Because it's unrealistically priced,' she admitted.

'Then get the vendors to lower it.'

'They're reluctant.' She sighed, and pulled a face. 'It's a divorce sale, you see, and they need every penny they can get. I've told them that they may not get a buyer unless they're prepared to be realistic, but you know what people are.'

He nodded and gave an impatient smile, eager to be away. 'Listen, I need to see Lisi. Can you tell me where she lives?'

Marian hesitated. 'I'm...I'm not sure that I should. She might not want me to.'

Philip met her eyes with an unwavering stare. 'Oh, I think she would,' he said pleasantly. 'But, of course, if you won't tell me—then I'll just have to find out for myself. Only it would save me a little time.' He gave her a lazy smile. 'Giving me more opportunity to look at houses.'

There was a long pause while she considered the subtext behind his words, and then she nodded. 'She lives at Cherry Tree Cottage—it's on Millbank Lane. A bright blue front door—it's easy enough to find.'

He folded up the house details and slid them into the pocket of his overcoat. 'Thanks very much.'

Marian looked at him anxiously. 'I don't know whether I should have told you.'

He gave a tight smile. 'I would have found her anyway.'

*   *   *

Lisi had just finished pinning the flouncy paper frill onto the birthday cake when there was a knock at the door, and she sighed. What she *didn't* need at the moment was an interruption! There were a million and one things to do before Tim's party—when the house would be invaded by five of his friends and she would have her work cut out to prevent six small boys from wrecking her little home!

She brushed some stray icing sugar from her hands and went to the front door, and there, standing on the step, was Philip, and her heart lurched with a combination of apprehension and lust.

He looked pretty close to irresistible, dressed casually in jeans which emphasised the long, muscular thrust of his thighs and a soft grey sweater which made the green eyes look even more dazzling than usual. He wore an old-fashioned flying jacket, and the sheepskin and worn leather only added to his rugged appeal.

She thought of Tim in the sitting room, watching a video, and the lurch of her heart turned into a patter of alarm.

'Hello, Philip,' she said calmly. 'This is a surprise.'

He gazed at her steadily. 'Is it? Surely you didn't think that I was going to go away without speaking to you again, Lisi?'

'I have nothing to say to you.'

'But I do,' he said implacably.

He can't make you do anything, she told herself. 'I'm afraid that it isn't convenient right now.'

He let his eyes rove slowly over her, and the answering flood of heat made him wish that he hadn't.

Her dark hair was scraped back from her face into a pony-tail and she wore cheap clothes—nothing special—a pair of baggy cotton trousers and an old sweater which clung to the soft swell of her breasts. There was a fine line of flour running down her cheek which made him think of warpaint.

And she looked like dynamite.

'Been cooking, have you?'

'*Am* cooking,' she corrected tartly. 'Busy cooking.'

'Mum-mee!'

Lisi froze as green eyes lanced through her in a disbelieving question.

'Mum-mee!' A child who was Lisi's very image appeared, and Tim came running out from the sitting room and up to the door, turning large, interested blue eyes up at the stranger on the doorstep. 'Hello!'

Lisi had always been proud of her son's bright and outgoing nature—she had brought him up to be confident—but at that moment she despaired of it. Why couldn't he have been shy and retiring, like most other boys his age? 'I really must go, Philip, you can see I'm really—'

He ignored her completely. 'Hello,' Philip said softly as he looked down at the shiny black head. 'And what's your name?'

The boy smiled. 'I'm Tim, and it's my birthday!' he said. 'Who are you?'

'I'm Philip. A friend of Mummy's.'

Tim screwed his eyes up. 'Mummy's boyfriend?'

Lisi saw the cold look of distaste which flickered across his face, and flinched.

'Does Mummy have lots of boyfriends, then?' Philip asked casually.

'*Tim*,' said Lisi, a note of desperation making her voice sound as though it was about to crack, 'why don't you go and colour in that picture that Mummy drew for you earlier?'

'But, *Mum*-mee—'

'Please, darling,' she said firmly. 'And you can have a biscuit out of the tin—only one, mind—and Mummy will come and help you in a minute, and we can organise all the games for your party. Won't that be fun? Run along now, darling.'

Thank heavens the suggestion of an unsolicited biscuit had captured his imagination! He gave Philip one last, curious look and then scampered back towards the sitting room.

Lisi tried to meet the condemnatory green stare without flinching. 'It's his birthday,' she explained. 'And I'm busy organising—'

'So *that* was why you had to ring your mother,' he observed softly.

It was not the aggressive question she had been expecting and dreading. She stared at him uncomprehendingly. *'What?'*

'The night you slept with me,' he said slowly. 'I wondered why you should bother to do that, when we were only *supposedly* going for a quick drink,' he added witheringly. 'I guess you had to arrange for your mother to babysit. Poor little soul,' he finished. 'When Mummy jumps into bed with a man whenever the opportunity presents itself.'

For a moment, Lisi couldn't work out what he was talking about, and then his words began to make sense. Tim was a tall boy, as Marian had said. He looked older than his years. And Philip didn't even suspect that the child might be his. God forgive me, she thought. But this is something I have to do. For all our sakes. He hates me. He thinks the worst of me—he's made that heartbreakingly clear. What good would it do *any* of us if he found out the truth?

'I have never neglected my son, Philip,' she said truthfully.

Did this make them quits? All the time he hadn't told her about Carla, lying desperately sick in her hospital bed— Lisi had carried an awesome secret, too. A baby at home. And who else? he wondered. 'So where's the father?' he demanded. 'Was he still on the scene when you stripped off and climbed into my bed?'

'How dare you say something like that?'

'It was a simple question.'

She jerked her head in the direction of the sitting room door. 'Just keep your voice down!' she hissed, and then met the fury in his eyes. 'Oh, what's the point of all this? You've made your feelings about me patently clear, Philip. There is nothing between us. There never was—other than a night of mad impetuosity. We both know that. End of story. And now, if you don't mind—I really do have a party to organise.'

He made to turn away. Hadn't a part of him nurtured a tiny, unrealistic hope that her behaviour that night had been a one-off—that it had been something about *him* which had made her so wild and so free in his bed? And all the time she'd had a child by another man! It was a fact of modern life and he didn't know why he should feel so bitterly disappointed. But he did.

'Goodbye, Philip.' Her overwhelming feeling was one of relief, but there was regret as well. She couldn't have him—she would never have him—not when his fundamental lack of respect for her ran so deep. But that didn't stop a tiny, foolish part of her from aching for what could never be.

He looked deep into her eyes and some sixth sense told him that all was not how it seemed. Something was not right. She was tense. Nervous. More nervous than she had any right to be, and he wondered why.

She started to close the door when he said, 'Wait!'

There was something so imperious in his command, something so darkly imperative in the glacial green gaze that Lisi stopped in her tracks. 'What?'

'You didn't say how old Tim was.'

She felt the blood freeze in her veins, but she kept her face calm. 'That's because you didn't ask.'

'I'm asking now.'

A thousand thoughts began to make a scrabbled journey through her mind. Could she carry it off? Would he see through the lie if she told him that Tim was four? It was credible—everybody said that he could easily pass for a four-year-old.

Her hesitation told him everything, as did the blanching of colour from her already pale face. He felt the slow, steady burn of disbelief. And anger. 'He's mine, isn't he?'

If she had thought that seeing him again was both nightmare and dream, then this was the nightmare sprung into worst possible life. She stared at him. 'Philip—'

'*Isn't* he?' he demanded, in a low, harsh voice which cut through her like a knife.

She leant on the door for support, and nodded mutely.

'Say it, Lisi! Go on, say it!'

'Tim is your son,' she admitted tonelessly, and then almost recoiled from the look of naked fury in his eyes.

'You bitch,' he said softly. 'You utter little bitch.'

She had played this unlikely scenario in her mind many times. Philip would magically appear and she would tell him about Tim, but she had never imagined a reaction like this—with him staring at her with a contempt so intense that she could have closed her eyes and wept.

'Go away,' she whispered. 'Please, just go away.'

'I'm not going anywhere. I want to know everything.'

'Philip.' She sucked in a ragged breath. Should she appeal to his better nature? Surely he must have one? 'I *will* talk to you, of course I will—'

'Well, thanks for nothing!' he scorned.

'But not now. I can't. Tim will come out again in a minute if I'm not back and it isn't fair—'

'*Fair?*' he echoed sardonically. 'You think that what you have done is *fair*? To deny me all knowledge of my own flesh and blood? And then to lie about it?'

'I did not lie!' she protested.

'Oh, yes, you did,' he contradicted roughly. 'It was—to use your own words, my dear Lisi—a lie by omission, wasn't it? Just now, when I asked you his age, you thought about concealing it from me.' His mouth hardened into a cruel, contemptuous line. 'But I'm afraid your hesitation gave you away.'

'Just go,' she begged. 'Don't let Tim hear this. Please.'

He hardened his heart against the appeal in her eyes. He had lived with death and loss and all the time she had brought new life into the world and had jealously kept that life to herself. As if they had stumbled across unexpected treasure together, and she had decided to claim it all for herself.

'What time does his party finish?'

She could scarcely think. 'At around s-six.'

'And what time does he go to bed?'

'He'll be tired tonight. I should be able to settle him down by seven.'

'I'll come at seven.'

She shook her head. 'Can't we leave it until tomorrow?' she pleaded.

He gave her a look of pure scorn. 'It has already been left three years too long!'

'Then one more night won't make any difference. Sleep on it, Philip—you won't feel so...so...angry about it in the morning.'

But he couldn't ever imagine being rid of the rage which was smouldering away at the pit of his stomach. 'How very naive you are, Lisi—if you think that I'll agree to that. Either I come round tonight once Tim has gone to sleep, or I march straight in there now and tell him exactly what his relationship to me is.'

'You wouldn't do that.'

'Just try me,' he said, in a voice of soft menace.

Lisi swallowed. 'Okay. I'll see you here. Tonight. Unless...' she renewed the appeal in her eyes '—unless you'd rather meet on...neutral territory? I could probably get a babysitter.'

But he shook his head resolutely. 'Thanks, but no thanks,' he said coldly. 'Maybe I might like to look in on my sleeping son, Lisi. Surely you wouldn't deny me that?'

My sleeping son. The possessive way that he said it made Lisi realise that Philip Caprice was not intending to be an absentee father. Already! How the hell was she going to cope with all the implications of *that*?

But what about Tim? prompted the voice of her conscience. What about him?

'No, I won't deny you that,' she told him quietly. 'I'll see you here tonight, around seven.'

He gave a brief, mock-courteous nod and then turned on his heel, walking away from her without a second glance, the way he had done the night his son had been conceived.

She shut the door before he was halfway down the path, and looked down to see that her hands were shaking.

She waited until her breath had stopped coming in short, anxious little breaths, but as she caught a glance at her reflection in the mirror she saw that her face was completely white, her eyes dark and frightened, like a trapped animal.

I must pull myself together, she thought. She had a son and a responsibility to him. Today was his party—his big day. She had already messed up in more ways than one. She mustn't let the complex world of adult relationships ruin it for him.

She forced a smile onto her lips and hoped that it didn't look too much like a grimace, and then she opened the door to the sitting room, where her beloved son sat with his dark head bent over his colouring, his little tongue protruding from between his teeth, just the way hers did. He's my son, too, she told herself fiercely. Not just Philip's.

'Hello, darling,' she said softly. 'Shall Mummy come and help for a bit?'

Tim looked up, his eyes narrowed in that clever way of his, and Lisi stared at him with a sudden, dawning recognition. His eyes might be blue like hers, but that expression was pure Philip. Why had she never seen it before? Because she had deliberately blinded herself to it as too painful?

'Mum-mee,' said Tim, and put his crayon down firmly on top of the paper. 'Who was that man?'

Not now, she told herself. How he must be told was going to take some working out.

'Oh, he's just a friend, darling,' she said, injecting her voice with a determined cheerfulness. 'A friend of Mummy's.'

But the words rang hollow in her ears.

CHAPTER FIVE

THE hours ticked by so slowly while Philip waited. He felt as though the whole landscape of his life had been altered irrevocably—as if someone had detonated a bomb and left a familiar place completely unrecognisable.

He went through the motions of working. He faxed the States. He replied to his e-mails. He made phone-calls to his London office, and it seemed from the responses given by his staff that he must have sounded quite normal.

But he didn't feel in the least normal. He had just discovered that he was the biological father of a child who was a complete unknown to him and he knew that he was going to have to negotiate some paternal rights.

Whether Lisi Vaughan liked it or not.

He deliberately turned his thoughts away from her. He wasn't going to think about her. Thinking about her just made his rage grow, and rage would not help either of them come to some kind of amicable agreement about access.

Amicable?

The word mocked him. How could the two of them ever come to some kind of friendly understanding after what had happened?

He went for a long walk as dusk began to fall, looking up into the heavy grey clouds and wondering if the threatened snow would ever arrive, and at seven prompt he was knocking on her door.

She didn't answer immediately and his mouth tightened. If the secretive little witch thought that she could just hide

inside and he would just go away again, then she was in
for an unpleasant surprise.

The door opened, and he was unprepared for the impact
of seeing her all dressed up for a party. Red dress. Red
shoes. Long, slim legs encased in pale stockings which had
a slight sheen to them. He had never seen her in red before,
but scarlet had been the backdrop to her beauty when she
had lain with such abandon on his bed. Scarlet woman, he
thought, and felt the blood thicken in his veins.

'You'd better come in,' said Lisi.

'With pleasure,' he answered, grimly sarcastic.

She opened the door wider to let him in, but took care
to press herself back against the wall, as far away from him
as possible. She was only hanging onto her self-possession
by a thread, and if he came anywhere near her she would
lose it completely. But he still came close enough for her
to catch the faint drift of his aftershave—some sensual
musky concoction which clamoured at her senses.

He followed her into the sitting room, where the debris
from the party still littered the room. He wondered how
many children there had been at the party. Judging by the
clutter left behind it could easily have run into tens.

There were balloons everywhere, and scrunched up
wrapping paper piled up in the bin. Half-eaten pieces of
cake and untouched sandwiches lay scattered across the paper cloth which covered the table.

Philip frowned. 'Weren't they hungry?'

'They only ever eat the crisps.'

'I see.' He looked around the room in slight bemusement.
'They certainly know how to make a mess, don't they?'

Lisi gave a rueful smile, thinking that maybe they *could*
be civil to one another. 'I should have cleared it away, but
I wanted to read Tim a story from one of his new books.'

The mention of Tim's name reminded him of why he
was there. 'Very commendable,' he observed sardonically.

'Can I...?' She forced herself to say it, even though his manner was now nothing short of hostile. But she had told herself over and over again that nothing good would come out of making an enemy of him, even though the look on his face told her that she was probably most of the way there. 'Can I get you a drink?'

'In a minute. Firstly, I want to see Tim.'

She steeled herself not to react to that autocratic demand. 'He's only just gone to sleep,' she said. 'What if he wakes?'

'I'll be very quiet. And anyway, what if he *does* wake?'

'Don't you know *anything* about children?' she asked, but one look at his expression made her wonder how she could have come out with something as naive and as hurtful as that.

'Actually, no.' He bit the words out precisely. 'Because up until this morning, I didn't realise that I might have to.'

'Just wait until he's in a really deep sleep,' she said, desperately changing the subject. 'He might be alarmed if he wakes up to find a strange man...' Her words tailed off embarrassedly.

He gave a bitter laugh. 'A strange man in his room?' he completed acidly. 'You mean it doesn't happen nightly, Lisi?'

It was one insult too many and on top of all the tensions of the day it was just too much. Her hand flew up to his face and she slapped him, hard. There was a dull ringing sound as her palm connected, but he didn't react at all, just stood there looking at her, his expression unreadable.

'Feel better now?'

She bit her lip in horror. She had never raised her hand to anyone in her life! 'What do you think?'

He turned away. He didn't want her looking at him all vulnerable and lost like that. He wanted to steel his heart against her pale beauty and the black hair which streamed down her back, tied back with a scarlet ribbon which matched the dress. 'You don't want to hear what I think,' he said heavily. 'I'll take that drink now.'

She went into the kitchen and took wine from the fridge and handed him the bottle, along with two glasses. 'Maybe you could just open that, and I'll clear up a little,' she said.

He sat down in one of the squashy old armchairs and began to open the wine, but his eyes followed her as she moved around the room, deftly clearing the table and bundling up all the leftover party food into the paper cloth.

He wished that she would go and put on the baggy trousers she had been wearing this morning. The sight of the shiny red material stretching over the pert swell of her bottom was making him have thoughts he would rather not have. He was here to talk about his son, not fantasise about taking her damned dress off.

She had lit the fire, and the room flickered with the shadowed reflections of the flames. On the now-cleared table he saw her place a big copper vase containing holly, whose bright berries matched the scarlet of her dress. It was, he thought, with bitter irony, a delightfully cosy little scene.

She took the glass of wine he handed her and sat in the chair facing his, her knees locked tightly together, wishing that she had had the opportunity to change from a dress which was making her uncomfortably aware of the tingling sensation in her breasts. Just what did he do to her simply by looking? She twisted the stem of her glass round and round. 'What shall we drink to?'

He studied her for a long moment. 'How about to truth?'

She took a mouthful and the warmth of the liquor started to unravel the knot of tension which had been coiled up in the pit of her stomach all day. She stared at him. 'Do you really think that *you* have a monopoly on truth? Why the hell do you think I didn't contact you and tell you when I found out I was pregnant?'

'What goes on in your mind is a complete mystery to me.'

Because you don't know me, thought Lisi sadly. And now you never will. Philip's opinion of her would always be distorted. He saw her as some kind of loose woman who would fall into bed with just about any man. Or as a selfish mother who would deliberately keep him from his own flesh and blood.

'Think about the last words you said to me,' she reminded him softly, but the memory still had the power to make her flinch. 'You told me you were married. What was I supposed to do? Turn up on your doorstep with a bulging stomach and announce that you were about to be a daddy? What if your wife had answered the door? I can't imagine that she would have been particularly overjoyed to hear that!'

He didn't respond for a moment. He had come here this morning intending to tell her about the circumstances which had led to that night. About Carla. But his discovery of Tim had driven that far into the background. There were only so many revelations they could take in one day. Wouldn't talking about his wife at this precise moment muddy the waters still further? Tim must come first.

'You could have telephoned me,' he pointed out. 'The office had my number. You could have called me any time.'

'The look on your face as you walked out that night made me think that you would be happy never to see me again. The disgust on your face told its own story.'

Self-disgust, he thought bitterly. Disgusted at his own weakness and disgusted by the intensity of the pleasure he had experienced in her arms. A relative stranger's arms.

He put the wineglass down on the table and his eyes glittered with accusation.

'The situation should never have arisen,' he ground out. 'You shouldn't have become pregnant in the first place.'

'Tell me something I don't know! I didn't exactly *choose* to get pregnant!'

'Oh, really?' The accusation in his voice didn't waver. 'You told me that it was safe.' He gave a hollow laugh. 'Safe? More fool me for believing you.'

Her fingers trembling so much that she was afraid that she might slop wine all over her dress, Lisi put her own glass down on the carpet. 'Are you saying that I lied, Philip?'

His cool, clever eyes bored into her.

'Facts are facts,' he said coldly. 'I realised that we were not using any protection. I offered to stop—' He felt his groin tensing as he remembered just when and how he had offered to stop, and a wave of desire so deep and so hot swept over him that it took his breath away. He played for time, slowly picking up his glass and lifting it to his lips until he had his feelings under control once more.

'I offered to stop,' he continued, still in that hard, cold voice. 'And you assured me that it was safe. Just how was it safe, Lisi? Were you praying that it would be—because you were so het-up you couldn't bear me to stop? Or were you relying on something as outrageously unreliable as the so-called "safe" period?'

'Do you really think I'd take risks like that?' she demanded.

'Who knows?'

She gave a short laugh. If she had entertained any lingering doubt that there might be some fragment of affection for her in the corner of his heart, then he had dispelled it completely with that arrogant question.

'For your information—I was on the pill at the time—'

'Just in case?' he queried hatefully.

'Actually—' But she stopped short of telling him why. She was under no obligation to explain that, although she had broken up with her steady boyfriend a year earlier, the pill had suited her and given her normal periods for the first time in her life and she had seen no reason to stop taking it. 'It's none of your business why I was taking it.'

I'll bet, he thought grimly. 'So why didn't it work?'

'Because…' She sighed. 'I guess because I had a bout of sickness earlier that week. In the heat of the moment, it slipped my mind. It was a million-to-one chance—'

'I think that the odds were rather higher than that, don't you?' He raised his eyebrows insolently. 'You surely must have known that there was a possibility that it would fail?'

Unable to take any more of the cold censure on his face, she leaned over to throw another log on the fire and it spat and hissed back at her like an angry cat. 'What do you want me to say? That I couldn't bear for you to stop?' Because that was the shameful truth. At the time she had felt as if the world would come to an abrupt and utter end if he'd stopped his delicious love-making. But she hadn't *consciously* taken a risk.

'And couldn't you, Lisi? Bear me to stop?'

She met his eyes. The truth he had wanted, so the truth he would get. 'No. I couldn't. Does that flatter your ego?'

His voice was cold. 'My ego does not need flattering. And anyway—' he topped up both their glasses '—how it happened is now irrelevant—we can't turn the clock back, can we?'

His words struck a painful chord and she knew that she had to ask him the most difficult question of all. Even if she didn't like the answer. 'And if you could?' she queried softly. '*Would* you turn the clock back?'

He stared at her in disbelief. Was she really that naive? 'Of course I would!' he said vehemently, though the way her mouth crumpled when he said it made him feel distinctly uncomfortable. 'Wouldn't you?'

She gave him a sad smile. He would never understand— not in a million years. 'Of course I wouldn't.'

'You *wouldn't*?'

'How could I?' she asked simply. 'When the encounter gave me a son.'

He noted her use of the word *encounter*. Which told him precisely how *she* regarded what had happened that night. Easy come. His mouth twisted. Easy go. She certainly had not bothered to spare his feelings, but then why should she? He had not spared hers. There was no need for loyalty between them—nothing at all between them, in fact, other than an inconvenient physical attraction.

And a son.

'He looks like you,' he observed.

'That's what everyone says,' said Lisi serenely, and saw to her amazement that a flicker of something very much like…disappointment…crossed his features. 'And it's a good thing he does, isn't it?' she asked him quietly.

'Meaning?'

'Well, I would hate him to resemble a father who wished that the whole thing never happened.'

'Lisi, you are wilfully misunderstanding me!' he snapped.

She shook her head. 'I don't think so. You would wish him unborn, if you could.'

'You can't wish someone unborn!' he remonstrated, and then his voice unexpectedly gentled. 'And if I really thought the whole situation so regrettable, then why am I here? Why didn't I just stay away when I found out, as you so clearly wanted me to?'

She shrugged. 'I don't know.'

'Then I'll tell you.' He leaned forward in the chair. 'Obviously the circumstances of his conception are not what I would have chosen—'

'What a delightful way to phrase it,' put in Lisi drily.

'But Tim is here now. He exists! He is half mine—'

'You can't cut him up in portions as you would a cake!' she protested.

'Half mine in terms of genetic make-up,' he continued inexorably.

'Now you're making him sound like Frankenstein,' observed Lisi, slightly hysterically.

'Don't be silly! I want to watch him grow,' said Philip, and his voice grew almost dreamy. 'To see him develop into a man. To influence him. To teach him. To be a father to him.'

Lisi swallowed. This didn't sound like the occasional contact visit to her. But she had denied him access for three whole years, wouldn't it sound unspeakably mean to object to that curiously possessive tone which had deepened his voice to sweetest honey?

And besides, what was she worrying about? He lived in London, for heaven's sake—and, although Langley was commutable from the capital, she imagined that he would soon get tired of travelling up and down the country to see Tim.

She knew how fickle men could be. She thought of Dave, her best friend Rachel's husband, who had deserted Rachel just over a year ago. They had a son of Tim's age and Dave's visits to see him had dwindled to almost nothing. And that was from a man who had fallen in love with and married the mother of his child. Who had seen that child grow from squalling infant to chubby toddler. If *he* had lost interest—then how long would she give Philip before he tired of fatherhood?

'I'd like to see him now, please.'

This time there was no reason not to agree to his request, but Lisi felt almost stricken by a reluctance to do so. Something was going to end right here and now, she realised. For so long it had been just her and Tim—a unit which went together as perfectly as peaches and cream. No one else had been able to lay claim on him and, since her mother had died, she had considered herself to be his only living relation. He was hers. All hers—and now she was going to have to relinquish part of him to his father.

A lump rose in the back of her throat and she swallowed it down.

Philip was staring at her from between narrowed eyes. Did her eyes glitter with the promise of tears? 'Are you okay?'

'Of course I'm okay,' she answered unconvincingly. 'Why shouldn't I be?'

'Because you've gone so pale.'

'I *am* pale, Philip—you know that.' He had told her so that night in his arms. 'Pale as the moon,' he had whispered, as his lips had burned fire along her flesh. 'Come with me,' she said slowly.

The two of them walked with exaggerated care towards the closed door with its hand-painted sign saying, 'Tim's Room'.

Lisi pushed the door open quietly and tiptoed over to the bed, where a little hump lay tucked beneath a Mickey-Mouse duvet, and Philip was surprised by the clamour of a far-distant memory. So she still had a thing about Disney, did she?

He went to stand beside her, and looked down, unprepared for the kick of some primitive emotion deep inside him. The sleeping child looked almost unbearably peaceful, with only one small lock of dark hair obscuring the pure lines of a flawless cheek. His lashes were long, he realised—as long as Lisi's—and his mouth was half open as he took in slow, steady breaths.

'So innocent,' he said, very softly. 'So very innocent.'

It was such a loaded word, and Lisi felt a strange, useless yearning. He thought *her* the very antithesis of innocence, didn't he? If only it could be different. But she knew in her heart that it never could. She nodded, gazing down with pride at the shiny-clean hair of her son. Their son. He looked scrubbed-clean and contented. Good enough to eat.

She stole a glance at Philip, who was studying Tim so intently that she might as well not have existed. Strange now how *his* profile should remind her of Tim's. Had that been because he had not been around to make any comparisons? How much else of Tim was Philip? she wondered. What untapped genetic secrets lay dormant in that sweet, sleeping form?

Philip turned his head and their eyes made contact in a moment of strange, unspoken empathy. She read real sadness in *his* eyes. And regret—and wondered what he saw in hers.

He probably didn't care.

She put her finger onto her lips and beckoned him back out. She did *not* want Tim to wake and to demand to know what this man was doing here. Again. She shut the door behind them and went back into the sitting room, where Philip stood with his back to the fire, looking to all intents and purposes as if he were the master of the house.

But he never would be. She must remember that. In fact, it was almost laughable to try to imagine Philip Caprice living in this little house with her and Tim. The ceiling seemed almost too low to accommodate him, he was so tall. She tried to picture them all cramming into the tiny bathroom in the mornings and winced.

'Would you like some more wine?' she asked.

He shook his head. 'No, thanks. Coffee would be good, though.'

She was glad of the opportunity to escape to the kitchen and busy herself with the cafetière. She carried it back in with a plate of biscuits to find him standing where she had left him, only now he was staring deep into the heart of the fire with unseeing eyes.

He took the cup from her and gave a small smile of appreciation. 'Real coffee,' he murmured.

At that moment she really, really hated him. Did he have any idea just how *patronising* that sounded? 'What did you expect?' she asked acidly. 'The cheapest brand of instant on the market?'

He shook his head, still dazed by the emotional impact of seeing his son. 'You're right—if anything was cheap it was my remark.'

And what about the others? she wanted to cry out. The intimation that she had deliberately got pregnant. Wasn't that the cheapest remark a man could ever make to a woman? He wasn't taking *those* back, was he?

'So who else knows?' he demanded.

Lisi blinked. 'Knows what?'

'About Tim,' he said impatiently. 'How many others are privy to the secret I was excluded from?

She shook her head. 'No one. No one knows.'

'No-one at all?' he queried disbelievingly.

'No. Why should they? As far as anyone knew—we simply had a professional relationship. Even Jonathon thought that—and nobody was aware that I went up to your room at the hotel that night.' She shuddered, thinking how sordid that sounded. She bit her lip. 'The only person I told was my mother, just before she died.'

'You told her the whole story?' he demanded incredulously.

Again, she shook her head. 'I edited it more than a bit.'

'Was she shocked?'

Lisi shrugged. 'A little, but I made it sound…' She hesitated. She had made it sound as though she had been in love with him, and that bit she had found surprisingly easy. 'I made it sound rather more than it had been.' And her mother had pleaded with her to contact him. But then the bit she had omitted to tell her mother had been that Philip had already been married.

He looked at her and gave a heavy smile. 'My parents will want to meet him,' he said, wondering just how he was going to tell his elderly parents that he, too, was a parent.

'Your p-parents?'

His eyes were steady. 'But of course. What did you expect?'

What *had* she expected? Well, for one thing—she had expected to live the rest of her life without ever seeing Philip again. 'I don't know,' she admitted. 'I haven't really thought it through.'

'He's in my life now, too, Lisi,' he said simply. 'And I don't come in a neat little box marked "Philip Caprice"— to be opened up at will and shut again when it suits you. I have family who will want to get to know him. And friends, too.'

And girlfriends? she wondered. Maybe even one particular girlfriend who was very special to him? Maybe even... She raised troubled aquamarine eyes to his. 'Have you married, again, Philip?' she asked quietly.

'No.'

She felt the fierce, triumphant leap of her heart and despaired at herself. Fool, she thought. Fool! 'So where do we go from here?'

He despised himself for the part of him which wanted to say, Let's go to bed—because even though the distance between them was so vast that he doubted whether it could ever be mended, that didn't stop him from being turned on by her. He shifted uncomfortably in the chair. Very turned on indeed. He met her questioning gaze with a look of challenge. 'You tell Tim about me as soon as possible.'

Her mouth fell open. '*Tell* him?'

'Of course you tell him!' he exploded softly. 'I'm back, Lisi—and I'm staking my claim.'

It sounded so territorial. So loveless. 'Oh, I see,' she said slowly.

He narrowed his eyes. 'Just how were you planning to explain to him about his father? If I hadn't turned up.'

'I honestly don't know. It's not something I ever gave much thought to. He's so young, and whenever he asked I just said that Mummy and Daddy broke up before he was born and that I hadn't seen you since.' It had seemed easier to bury her head in the sand than to confront such a painful issue. 'Maybe one day I might have told him who his real father was.'

'When?' he demanded. 'When he was five? Six? Sixteen?'

'When the time was right.'

'And maybe the time never *would* have been right, hmm, Lisi? Did you think you could get away with keeping me anonymous for the rest of his life, so that the poor kid would never know he had a father?'

She met the burning accusation in his eyes and couldn't pretend. Not about this. 'I don't know,' she whispered.

He rose to his feet. 'Well, just make sure you do it. And soon. I don't care how you do it—just tell him!'

She nodded. She wanted him gone now—with as long a space until his next visit as possible. 'And when will we see you again? Some time after Christmas?'

He heard the hopeful tinge to her question and gave a short laugh. 'Hard luck, Lisi,' he said grimly. 'I'm afraid that I'm not going to just conveniently disappear from your life again. I'm intending to be around quite a bit. Just call it making up for lost time, if it makes you feel better. And it's Christmas very soon.'

'Christmas?' she echoed, in a horrified whisper.

'Sure.' His mouth hardened into an implacable line. 'I was tempted to buy him a birthday present today, but I didn't want to confuse him. However, there's only a week to go until Christmas and some time between now and then he needs to know who I am.' His eyes glittered. 'Because you can rest assured that I will be spending part of the holiday with him.'

She wanted to cry out and beg him not to disrupt the relatively calm order of her life, but as she looked into Philip's strong, cold face she knew that she would be wasting her breath. He wasn't going to go away, she recognised, and if she tried to stop him then he would simply bring in the best lawyers that money could buy in order to win contact with his child. She didn't need to be told to know that.

'Understood?' he asked softly.

'Do I have any choice?'

'I think you know the answer to that. Don't worry about seeing me to the door. I'll let myself out.'

As if in a dream she watched him go and shut the front door quietly behind him, and only when she had heard the last of his footsteps echoing down the path did she allow herself to sink back down onto the chair and to bury her head in her hands and take all that was left to her.

The comfort of tears.

CHAPTER SIX

LISI was woken by the sound of the telephone ringing, and as she picked it up she was aware that something was not as it should be.

'Hello?'

'Lisi, it's Marian.'

Sleepily, Lisi wondered what her boss was doing ringing her this early in the morning... She sat bolt upright in bed. That was it! That was what was not right! She had over-slept—she could tell that much by the light which was filtering through the curtains. 'What time is it?' she asked urgently.

'Nine-thirty, why—?'

'Wait there!' swallowed Lisi, and left the receiver on the bed while she rushed into Tim's bedroom. What was the matter with him? Why hadn't he woken at his usual unearthly hour? Had Philip Caprice climbed in through one of the windows in the middle of the night and kidnapped his son?

But to her relief her son was sitting on his bed, engrossed in playing with some of his new birthday toys. He looked up as Lisi flew into the room, and smiled.

''Lo, Mum-mee,' he said happily. 'Me playing with tractor!'

'So I see! And a lovely tractor it is too, darling,' said Lisi, charging across the room to drop a kiss on top of his head. 'Mummy's just talking to Marian on the telephone and then we'll have a great big breakfast together!'

But Tim's head was bent over his toy again and he was busy making what he imagined to be tractor noises.

On the way back to speak to Marian, Lisi reflected how different things felt this morning. She no longer felt weak or intimidated by Philip. He had decided that he wanted contact and there was nothing she could do about it—but he could do all the legwork. She would just be polite. Icily polite.

Because during the middle of her largely sleepless night she had come to her senses and a great sense of indignation had made her softly curse his name.

He had been so busy attacking her that she hadn't really had time to consider that he had shown no remorse about betraying his wife. Nor any shame for his part in what had happened. Philip obviously wanted to make her the scapegoat—well, tough! He should look to himself first!

She picked the phone back up. 'Hello, Marian—are you still there?'

'Just about,' came the dry reply. 'Where did you go—Scotland?'

'Very funny.'

'You sound more cheerful today,' observed Marian.

'I am,' said Lisi. '*Much* happier!'

There was a short pause. 'I don't know if you're going to be after what I'm about to tell you.'

A sudden sense of foreboding filled Lisi with dread. This was something to do with Philip. 'What is it?'

'It's Philip Caprice.'

Exasperation and impatience made Lisi feel like screaming—until she reminded herself that the worst had already been exposed. There was nothing he could do to hurt and upset her now. 'What now?' she asked.

'He wants you to show him round a property later this morning.'

'He has to be kidding! Did you tell him that I'm off now until after Christmas?'

'I told him that yesterday. Lisi, has something happened between you two?'

'Apart from the very obvious?' she asked tartly.

'You know what I mean.'

Yes, she knew what Marian meant and she guessed that it was pointless keeping it from her boss—especially as she had already guessed that Philip was Tim's father.

'I told him,' she said flatly.

'You *told* him?'

'He guessed,' Lisi amended.

'And?'

Lisi sighed. She had planned to get onto the phone first thing and tell Rachel all about it, but just then she badly needed to confide in somebody, and Marian was older and wiser. Lisi suspected that she had known straight away that a man as discerning as Philip would be bound to guess eventually.

'He wants to be involved.'

'With you?'

'Oh, no,' said Lisi with a hollow laugh. 'Definitely not with me. With Tim.'

'I see.' Marian's voice sounded rather strained. 'That explains it, then.'

That sense of foreboding hit her again. 'Explains what?' she asked, her voice rising with a kind of nameless fear.

'He really *does* want to buy somewhere here. In Langley.'

Lisi's mouth thinned. 'I see.'

'And that's not the worst of it.'

'What do you mean?'

'He wants *you* to show him around a property—'

'But I'm on *holiday*, Marian!'

'I already told him that.'

'And even if I weren't—I don't *want* to show him around a property!'

'He's…well, he's insisted, dear.'

'He can't insist,' whispered Lisi. 'Can he?'

Another pause. 'He *is* the customer,' said Marian apologetically, and suddenly Lisi understood. Marian was a businesswoman—and business was business was business. Philip Caprice was a wealthy and influential man and if he said jump, then presumably they would all have to leap through hoops for him.

She thought of all the times when Marian had let her have the morning, or even a couple of days, off work. When Tim had been ill. Or when she had taken him to have his inoculations. She was an understanding and kind employer, and Lisi owed her.

'Okay,' she sighed. 'I can probably arrange for Rachel to look after Tim. When does he want to look round?'

'Later on this morning. Think you can manage it? You can even leave Tim in here with us, if it's difficult.'

'I'm sure Rachel will be able to have him.'

'Good!' Marian's voice grew slightly more strained. 'There's just one more thing, Lisi.'

Lisi tried to inject a note of gallows humour into her voice. 'Go on, hit me with it!'

'The property in question…it's…it's The Old Rectory.'

The world spun. It was a cruel trick. A cruel twist of fate. Was he planning to hurt her even more than he already had done? Lisi heard herself speaking with a note of cracked desperation. 'Is this some kind of joke, Marian?'

'I wish it was, dear.'

Lisi didn't remember putting the phone down, she just found herself sitting on the bed staring blankly at it. He couldn't, she thought fiercely. He couldn't do this to her!

The Old Rectory.

The house she had grown up in. The house her mother had struggled to keep on, even after the death of her father, when everyone had told her to downsize and to move into something more suitable for a mother and her daughter on their own.

But neither of them had wanted to. A house could creep into your heart and your soul, and Lisi and her mother had preferred to put on an extra sweater or two in winter. It had kept the heating bills down at a time when every penny had counted.

After her mother had died, Lisi had reluctantly sold the house, but by then she had needed to. Really needed to, because she'd had a baby to support. She had bought Cherry Tree Cottage and invested the rest of the proceeds of the sale, giving just enough for her and Tim to live on. To fall back on.

And now Philip Caprice was going to rub her nose in it by buying the property for himself!

Over my dead body! she thought.

She gave Tim his breakfast.

'I want birthday cake,' he had announced solemnly.

'Sure,' said Lisi absently, and began to cut him a large slice.

'*Can* I, Mum-mee?' asked Tim, in surprise.

She glanced down at the sickly confection and remembered feeding Philip birthday cake all those years back and her heart clenched. She looked into Tim's hopeful face and relented. Oh, what the heck—it wouldn't hurt for once, would it?

While Tim was chomping his way through the cake, she phoned Rachel, who agreed to look after him without question.

'Bless you!' said Lisi impulsively.

'Is everything okay?'

She heard the doubt in Rachel's voice and wondered if she sounded as mixed-up and disturbed as she felt. Probably. 'I'll tell you all about it later,' she said grimly.

'Can't wait!'

Lisi went through the mechanics of getting ready. She ran herself a bath and left the door open and Tim trotted happily in and out. She wondered whether Philip was prepared for the lack of privacy which caring for a young child inevitably brought. And then she imagined him lording it in her old family home and she could have screamed aloud with fury, but for Tim's sake—and her own—she won the inner battle to stay calm.

She supposed that she ought to dress as if for work and picked out her most buttoned-up suit from the wardrobe. Navy-blue and pinstriped, it had a straight skirt which came to just below the knee and a long-line jacket. With a crisp, white blouse and her hair scraped back into a chignon, she thought that she looked professional. And prim.

Good!

The scarlet dress had been a big mistake last night. He might not like or respect her, but it was obvious that he still felt physically attracted to her. She had seen the way he'd watched her last night, while trying to appear as if he hadn't been. And she had seen the tension which had stiffened his elegant frame, had him shifting uncomfortably in his chair. It had been unmistakably a sexual tension, and Lisi wasn't fooling herself into thinking that it hadn't been mutual.

Later that morning, after she had deposited Tim and some of the leftover party food at Rachel's house, Lisi walked into the agency to find Philip waiting for her.

His face was unsmiling and his eyes looked very green as he nodded at her coolly. 'Hello, Lisi,' he said, speaking as politely and noncommittally—as if this were the first time he had ever met her.

Marian was sitting at her desk looking a little flustered. 'Here are the keys,' she said. 'The owners are away.'

Her heart sinking slightly, Lisi took them. She had hoped that one of the divorcing couple would be in. At least the presence of a third party might have defused the atmosphere. She could not think of a more unpalatable situation than being alone in that big, beautiful house with Philip.

Unpalatable? she asked herself. Or simply dangerous?

'We can walk there,' she told him outside. 'It's just up the lane.'

'Sure.'

But once away from Marian's view, she no longer had to play the professional. 'So you're going through with your threat to buy a house in the village,' she said, in a low, furious voice.

'I think it makes sense, under the circumstances,' he said evenly. 'Don't you?'

Nothing seemed to make sense any more—not least the fact that even in the midst of her anger towards him—her body was crying out for more of his touch.

Was that conditioning? Nature's way of ensuring stability? That a woman should find the father of her child overwhelmingly attractive? No. It couldn't be. Rachel had completely gone off Dave—she told Lisi that the thought of him touching her now made her flesh creep. But then Dave *had* run off with one of Rachel's other supposed 'friends'.

Lisi reminded herself that Philip was not whiter-than-white, either. *He* had been the one who had been attached—more than attached. He had actually been married, and yet his anger all seemed to be directed at her. His poor wife! It was, Lisi decided, time to start giving as good as she got.

Her rage was almost palpable, thought Philip as he looked at the stiff set of her shoulders beneath the starchy-looking suit she wore. He suspected that she had dressed in a way to make herself seem unapproachable and unattractive to him, but if that *had* been the case, then she had failed completely.

'This is in the same direction as *your* house,' he observed as she took him down the very route he had used last night.

She stopped dead in her tracks and gave him a coolly questioning stare. 'You didn't know?'

'I've only seen the details.'

'It's just down the bloody *road* from me!'

'Handy,' he murmured.

She didn't want him making jokey little asides. That kind of comment could lull you into false hopes. She preferred him hostile, she decided.

Her breath caught in her throat as they walked past her cottage to the end of the lane, where, beside the old grey Norman church, stood the beautiful old rectory. And her heart stood still with shock.

The place was practically falling down!

The yew hedge which her mother had always lovingly clipped had been allowed to overgrow, and the lawn was badly in need of a cut.

'Not very well presented,' Philip observed.

'They're getting divorced,' explained Lisi icily. 'I don't think that house-maintenance is uppermost in their minds at the moment.'

He turned away. People sometimes said to him that death must be easier to bear than divorce. When a couple divorced they knowingly ripped apart the whole fabric of their lives. Only anger was left, and bitterness and resentment.

'At least Carla died knowing that you loved her, and she loved you,' his mother had said to him softly after the funeral and then, like now, he had turned away, his face a mask of pain. What would his mother say if she knew how he had betrayed that love?

And the woman who had tempted him stood beside him now, mocking him and tempting him still in her prissy-looking worksuit. He would be tied to Lisi for ever, he realised—because children made a bond between two people which could never be broken.

'Philip?' Her voice had softened, but that was instinctive rather than intentional for she had seen the look of anguish which had darkened the carved beauty of his features. 'Shall we go inside, or did you want to look round the garden first?'

He shook his head. 'Inside,' he said shortly.

Lisi had not been inside since the day when all the packing crates had made the faded old home resemble a warehouse. She had perched on one waiting for the removals van to arrive, her heart aching as she'd said goodbye to her past. Tim had lain asleep in his Moses basket by her feet—less than six months at the time—gloriously unaware of the huge changes which had been taking place in his young life.

Unbelievable to think that this was the first time she had been back, but Marian had understood her reluctance to accompany clients around her former home. Until Philip Caprice had swanned into the office and made his autocratic demand Lisi hadn't set foot inside the door.

Until today.

Lisi had to stifle a gasp.

When she had lived here with her mother there had been very little money, but a whole lot of love. Surfaces had been dusted, the floorboards bright and shiny, and there had always been a large vase of foliage or the flowers which had bloomed in such abundance in the large gardens at the back.

But now the house had an air of neglect, as if no one had bothered to pay any attention in caring for it. A woman's tee shirt lay crumpled on one corner of the hall floor and a half-empty coffee cup was making a sticky mark on the window-ledge. Lisi shuddered as she caught the drift of old cooking: onions or cabbage—something which lingered unpleasantly in the unaired atmosphere.

She knew from statistics that most people decided to buy

a house within the first few seconds of walking into it. At least Philip was unlikely to be lured by this dusty old shell of a place. She thought of the least attractive way to view it, and she, above all others, knew the place's imperfections.

'The kitchen is along here,' she said calmly, and proceeded to take him there, praying that the divorcing couple had not had the funds to give the room the modernisation it had been crying out for.

She led the way in and let out an almost inaudible sigh of relief. Not only was the kitchen untouched, but it had clearly been left during some kind of marital dispute—for a smashed plate lay right in the centre of the floor. Pots and pans, some still containing food, lay on the surface of the hob, and there was a distinctly nasty smell emanating from the direction of the fridge.

He waited for her to make some kind of fumbling apology for the state of the place, but there was none, she just continued to regard him with that oddly frozen expression on her face.

'Like it?' she asked flippantly.

He narrowed his eyes. 'Hardly. Where's the dining room?'

'I'm afraid that it's some way from the kitchen,' she said, mock-apologetically. 'It isn't a terribly well-designed property—certainly not by modern standards.'

'You really don't want me to buy this house, do you, Lisi?'

'I don't want you to buy any house in Langley, if you must know.' And especially not this one. She put on her professional face once more. 'Would you like to see the dining room?'

'I can't wait,' he answered sardonically.

The dining room looked as though it had never had a meal eaten in it; instead there was a pile of legal-looking papers heaped up on the table, as if someone had been using it for a office. Philip looked around the room slowly, but said nothing.

'Where next?' asked Lisi brightly.

'To the next enchanting room,' he murmured.

Perversely, his criticism stung her, making her realise that she was still more attached to the place than she was sure she should be. How she wished he could have seen it when *she* had lived here, particularly at this time of the year. At Christmas it had come into its own. The hall used to be festooned with fresh laurel from the garden and stacks and stacks of holly and great sprigs of mistletoe had been bunched everywhere.

The choir would come from the church next door on Christmas Eve, and drink sherry and eat mince pies and the big, wide corridors would echo with the sound of excited chatter, while in the sitting room a log fire had blazed out its warmth.

Fortunately—or unfortunately in Lisi's case—no neglect could mar the beauty of the sitting room. The high ceiling and the carved marble fireplace drew the attention away from the fact that the curtains could have done with a good clean.

Philip nodded and walked slowly around the room, his eyes narrowing with pleasure as he looked out of the long window down into the garden beyond.

A winter-bare garden but beautiful nevertheless, he thought, with mature trees and bushes which were silhouetted against the curved shapes of the flower beds.

Lisi wandered over to the window and stood beside him, past and present becoming fused for one brief, poignant moment.

'You should see it in springtime,' she observed fondly.

He heard the dreamy quality of her voice which was so at odds with her attitude of earlier. 'Oh?'

'There are bulbs out everywhere—daffodils and tulips and narcissi—and over there...' she pointed to where a lone tree stood in the centre of the overgrown lawn '...underneath that cherry, the first snowdrops come out and the lawn is sprinkled with white, almost as if it had been snowing.'

The sense of something not being as it should be pricked at his senses. Instincts, Khalim had taught him. Always trust your instincts.

'You seem to know this house very well for someone who only works part-time in the estate agency,' he observed softly.

She turned to face him. What was the point of hiding it from him? 'You're very astute, Philip.'

'Just observant.' His dark brows winged upwards in arrogant query. 'So?'

'I used to live here.' No, that remark didn't seem to do the place justice. 'It was my childhood home,' she explained.

There she was, doing it again—that vulnerable little tremble of her mouth which made him want to kiss all her hurt away.

'What happened?' he asked abruptly.

'After my father died, it was just my mother and me—'

He sounded incredulous. 'In this great barn of a place?'

'We loved it,' she said simply.

He let his eyes roam once more over the high ceilings. 'Yes, I can see that you would,' he said slowly.

'We couldn't bear to leave it. When my mother died, I had to sell up, of course—because there was Tim to think about by then.'

'So you sold this and bought the cottage?' he guessed. 'And presumably banked the rest?'

She nodded.

He thought of her, all alone, struggling along with a little baby, and he felt the sharp pang of conscience. 'Lisi, why in God's name didn't you contact me? Even if I hadn't been able to offer you any kind of future—don't you think that I would have paid towards my son's upkeep?'

She gave him a look of icy pride. 'I wasn't going to come begging to you, cap in hand! I had to think of what was best for everyone, and I came to the conclusion that the best thing would be to cut all ties.'

'And did you enjoy playing God with people's lives?'

She heard his bitterness. 'I thought it would only complicate things if I tried to involve you—for you, for me, for Tim. And for your wife, of course,' she finished. 'Because if it had been me, and my husband had done what you did to her—it would have broken my heart.' She looked at him and her eyes felt hot with unshed tears for the dead woman she had unknowingly deceived. But not Philip—his betrayal had been cold-bloodedly executed. 'Did she know, Philip? Did your wife ever find out?'

'No,' he said flatly. 'Carla never knew anything about it.'

'Are you sure? They say that wives always know—only sometimes they pretend not to.' She stared at him as if she were seeing him for the first time. 'How could you do it? How could you do that to her and live with yourself afterwards?'

Her condemnation of him was so strong that he felt he could almost reach out and touch it, but he knew he couldn't let her stumble along this wrong track any longer, no matter how painful the cost of telling her.

'She didn't know,' he ground out, 'because she wasn't aware. Not of me, or you, or what happened. Not aware of anything.'

She blinked at him in confusion. 'What are you talking about?'

'The night I made love to you—my wife hadn't spoken to me for eighteen months.'

Foolish hope flared in her heart, putting an entirely different perspective on events. 'You mean...you mean that you were *separated*?'

He gave a bitter laugh at the unwitting irony of her words. 'In a sense, yes—we had been separated for a long time. You see, the car crash happened *before* I met you, Lisi, not after. It left her in a deep coma from which she never recovered. She didn't die for several months after...after...'

'After what?' she whispered.

His eyes grew even bleaker. 'After I made love to you. You must have been about six months pregnant when she died.'

CHAPTER SEVEN

THE sitting-room of her childhood retreated into a hazy blur and then came back into focus again and Lisi stared at Philip, noting the tension which had scored deep lines down the side of his mouth.

'I don't understand,' she said.

'Don't you?' He gave a short laugh. 'My wife—'

His wife. His *wife*. 'What was her name?'

He hesitated, then frowned. What was it to her? 'Carla,' he said, grudgingly.

Carla. A person who was referred to as a 'wife' was a nebulous figure of no real substance, but Carla—Carla existed. Philip's wife. Carla. It hurt more than it had any right to hurt. 'Tell me,' she urged softly.

He wasn't looking for her sympathy, or her understanding—he would give her facts if she wanted to hear them, but he wanted nothing in return.

'It happened early one autumn morning,' he began, and a tale he had not had to recount for such a long time became painfully alive in his mind as he relived it. 'Carla was driving to work. She worked out of London,' he added, as if that somehow mattered. 'And visibility was poor. There were all the usual warnings on the radio for people to take it easy, but cars were driving faster than they should have done. A lorry ran into the back of her.' He paused, swallowing down the residual rage that people were always in a hurry and stupid enough to ignore the kind of conditions which led to accidents.

'When the paramedics arrived on the scene, they didn't think she'd make it. She had suffered massive head injuries.

98

They took her to hospital, and for a while it was touch and go.'

Lisi winced. What words could she say that would not sound meaningless and redundant? He must have heard the same faltering platitudes over and over again. She nodded and said nothing.

'Her body was unscathed,' he said haltingly. 'And so was her face—that was the amazing thing.' But it had been a cruel paradox that while she had lain looking so perfect in the stark hospital bed—the Carla he had known and loved had no longer existed. Smashed away by man's disregard for safety.

'I used to visit her every day—twice a day when I wasn't out of London.' Sitting there for hours, playing her favourite music, stroking the cold, unmoving hand and praying for some kind of response, some kind of recognition he was never to see again. Other than one slight movement of her fingers which had given everyone false hope. 'But she was so badly injured. She couldn't speak or eat, or even breathe for herself.'

'How terrible,' breathed Lisi, and in that moment her heart went out to him.

'The doctors weren't even sure whether she could hear me, but I talked to her anyway. Just in case.'

He met a bright kind of understanding in her eyes and he hardened his heart against it. 'I was living in a kind of vacuum,' he said heavily. 'And work became my salvation, in a way.' At work he had been forced to put on hold the human tragedy which had been playing non-stop in his life. He gave her a hard, candid look. 'Women came onto me all the time, but I was never...'

She sensed what was coming. 'Never what, Philip?'

'Never tempted,' he snarled. 'Never.' His mouth hardened. 'Until you.'

So she *was* the scapegoat, was she? Was that why he

had seemed so *angry* when he had walked back into her life? 'You make me sound like some kind of *femme fatale*,' she said drily.

He shook his head. That had been his big mistake. A complete misjudgement. Uncharacteristic, but understandable under the circumstances. 'On the contrary,' he countered. 'You seemed the very opposite of a *femme fatale*. I thought that you were sweet, and safe. Innocent. Uncomplicated.'

Achingly, she noted his use of the past tense.

'Until that night. When we had that celebratory drink.' He walked back over to the window and stared out unseeingly. 'I'd only had one drink myself—so I couldn't even blame the alcohol.'

Blame. He needed someone to blame—and she guessed that someone was her. 'So I was responsible for your momentary weakness, was I, Philip?'

He turned around and his face was a blaze of anger. 'Do you make a habit of getting half-cut and borrowing men's hotel rooms to sleep it off?' he ground out, because this had been on his mind for longer than he cared to remember. 'Do you often take off all your clothes and lie there, just waiting, like every man's fantasy about to happen?'

'Is that what you think?' she asked quietly, even though her heart was crashing against her ribcage.

'I'm not going to flatter myself that I was the first,' he said coldly. 'Why should I? You didn't act like it was a once-in-a-lifetime experience.'

His words wounded her—but what defence did she have? If she told him that it had *felt* like that, for her, then she would come over at best naive, and at worst—a complete and utter liar.

'I'll take that as a compliment,' she said, and regretted it immediately. 'I'm sorry,' she amended. 'I shouldn't be flippant when you're telling me all this.'

Oddly enough, her glib remark did not offend him. 'It was a long time ago,' he said heavily. 'I don't want to be wrapped up in cotton wool for the rest of my life.'

'Won't you tell me the rest?' she asked slowly, because she recognised that he was not just going to go away. And if he *was* around in her life—then how could they possibly form any kind of relationship to accommodate their son, unless she knew all the facts? However painful they might be.

He nodded. 'That night I left you I went straight to the hospital. The day before Carla had moved her fingers slightly and it seemed as if there might be hope.'

She remembered that his mood that day had been almost high. So that had been why. His wife had appeared to be on the road to recovery and he had celebrated life in the oldest way known to man. With her.

'But Carla lay as still as ever, hooked up to all the hospital paraphernalia of tubes and drips and monitors,' he continued.

He had sat beside her and been eaten up with guilt and blame and regret as he'd looked down at her beautiful but waxy lips which had breathed only with the aid of a machine. Carla hadn't recognised him, or had any idea of what he had done, and yet it had smitten him to the hilt that he had just betrayed his wife in the most fundamental way possible.

His mouth twisted. To love and to cherish. In sickness and in health. Vows he had made and vows he had broken.

He had always considered himself strong, and reasoned and controlled—and the weakness which Lisi had exposed in his character had come as an unwelcome shock to which had made him despise himself.

And a little bit of him had despised her, too.

'She died a few months later,' he finished, because what else was there to say? He saw her stricken expression and guessed what had caused it. 'Oh, it wasn't as a result of what you and I did, Lisi, if that's what you're thinking.'

'The thought had crossed my mind,' she admitted slowly. 'Even though I know it's irrational.'

Hadn't he thought the same thing himself? As though Carla could have somehow known what he had done.

'What did you do?' she questioned softly.

There was silence in the big room before he spoke again.

'I went to pieces, I guess.' He saw the look of surprise in her eyes. 'Oh, I functioned as before—I worked and I ate and I slept—but it was almost as if it was happening to another person. I think I was slowly going crazy. And then Khalim came.'

'Khalim?' she asked hesitantly.

'Prince Khalim.' He watched as the surprise became astonishment, and he shrugged. 'At the time he was heir to a Middle-Eastern country named Maraban—though of course he's ruler now.'

'How do you know him?' asked Lisi faintly.

'We were at Cambridge together—and he heard what had happened and he came and took me off to Maraban with him.'

'To live in luxury?'

He smiled at *this* memory as he shook his head. 'The very opposite. He told me that the only way to live through pain and survive it was to embrace it. So for two months we lived in a tiny hut in the Maraban mountains. Just us. No servants. Nothing. Just a couple of discreet bodyguards lurking within assassination distance of him.'

Her eyes grew wide with fascination. 'And what did you do?'

'We foraged for food. We walked for hours and sometimes rode horses through the mountains. At night we would read by the light of the fire. And he taught me to fight,' he finished.

'To *fight*?'

He nodded. 'Bare-knuckled. We used to beat hell out of each other!'

'And didn't he...*mind*?'

Philip shook his head. 'Out there, in the mountains—we were equals.' Indeed, he suspected that Khalim had learned as much from the experience as he had—for certainly the two men who had emerged from their self-imposed exile had been changed men.

She had wondered what had brought about the new, lean, hard Philip. Why he had looked so different—all the edges chiselled away. She swallowed. 'And then?'

'Then he offered me a job, working as his emissary. It took me all over the world.'

'And did you enjoy it?'

'I loved it.'

'But you left?'

He nodded.

'Why?'

'The time had come. Everything has its time of closure. Khalim fell in love with an English woman. Rose.'

His mouth curved into a warm and affectionate smile and Lisi felt the dagger of jealousy ripping through her.

'Khalim and I had developed the closeness of brothers—in so much as his position allowed. It was only right that Rose should have him all to herself once they were married.'

In all the time she had been listening to his story, Lisi had been entranced, but as he drew to the end of it reality reared its head once more.

She gave a little cough. 'Would you like to see upstairs now?'

'No, thanks—I've seen enough.'

Thank God! She nodded understandingly. 'Well, I'm sure

we'll be getting a lot more properties on the market—especially after Christmas.'

He gave a slow smile as he realised what she was thinking. 'You may have misunderstood me, Lisi,' he said silkily. 'I want this house and I want you to put an offer in.'

'But it's overpriced! You know it is!' she declared desperately. 'Ridiculously overpriced!'

He wondered whether she tried to put *other* buyers off in quite such an obvious way, but somehow doubted it. 'So Marian Reece told me.'

'And they've stated *unequivocally* that they can't possibly accept anything other than the full asking price.'

'Then offer it to them,' he said flatly.

She could not believe her ears. This was Philip Caprice speaking—the man famed for driving the hardest bargain in the property market! 'Are you serious?' she breathed.

He saw the way her lips parted in disbelief and he felt a wild urge to kiss them, to imprison her in his arms and to take the clips from her hair and have it tumble down over that masculine-looking jacket. His eyes slid down past the pencil skirt to the creamy tights which covered her long legs and that same wildness made him wonder what she would do if he began to make love to her.

Should he try? See if she would respond with passion and let him slide his hand all the way up her legs and touch her until she was begging him for more. He struggled to dampen down his desire.

'I've never been more serious in my life,' he said, and then his voice became clipped. 'Tell the vendors that my only condition is that I want *in* and I want them out. So let's tie up the deal as quickly as possible, shall we?'

If she could have had a wish at that moment, it would have been to have been given a huge sum of money—enough to buy back her own home herself instead of letting it go to Philip Caprice. Couldn't he guess how much she loved the place? Wasn't he perceptive enough to realise how heartbreaking she was going to find it, with *him* living here.

Or maybe he just didn't care.

He was walking around the room now, touching the walls with a proprietorial air she found utterly abhorrent. She gritted her teeth behind a forced smile. 'Very well. I'll get that up and running straight away.' There was a question in her eyes. 'Though it's going to need a lot of work to get it up to the kind of specifications I imagine you'll be looking for.'

His answering smile was bland. 'Just so.'

'You certainly couldn't expect to be in before Christmas. Probably not until springtime at the earliest,' she added hopefully.

Her wishes were beautifully transparent, but, unfortunately for her, they were not going to come true. 'Not Christmas, certainly,' he agreed, and saw her visibly relax. 'But I think spring is a rather pessimistic projection.'

'All the builders and decorators around here are booked up for *months* in advance!' she told him, trying to keep the note of triumph from her voice.

'Then I shall just have to bring people down from London, won't I?'

She glared at him. 'As you wish,' she said tightly. 'And now, if there's nothing further, I'll call into the office and then I really must get back—'

'To Tim?' he interjected softly.

How she wished he wouldn't use that distinctly possessive tone! He might be Tim's father—but the two had barely exchanged a few words. He couldn't just walk back into their lives unannounced and expect to be an equal partner!

'Yes, to Tim,' she said coldly, and began to walk towards

the hall, her high heels clip-clopping over the polished floorboards.

'Oh, Lisi?'

She stopped, something in his tone warning her that she was not going to like his *next* words, either. She turned round, wishing that he were ugly, and that he didn't have those piercing green eyes which could turn her knees to jelly. 'Yes?'

'We haven't discussed Christmas yet, have we?'

'Christmas?' she echoed stupidly. 'What about it?'

'I want to spend it with Tim.'

She fought down the urge to tell him that he could take a running jump, but she knew that open opposition would get her nowhere. Softly, softly it must be.

She put on her most reasonable smile. 'I'm afraid you can't. I'm really sorry.'

Yeah, she sounded *really* sorry. He kept his face impassive. 'Oh? And why's that?'

'Because we've already made arrangements for Christmas.'

'Then unmake them,' he said flatly. 'Or include me.'

She drew in a deep breath. 'We've arranged to have lunch with my friend Rachel and her son, Blaine—he's Tim's best friend. I couldn't possibly take you along with us!'

He thought about it. 'I'm supposed to be having lunch with my parents,' he reflected. 'But I'll drive down here afterwards. We can all have tea and Christmas cake together, can't we, Lisi?'

'No!'

'Why not?'

'Because...because he doesn't know who you are!'

He narrowed his eyes, but not before she had seen the flash of temper in them. 'You mean you haven't told him yet?'

'When?' she demanded angrily. 'In the hour I had this morning between waking up and being summoned into the office at your bidding?'

The accusation washed over him. 'I thought that it was important for you to see where I was buying.'

'Why?'

'Because eventually Tim will come to stay with me. Naturally.'

Feeling as though her world were splintering all around her, Lisi prayed that it didn't show. Keep calm, she told herself. He may be powerful and rich, but he can't just ride roughshod over your wishes. He can't.

She drew a deep breath.

'Listen, Philip—I can understand that you want to build a relationship with Tim—'

'How very good of you,' he put in sarcastically.

'But he doesn't know you properly, and until he does then I'm afraid that I cannot permit him to stay with you. In fact, he probably won't want to come up to the house without me.'

The expression on his face grew intent. 'I want bathtimes and bedtimes and all the normal things which fathers do, and if you think I'm cracking my skull on the ceiling of your cottage every time I stand up, then you've got another think coming!'

She opened her mouth to object and then shut it again, because she could see from his unshakable stance that to argue would be pointless. 'I can't see that happening for a long time,' she said coldly.

'We'll see.' He gave a bland smile. 'And in the meantime, I'll be around on Christmas afternoon. Shall we say around five?'

She couldn't bring herself to answer him, and so she nodded instead.

CHAPTER EIGHT

'TIM, darling—*please* don't eat any more—you'll be sick!
'*One* more, Mum-mee!'

Lisi lunged towards him, but he had crammed another chocolate in his mouth before she could stop him. She took the stocking away from him firmly. 'That's enough chocolate!' she said sternly. 'We've got tea to get through next.' And her face fell.

Rachel leaned across the table, holding a bottle of port. 'Have a glass?' she suggested. 'You haven't got far to go, and it *is* Christmas Day!'

'You don't need to remind me,' said Lisi gloomily. She looked down at her son, who was busy licking chocolate off the inside of the wrapper. 'Put that down, darling, and go away and play with Blaine until it's time to go!'

To her relief, Tim went scampering off, and, after a swift glance at her wrist-watch, Lisi curled her feet up underneath her. Another hour until the avenging Caprice appeared on her doorstep. 'I could just go to sleep.' She yawned.

'On Christmas Day? Show me the mother of a child under ten who couldn't, and I'll show you a liar!' chortled Rachel, and then a look of concern criss-crossed her brow as she glanced across at her friend. 'You okay?'

Lisi shrugged. 'As okay as anyone can be when they're having their arm twisted.' She had told Rachel everything. She had seen no cause not to. There was no longer any point in keeping anything back. People would know—or guess—soon enough when she and Tim started traipsing down the lane for cosy afternoons and evenings with him.

'I still can't believe he's bought The Old Rectory,' said

108

Lisi crossly. 'And what is even more unbelievable is that he railroaded his lawyers into rushing through the deal. They complete in the New Year,' she finished. 'What a wonderful way to start the year—Philip Caprice firmly ensconced in my old family home.'

'I think it's rather romantic,' sighed Rachel.

'*Romantic?*' squeaked Lisi.

'Mmm. I can't imagine Dave doing something like that—even if he could afford to.'

'But you wouldn't want him to, would you?' asked Lisi, raising her eyebrows in surprise. 'I thought you said that if you never saw him again, it would be much too soon?'

Rachel shrugged and swirled her port around in the glass, so that it looked like a claret-coloured whirlpool. 'I suppose not. It's just that sometimes I get lonely—well, often, actually—and Christmas is the worst. Even if Dave wasn't the most wonderful husband in the world, at least he was *there*. I guess I miss having a man around the place.'

And that was the difference between them, thought Lisi—she had been content enough with her single status. Not that she had been anti-men, or anything like that—she just hadn't particularly missed having a partner. Until she reminded herself that she had never actually *had* a partner.

'I'd better think about making a move,' she said reluctantly, thinking how warm and cosy it was by Rachel's fireside.

Rachel nodded. 'You'll need to change.'

'Will I hell? There's nothing wrong with this dress!'

'Except that Tim has smeared chocolate all over it,' commented Rachel, with a smile.

Lisi looked down at her dress to see several brown, sticky thumbprints! She smiled at her friend. 'We've had a wonderful time today,' she said softly.

'Me, too.'

'Sure you won't come over for a drink later on?'

Rachel pulled a face and giggled. 'And face the daunting Philip Caprice after what you've told me about him? Er, I'll take a rain check, thanks, Lisi!'

Lisi packed up their presents in a carrier bag and wrapped Tim up warmly in his little duffle-coat and the brand-new bobble hat and matching scarf which Santa had brought him. She kissed Rachel and Blaine goodbye and they set off home in the crisp air.

Although it was only just past four, it was already pitch-black and there was a curious silence which had descended over the whole village. But then it *was* Christmas Day. Everyone was inside, making merry with their families—falling asleep after their big lunches, or playing games or watching weepie films on television.

She let them in and thought how cold the house was. Better light a fire. She drew the curtains and knelt in front of the brand-new toy railway track and began to push one of the trucks around it with her finger. 'Choo-choo,' she chanted. 'Choo-choo!'

'*Me*, Mum-mee! Me play with the train!'

She smiled. 'Go on, then, and I'll light the fire.'

She efficiently dealt with the logs and paper until the blaze was spitting and glowing. She put the big fire-guard in front of it, and went into her bedroom to change.

She had just stripped off her dress and was standing in her bra and pants when there was a knock at the front door and she glanced at her watch in horror. He couldn't be here! Not yet. But who else would it be on Christmas afternoon?

Saying a few choice words underneath her breath, she dragged on her dressing gown and opened the front door to find his tall figure dominating her view, blotting out the moon completely. He was carrying presents, but she barely gave them a second glance. Not only had he demanded this visit—he didn't even have the courtesy to be on time!

'You're early!' she accused.

He thought that no woman had the right to look as sexy as that—not when she was wearing an old flannelette dressing gown which had clearly seen better days—but Lisi did. Maybe it was something to do with the fact that he knew only too well what fabulous curves lay beneath its rather shapeless covering. Or because, for once, she had let her hair fall free and unfettered, spilling in abundant ebony streams to her waist. He had only ever seen it loose once before and he felt the blood begin to sing in his veins as he remembered just when.

'And a very happy Christmas to you, too,' he replied sardonically. 'I left my parents slightly ahead of schedule because they predicted snow—'

'Where?' asked Lisi, theatrically peering at the sky and then at the ground. 'I don't see any snow!'

He tried to take into consideration the fact that she had obviously been changing. 'My apologies,' he murmured. 'And now, do you think I can come inside? It's getting pretty chilly standing here.'

She held the door open ungraciously, but as she closed it on the bitter night she reminded herself that she had vowed there would be no unpleasantness. Not in front of Tim. And especially not today, of all days.

Philip lowered his voice. 'Have you told him?'

She bit her lip. 'Not yet.'

He looked at her in disbelief. 'Hell, Lisi—it's been a week!'

She shook her head. 'I just couldn't work out how to do it—it's not something you can come out with very easily and explain to a child of three. ''By the way, darling—you know that strange man who turned up on the doorstep on your birthday? Well, he's your daddy!'''

'There's no need to make it sound so—'

'So like the truth?'

He sighed. 'So when *are* you going to tell him?'

'Not *me*, Philip. Us. You, mainly.'

'*Me?*'

'Yes, you! I'll leave you to do the talking—I'm sure
you'll put it in the most diplomatic way possible.' Hot tears
stung at her eyes and she turned away before he could see
them. 'I just haven't got a clue what to say. *Tim!*' she
called. 'Tim!'

'Is it Faver Chrissmas 'gain?' squeaked a little voice and
Tim came pelting out and almost collided with the tall figure in the hall. He looked up at him with huge aquamarine
eyes.

So like Lisi's eyes, thought Philip. 'Hello,' he said.

'You're Mum-mee's friend!' announced Tim triumphantly.

'That's right! And I've come to have tea with you both—
if that's okay with you?'

'Did Faver Chrissmas bring you lots of presents?'

'Not lots,' said Philip gravely. 'Some.'

'I got lots!'

Philip smiled. 'Do you want to show me?'

Tim nodded excitedly and eyed the brightly wrapped par-
cels in Philip's arms with interest. 'Who are *those* presents
for?' he asked coyly.

Philip laughed. 'They're for you. We'll open them when
Mummy has changed out of her dressing gown.' He shot
Lisi a questioning look and she realised that she had been
standing there just gawping.

'I'll go and get changed.' She nodded, wondering just
how he had always had the knack of seeming to be in
charge!

She shut the bedroom door behind her, her heart thundering just with the knowledge that *he* was here, such a
short distance away, and that she was standing in her underwear and looking at it critically in the mirror.

A functional peach-coloured bra and knickers which

didn't even match—but who cared? She certainly wasn't planning for him to get a glimpse of them.

But you would like him to, wouldn't you? taunted a mischievous voice in her head, and she shook her head at her reflection in the mirror.

She still wanted him, yes—but things were complicated enough as they were. Resuming a physical relationship with him would only add to those. She gave a wry smile as she pulled on a pair of old blue jeans and an ice-blue sweater. Who was she kidding? As if a few short hours in someone's arm could be defined as a relationship.

She raked the brush through her hair, tempted to tie it back—but decided that she couldn't leave him sitting out there waiting for her for much longer, so she left it loose.

She walked back into the sitting room to find that he was playing trains with Tim, and when he looked up his eyes were quietly smouldering.

'Is—everything okay?' she asked.

He steeled himself against the impact of her beauty, and jerked his head towards the roaring fire instead. He stood up and came to stand beside her, lowering his voice into an undertone so that only she could hear. 'Do you usually leave Tim here on his own, while you titillate yourself in the next room?'

For a moment she didn't quite get his drift, and when she did her mouth set itself into a mulish line. So he thought he could walk back into their lives and start criticising her skills as a mother, did he?

'I was hardly titillating,' she answered icily, gesturing to her casual clothes with an angry, jerking motion. 'Just getting changed out of a dress which Tim had liberally smeared with chocolate.'

'Lisi, he was alone in the room with a fire—for heaven's sake! Do you really think that's safe for a three-year-old?'

The injustice of it stung her. 'I'll go and put the kettle

on,' she said, between gritted teeth, and marched out to the
kitchen.

He followed her, as she had known he would, but remained standing in the doorway so that he could keep an
eye on the toddler who was still engrossed in his new train-
set.

He saw the fury in the stiff set of her shoulders. 'Listen.
I wasn't meaning to be judgemental,' he said softly.

She clicked the kettle on and turned round, her eyes spitting pale blue fire. 'Like hell you weren't!'

'I was only just pointing out—'

'Well, don't!' she said, in a low, shaking voice. 'Do you
think I've brought him up in a house which has a fire and
not taught him that he is never to go near it?'

'Listen—'

'No, *you* listen! What do you think it's like as a single
parent living with a little boy? Have you ever stopped to
think about it?'

'Actually, no—but then it wasn't number one on my list
of priorities. Until now.'

She met the quizzical green stare fearlessly. 'Even taking
a bath has to be planned with all the attention you would
give to a military campaign!' she declared. 'As for going
to the bathroom—well, you don't want to know!'

He glanced back towards Tim and then at her again. It
had never occurred to him. Why should it? People rarely
considered the practical problems of child-rearing unless
they were contemplating taking the plunge themselves. He
sighed. 'You're right. I had no right—'

'No, you didn't!' she agreed furiously. 'You have only
to take a look at him to realise that he is a happy, contented
little boy. The world is full of dangers, Philip—and I have
had to teach him about them all. Never to talk to strangers.
Never to approach a dog that might bite him. The fact that
the roads aren't safe—' She saw him flinch, and wished

she hadn't chosen an example which would remind him of Carla. 'I'm sorry.'

He shook his head. 'The cotton-wool remark still holds true. I shouldn't have said what I did.'

'No, you shouldn't!' She pointed to the kitchen cupboards with an air of frustration. 'I've had all these cupboards child-proofed so that he can't get into them. I don't leave bottles of bleach lying around the place for him to find—and there's a stair-gate at the foot of the stairs! Please credit me with a little more sense and caring, Philip! He has had it drummed into him from the word go that fires are dangerous and must be treated with respect and caution—and that Mummy is the only person who touches the fire.'

He watched her warm the pot and then make the tea. He had been lucky in a way, he guessed. She could have been the kind of mother who didn't care—who saw Tim as a mistake who had taken away her youth and her freedom. But she had created a home for him, a warm and loving home, he realised.

She was right. You had only to look at the child to see that he was happy and contented and well cared for. Stimulated, too—to judge from his conversation.

'Can I do anything?' he asked.

She couldn't resist it. 'Better go back in and keep your eye on Tim,' she said sweetly. 'I can manage here.'

He nodded, and his gaze swept over her, beguiling her and capturing her in its intense green light. 'And we'll tell him?'

Lisi swallowed. She couldn't keep putting it off. *They* couldn't keep putting it off. 'I have no choice, do I?' she asked quietly, but noticed that he didn't bother answering that—he didn't need to—just turned away and walked back into the sitting room.

She carried the tea-tray through and brought in Christmas cake and mince pies and slices of Stollen.

Philip looked up as she began to unload it all onto the table and gave a rueful smile. 'Not sure if I can eat again—at least until the New Year.'

She forced herself to be conversational. They were shortly to drop the biggest bombshell into Tim's life—let him see that his mother and his father didn't actually hate one another.

'Did your mother feed you up?'

He nodded. 'It's my first Christmas here for years—in Maraban they don't celebrate it.'

Tim looked up. 'Where's Malaban?' he chirped.

'Maraban,' corrected Philip, and his eyes softened as he looked down at the interested face of his son. 'It's a country in the Middle East. A beautiful land with a great big desert—do you know what a desert is, Tim?'

He shook his dark head, mesmerised.

'It's made of sand—lots of sand—and only the very toughest of plants can grow there.'

'What telse?' asked Tim. 'In Malaban?'

Philip smiled. 'Oh, there are fig trees and wild walnut trees, and the mountain slopes are covered in forests of juniper and pistachio trees—'

'What's st-stachio tree?' piped up Tim. 'Like an apple tree?'

Philip shook his head. 'Not really. A pistachio is a nut,' he explained. 'A delicious pale green nut in a little shell—'

'He's too young for nuts!' put in Lisi immediately.

He guessed that he deserved that, and nodded. 'Oh, and there are lots of animals there, too,' he said. 'Jackals and wild boar and rare, pink deer.'

Tim's eyes were like saucers, thought Lisi. He probably thought that Philip was concocting a wonderful fairy-tale land, and, come to think of it, that was exactly what it sounded like.

'Do you live there?' asked Tim.

'I did. But not any more.'

'Why?'

'Because it was time for me to come back to England.'

'Why?'

'Tim—' began Lisi, but Philip shook his head.

'I used to work for a prince.'

Lisi looked at Tim—now he really *did* think that this was a story!

'A *real* prince?'

'Uh-huh. Prince Khalim. Only the prince got married and so it was time for me to move on.'

Tim nodded solemnly. 'Will you play trains with me?'

He met her eyes across the room. *Now*, they urged her, and Lisi knew that she must begin this particular story. She took time pouring tea, and gave Tim a beaker of juice, and then she went to sit down on the floor next to both of them and cleared her throat.

'Tim, darling?'

A train was chugged along the track by a small, chubby finger.

'Tim? Look at Mummy, darling.'

His long-lashed eyes locked on hers and she felt the almost painfully overwhelming love of motherhood. She steadied her breathing. 'Do you remember that once you asked me why you hadn't got a daddy?'

Philip stilled as Tim nodded.

'And I told you that he had gone away a long time ago and that I wasn't sure if he was ever coming back?'

Again Tim nodded, but this time Philip flinched.

'Well…' She hesitated, but in her heart she knew that there was no way to say this other than using clear and truthful words which a three-year-old would understand. 'Well, he did come back, darling and…'

Tim was staring up at Philip. 'Are *you* my daddy?'

He felt the prick of tears at the back of his eyes as he nodded. 'Yes, Tim,' he answered, his voice thickening. 'I am.'

Tim nodded, and bent his head to push the train around the track once more.

'Tim?' questioned Lisi tentatively, because she couldn't see the expression on his face, and when he lifted it it was unusually calm and accepting, as if he were told things like this every day of the week.

'An' are you going 'way again? To Malaban?' he asked casually, as if it didn't really matter, but Lisi could tell from that oddly fierce look of concentration on his little face that it did.

Philip shook his head, unable to speak for a moment. 'No, Tim,' he said eventually. 'I'm not going anywhere. I'm going to buy a house in the village and see you as many weekends as your mummy will let me.'

He met her gaze with a question in his eyes.

So if I don't let him, then I'm the big, bad witch, she thought bitterly.

'An' are you and Mummy getting married?'

The silence which greeted this remark made Lisi as uncomfortable as she had ever felt in her life. She shook her head. 'Oh, no, darling—nothing like that!'

'Why?'

Oh, *why* had she brought him up to be so alert and questioning? To pursue every subject until he was satisfied with the answers?

'Because not all mummies and daddies live together, now, do they?' she asked gently. 'Blaine's daddy doesn't live with Blaine's mummy any more, does he?'

'That's 'cos he's livin' with a witch!'

'A *witch*?' squeaked Lisi in confusion.

'That's what Blaine heard his Mum-mee say!'

Philip bit back a smile. He suspected that the word had been 'bitch'. 'I would like to get to know you a little better, if that's okay with you, Tim. And Mummy and I will be great friends, won't we, Lisi?'

'Oh, yes,' she agreed, but her eyes flashed him a different message entirely. 'Definitely.'

'So what have you got to say to all that?' asked Philip, and, unable to resist it for any longer, reached out his hand to ruffle the silky blackness of the little head.

Tim put his train down and looked up at her. 'Can I have more chocolate, Mum-mee?' he asked.

The question shattered the tension in the atmosphere, and Philip and Lisi both burst out laughing, their eyes colliding in a brief expression of shared joy that made her heart thunder beneath her breast. It's just relief, she told herself fiercely—nothing to do with her. Tim has accepted him, and he's got what he wanted.

Though she wouldn't have been human if she hadn't half hoped that he wouldn't.

She put more logs on the fire and then watched while Philip wholeheartedly entered into playing with Tim. For a man with little or no experience of children, she was forced to the conclusion that he was very good with them. If Tim's reaction was anything to go by.

He stared wide-eyed while Philip made a horse out of some balloons and then blew up some others and let the air whizz out of them in a sound which had Tim collapsing in peals of giggles.

She had taken all the remains of the tea back out to the kitchen, and when she returned it was to find them playing rough and tumble on the rug and she realised that there were some things that fathers could do, which mothers never could.

They both looked up as she walked in, both flushed with pleasure but tinged with a kind of guilt—identical expressions on their faces. How could I ever have thought that they weren't alike? thought Lisi with a touch of despair. The colouring might be hers, but Marian was right: he *did* have bits of Philip—lots of Philip—in him. Of course he did.

Gently, Philip lowered Tim back down onto the carpet, from where he had been sitting on his shoulders, and stood up.

'Am I interrupting your routine, Lisi?'

So I am the bringer of routine and order, and he provides the fun, does he? thought Lisi. Or was she being unfair?

Philip saw the look of discomfort which had pleated her brow and understood exactly what had caused it. She had agreed to let him get to know Tim, but she had probably not anticipated what a success it would be.

Neither had he.

A different child might have refused to answer him. Or spoken in sulky monosyllables. Not chatted so openly and with such obvious interest. And much of that must be down to her.

'It's your bathtime, Tim,' she said, with a quick glance at her watch, and then forced herself to meet Philip's gaze. 'Unless you'd like to?'

He would like to. He wanted to bath his son more than he had wanted anything in a long time, but he recognised that Lisi might now be feeling the outsider. He shook his head. 'No, you do it. He's used to you.'

'Philip do it!' demanded Tim, unwilling to lose sight of his new friend.

Philip shook his head. 'I have to make a few phone calls,' he said.

She carried Tim to the bathroom and wondered who he was phoning on Christmas Day. Obviously somebody very close to him. He had told her that he wasn't married—but that didn't preclude a girlfriend, did it?

But he kissed you, a voice reminded her. He kissed you passionately and told you that he still wanted you—would he betray a second woman if he got the opportunity?

He isn't going to *get* the opportunity, she told herself as she squirted bubble bath into the running water and watched it become big, foamy clouds. No matter how much *she* wanted to—it wasn't right. There was too much bitter history behind them and only potential heartache lay ahead if she was crazy enough to give in.

She let Tim splash around in the bath for ages, wondering whether Philip would stick around. He might just get the message and go. But he was still there, talking in a low voice into his mobile phone as she carried a sleepy, pyjama-clad Tim past the sitting room to his bedroom and tenderly put him into bed.

'Have you had a lovely Christmas, darling?' she asked him softly.

'Yes, Mum-mee.' His eyes opened wide. 'Is Philip coming tomorrow?'

She sincerely hoped not, but she made herself smile a placating smile. 'We'll see. Okay?'

He nodded against the pillow, letting his eyelids drift down, and then automatically stuck his thumb in his mouth.

He was almost asleep, but story-telling was sacrosanct and Lisi put her hand out and pulled out the nearest book, which just happened to be *Cinderella*. How very appropriate, she thought wryly, and began to read.

She waited until she was certain that he was sound asleep, then reluctantly made her way back to where Philip lay sprawled on the floor in front of the fire, his phone-call finished. He had, she noted with surprise, put all the toys neatly away, so that the room for once didn't look as though a bomb had hit it. She had never had anyone do that for her before.

She hovered in the doorway, unsure of what to say or do. She could hardly ask him to leave. 'Can I get you a drink of something?'

He heard the lack of enthusiasm in her voice. 'One for the road?' he suggested sardonically.

She shrugged. 'If you like.'

He shook his head, got to his feet and went over to where she stood. 'No, thanks. You must be tired.'

Again she had the sense of him dominating the room, of his raw masculinity exuding from every pore of that spectacular body. In an effort to distract herself, she said, rather awkwardly, 'It went well, I think, didn't it?'

'Yes.' He was aching to touch her, but he realised that he owed her something. 'Thank you, Lisi,' he said simply. 'For letting me.'

She wasn't going to read anything into what he said. This was a purely practical arrangement, solely for the welfare of Tim. 'I had no choice, did I?' she questioned tartly. 'I imagine that if I'd refused you would have sought some kind of legal redress.'

Her brittle words extinguished the warmth he had been feeling, but did absolutely nothing to put out the fire in his groin. He knew he shouldn't do this, but something drove him on—a need to see that cold, frozen look wiped clean off her beautiful face.

He reached his hand out to cup her chin, his thumb and his forefinger stroking along its outline almost reflectively.

Lisi shivered. Where he touched her, he set her on fire. She knew that she should move away but something was stopping her and she wasn't sure what. 'Please don't,' she whispered.

Her lacklustre words belied the shining darkness in her

eyes and the need to kiss her overpowered him. 'You want me to,' he whispered back.

'No—'

But he kissed the word away with his mouth, feeling its unresisting softness become as hard and as urgent as his.

She rocked against him—all the cold and the hunger and frustration she had experienced letting itself go as his mouth explored hers with a thoroughness guaranteed to set her on the path to inevitable seduction. She felt the prickling sensation as her breasts grew heavy and aroused, and a long-forgotten molten sweetness began to build up at the very core of her.

Her mind was spinning. She wanted to burrow her hands up beneath his sweater and to feel the warm bare silk of his skin once more, but she had been a mother for too long to let her own wishes be paramount. For one split-second she imagined what could—*would*—happen next, if she didn't put a stop to it.

They couldn't possibly let things progress naturally and make love in front of the fire—Tim might walk in at any second. Which left going to her bedroom and the embarrassment of silently getting undressed, of having to keep their voices—and moans—low, just in case they woke Tim.

She tore herself away.

What was she *thinking* of? She didn't want to make love to him!

He had never been so frustrated in his life. 'Lisi—'

'No!' She shook her head vehemently. 'I am *not* going to have sex with you, Philip. The first time was bad enough—'

'I beg to differ,' he murmured, thinking how magnificent she looked when she was angry.

She carried on as if he hadn't interrupted. 'When I discovered you were married I felt like hell—but at least I thought that you had been so overcome with desire that you had been unable to stop yourself. Desire for *me*,' she finished deliberately.

His eyes narrowed as he tried to work out exactly what she was getting at. 'I'm not sure that I understand you, Lisi.'

'It didn't even have to be me, did it? I was just a vessel for your more basic needs!' she carried on wildly. 'Anyone would have done! Your wife was sick and you were frustrated—that's what really happened, isn't it, Philip?'

He went rigid. 'My God,' he said, in disgust. 'You really know how to twist the knife, don't you?' He picked up his overcoat and walked to the front door and opened it without another word.

She wanted to call after him, to take back the hateful words which had seemed to come pouring out of her mouth like poison, but one look at the icy expression on his face as he turned round made her realise that it would be a futile gesture.

He gave a cold, hard smile. 'If your idea was to insult me so much that I would go away and never come back again, then you have just very nearly succeeded,' he said.

And, bizarrely, the thought that her hurt pride and resentment might have cost Tim a relationship with his father wounded her far more than anything else. 'Philip—'

He shook his head. 'Please don't say any more—I don't think I could take it. I'd better just tell you that this particular campaign won't work. You see, Tim is far more important to me than the obvious loathing you feel for me. I'm here, Lisi—and I'm here for the duration. Better get used to it.'

And without another word, he was gone.

CHAPTER NINE

MARIAN Reece pursed her lips together in a silent whistle. 'Good heavens—just how much do you think he's spending on that property?'

Lisi looked up from her computer, and, lo and behold— another upmarket van was cruising past the office towards The Old Rectory. What was it this time? Lisi peered out of the window and read from the gold lettering on the side of the van. 'Tricia Brady; Superior Interiors'. 'He's obviously having the place decorated now,' she said, with a sigh.

Marian's eyes goggled. 'And how!' she exclaimed. 'I've heard of her—she must have come all the way down from London. This early in the New Year, too—I'm surprised she wasn't fully booked.'

'She probably was,' said Lisi gloomily. 'She's probably got long blonde hair and legs up to her armpits and Philip probably just outrageously batted those beautiful eyes at her and she probably cancelled every engagement in her diary!'

Marian gave her a shrewd look. 'Do I detect a sign of the green-eyed monster?' she asked.

Lisi replaced the gloomy look with a fairly good impression of devil-may-care. 'Not at all,' she said airily. 'I expect that's exactly what happened. Either that or he's paying well over the odds.'

'He must be,' said Marian. 'It's only the middle of January—and already he's transformed the place! I've never known builders be quite so willing, or so efficient!'

'No,' said Lisi tonelessly.

Marian shot her a glance. 'How's it going between you two?'

'It's not between *us* two,' replied Lisi carefully. 'The only relationship I have with Philip is that we happen to share a child.'

'Only?' spluttered Marian, then sighed. 'And is it…amicable?'

Lisi sighed. She had vowed to keep it that way, but ever since her outburst on Christmas night he had been keeping his distance from her. He had been round three times to see Tim, and the atmosphere had been awkward, to say the least.

For a start, the house always seemed so much smaller when he was in it, and the unspoken tension between them was so strong that Lisi was surprised that Tim wasn't made uncomfortable by it.

But no. Tim didn't seem to notice anything or anyone— he was so enraptured by the man he had almost immediately taken to calling 'Daddy'.

The first time he'd done it, Lisi had spoken to him gently at bedtime that night. 'You don't have to say Daddy if you don't want to,' she suggested gently. 'Philip won't mind being called just Philip, I'm sure.'

He didn't answer and she wasn't even sure if he had registered her words or not, but he obviously had, because at the end of Saturday's visit Philip paused on his way out of the front door, his eyes spitting with undisguised rage.

'Did you tell Tim not to call me Daddy?' he demanded.

She sighed. 'That's not what I said at all.'

'That's what he told me!'

She kept her voice low, tried to stay calm, though heaven only knew—it wasn't easy. 'I merely suggested that he might find it easier to call you Philip. For the time being—'

'Until *you* decided that the time was right, I suppose?'

he questioned witheringly. 'And when would that be, Lisi? Some time? Never?'

She stuck to her guns. She was not going to let his hostility get to her. *She was not.* 'I just didn't want him to feel that he was being railroaded into anything—'

'By me?'

'Not by anyone!' she retorted, her voice rising. 'It's just such a huge thing to suddenly start calling you Daddy!'

He had moved a little closer, his body language just short of menacing—so how come she didn't feel in the least bit intimidated by it? How come she wanted to tell him to forget their stupid rows and to kiss her like he had done on Christmas night?

'Or is it just that *you* feel threatened by it, Lisi?'

'Threatened? Me?'

'Yes, you! Unwilling to share him, are you? Do you want all his love for yourself, is that it?'

'Oh, don't talk such rubbish!' she snapped. 'I was thinking of *Tim*!'

'So you claim. When it would clearly suit you far more to have me as far away from you as possible! Well, just don't use him as a pawn in our little disagreement—do you understand, Lisi!'

Little disagreement? If this was his idea of a little disagreement, then she'd hate to enter into all-out warfare with him!

Marian was still staring at her with a question in her eyes, and Lisi shook her head.

'No,' she said slowly, in answer to her boss's question. 'It isn't exactly what I'd call amicable—even though that's what we both wanted originally.'

'You should talk to him about it!' urged Marian.

But there didn't seem anything left to say, thought Lisi as she picked up the telephone which had just begun to ring. 'Good afternoon, Homefinders Agency.'

'Lisi? It's Philip.'

Of course it was Philip—no one else had a voice that rich, that deep, that dark. 'Hello, Philip,' she said, cursing her body's reaction as she felt the inevitable prickle of excitement. 'What can I do for you?'

Silently, he cursed. How shocked she would be if he answered that question truthfully.

'I'm up at the house,' he said.

'Here?' she questioned stupidly, her heart racing. 'In the village?'

'Yeah. I drove up early this morning.'

He was here, just down the road and he hadn't even bothered to tell her he was coming. Just why that should hurt so much she didn't know, but it did.

'I'm having the house decorated,' he was saying. 'Someone is over here now with some sample fabrics.'

She certainly wasn't going to pander to his ego by telling him that she had seen the plush van driving by. 'Really?' she asked pleasantly.

'Really,' he echoed, mocking her insincere tone. 'And I wondered whether you were free for half an hour?'

Her pulse began to race. 'Why?'

She could be so damned abrupt, he thought. 'I didn't know if you wanted to choose some colours for Tim's room.'

Time stopped. He seemed to be speaking in some strange, terrible language. 'T-Tim's room?' she croaked.

Something in the way she said it made him want to offer reassurance, until he remembered her monstrous accusation on Christmas night, and he hardened his heart against the tremor in her voice. Did she think that *he* didn't have feelings, too?

'That's right. He will *need* his own room, Lisi—surely you realise that?'

The only thing she realised was that she was fighting to

control her breath. 'I have to discuss this with you, and we can't do it on the phone,' she said.

'Then come up to the house.'

'I'm working.'

'Doesn't Marian owe you a few hours? For your un-scheduled work when I demanded that you show me around the rectory?'

'I'll ask her,' she said, in a low voice. 'I can't promise anything.'

His voice sounded noncommittal. 'Suit yourself. It's up to you, Lisi—you're the one who wants to talk.'

She put the phone down, feeling close to tears, and saw Marian looking at her with concern.

'Philip?' she asked.

'How did you guess?'

'Normal clients don't usually leave the agent looking as though the bottom has just fallen out of their world.'

Maybe it just had. Lisi cleared her throat. 'Marian—would it be possible to take an hour off? I need to talk to Philip and he's up at the rectory.'

'Of course it would.' Marian hesitated. 'Listen, my dear—have you thought about consulting a lawyer?'

Lisi shook her head. 'There's no point—it would achieve precisely nothing. He isn't being unreasonable. Tim adores him. He's his father—by law he is *allowed* contact. It's just me who has the problem with it.'

Marian nodded. 'Take as long as you need.'

Lisi gathered up her coat and wrapped herself up in it, but once outside it seemed to offer little protection against the bitter wind, although maybe it was the bitter heartache which was making her teeth chatter.

She trudged up the lane to The Old Rectory, and for a moment she stood stock-still with amazement, for she had seen the comings and goings of various vans and contractors, but had deliberately stayed away from the place, telling herself that it would be too traumatic to see her former home being completely changed.

But her amazement was tinged with admiration, because, whatever Philip was doing inside the house, on the outside, at least—his taste could not be faulted.

The exterior had been painted a cool, pale grey and all the mildew had been removed. Window frames were gleaming, as was the newly painted front door, and the garden had obviously been lovingly attacked by experts.

The front door was slightly ajar, and when she received no reply to her knock she pushed it open and walked into the hall where another shock awaited her. The walls were a deep, vibrant scarlet—red as holly berries—and the floorboards gleaming, with an exquisite long, silk runner in shades of deepest cobalt and scarlet and jade.

It looked utterly beautiful, she thought, and a lump rose in her throat as she called.

'Hello?'

'Hello, Lisi,' came a voice from upstairs. 'Come on up— we're up here.'

We? And then she remembered the interior design van.

With reluctant feet she made her way slowly upstairs in the direction of the voices she could hear speaking and laughing, and she felt a wave of objection that he should feel happy enough to laugh while her world seemed to be caving in.

To her horror, the voices were coming from the direction of a room she knew only too well—her old childhood bedroom—and her heart sank even further. Had he known, or guessed, she wondered, or was it simply coincidence which had made Philip select that particular room for Tim?

Drawing a deep breath, she walked straight in, and then stopped.

Two heads were bent close over a swatch of fabrics— one dark and nut-brown, the other blonde, and Lisi almost gave a hollow laugh. She had imagined Tricia Brady to be blonde with legs up to her armpits, and in that she had been uncannily accurate—but she had imagined the blonde hair to have come out of a bottle and for an aging face to be caked in heavy make-up.

But this woman fulfilled none of those criteria.

Her shiny blonde hair was fair and pale and completely natural, and when she lifted her head at the sound of Lisi's footsteps she didn't appear to be wearing any make-up at all. But then she didn't need to—skin that flawless and china-blue eyes that saucer-like did not need any help from nature to enhance them.

She was dressed practically and yet stunningly—in a pair of butter-soft suede trousers which must have cost what Lisi earned in a month. A cream silk shirt and a sheepskin-lined waistcoat completed the look and Lisi shuddered to think what her off-the-peg department store workaday suit must look like in comparison.

Philip smiled, but the expression on his face was as cool as it had been since Christmas. 'Lisi, hi,' he said. 'This is Tricia Brady—she's helping me with decor for the house.'

She's helping me. It didn't sound like a strictly working relationship, did it? thought Lisi indignantly. He could have said, Tricia is the designer, or, Tricia is working for me.

'Hello,' she said, thinking how wooden her voice sounded. 'I'm pleased to meet you.'

'Me, too.' Tricia grinned. 'I would shake hands, but my fingers are freezing—I keep telling Philip to turn the heating up, but he won't listen!'

'That's because people tend to go to sleep if it's too warm. Not good—but especially not good for people who are working,' he responded drily, but flashed her an answering smile.

Lisi felt sick, but she guessed that this was something she was going to have to get used to. If it wasn't Tricia it would be someone else. Some beautiful, expensively dressed woman who would temporarily or permanently share Philip's life one day.

And become a surrogate mother to Tim while he was here, she reminded herself, gritting her teeth behind a smile which pride forced her to make.

'Lisi is the mother of my son,' explained Philip. 'And so I thought she could give us some input on colours and fabrics.'

It was the coldest and most distancing description he could have given her—and yet, when she thought about it, how else could he have put it? She wasn't his girlfriend—current *or past*.

Pulling herself together, she walked over and looked down at the swatch of fabrics which Tricia was still holding. 'May I?' she asked pleasantly, and Tricia handed it to her.

She pretended to lose herself in them, though her mind was only half on the task—but she had spotted immediately the one which Tim would like the most.

'This one,' and she jabbed at the brightly coloured piece of material which depicted Mickey Mouse dancing all over it.

'Lisi likes Disney,' Philip explained with a smile, thinking how jerky and unnatural her movements were. 'She always has done, haven't you, Lisi?'

He was remembering her birthday cake, and so was she. That innocent start to a supposed friendship which had brought so much heartache in its wake. She nodded. 'Wh-what colour are you planning to do the walls?'

Tricia peered down at the fabric and pointed a perfect fingernail at several of the colours. 'We could pick out one of these shades,' she suggested and turned her head. 'What do you think, Phil?'

Phil?

Phil?

Lisi wanted to scream and to demand what right she had to call him by a nickname that *she* had never heard used before, but there was absolutely no point at all. Tricia could call him anything she liked, and probably did—in bed at night when he was making mad, passionate love to her.

'I like the...I like the yellow.' She swallowed.

'Mmm!' Tricia smiled. 'Perfect! Sunny and positive— and with all that glorious light flooding in—' She waved an expansive arm at the window. 'The room will look irresistible!' She shot a look at Philip, and her eyes glimmered. 'We could do it in the same colour as your London dining room, in fact—or would you rather something different down here?'

'Something a touch brighter, perhaps?' he murmured as Lisi turned abruptly away.

So Tricia had decorated his other home, too, had she? That was a pretty big compliment to pay a woman, no matter that she was being paid for her skills. To be selected to choose paints and fabrics for a man as discerning as Philip must mean that he rated her very highly indeed.

Lisi walked over to the window and looked out, the way she had done countless times before, as a child. She used to sit on the ledge for hours and watch the change as each new season came upon the garden, though she could never remember a scene so bare and unforgiving as the one which lay outside today.

'Shall we tackle the main bedroom today?' Tricia was asking.

Philip was watching Lisi and saw the way that her body had stiffened and some pernicious devil made him want to take Tricia up on her offer, but he decided against it.

'Not today, thanks, Trish,' he said casually. 'I have a few things I need to discuss with Lisi.'

'Oh. Okay. Well, call me later, if you like, and we'll sort out what needs doing. Nice to have met you, Lisi!'

Lisi turned around, wishing that her features would stop feeling as if they were made out of stone. 'Nice to have met you, too,' she managed.

There was silence in the room while Tricia gathered up her samples and put them all in a soft leather case, then she stood on tiptoe and kissed first Philip's right cheek, and then his left.

'See ya!' She smiled. 'I'll let myself out.'

'I'll call you,' he promised.

Lisi studied the floorboards with intense interest and not a word was spoken as they heard Tricia running down the stairs and the front door slamming behind her.

'Lisi?' he questioned softly.

She lifted her eyes to find herself imprisoned in a cool green gaze and her cheeks flooded with heat as she gave into the unwelcome but inevitable.

I want him, she thought suddenly, and the tip of her tongue flicked out to lick at the sudden unbearable dryness of her lips. I always have and I always will—and I can't bear the thought of anyone else having him. If he still wants me—if—then who on earth am I benefitting by turning him down? He is tied to me through Tim, she told herself with a fierce, primitive feeling of possession—and he will always be tied to me.

Now what was she playing at? he wondered. Why was she giving him that flushed and glittering look as though she wanted him to go and take her in his arms—especially as she had made so clear on Christmas night that physical closeness was the very last thing on her mind. Damn her, he thought, feeling his body immediately reacting to what looked like an unmistakable invitation in her eyes.

She didn't break the stare, just carried on looking at him, feeling her body begin to flower with need as his eyes darkened and then narrowed in a slowly dawning comprehension.

'Lisi?' he said again, only now his voice had thickened to honey. 'What the hell do you think you're doing?'

She wasn't going to play games; there was no time for games, and even if there were—wouldn't games be totally inappropriate between a couple who had been through what they had been through?

She moistened her lips again and saw the dull flush of awareness arrow up the carved cheekbones. 'Is Tricia *just* your designer?' she asked.

Her question told him everything. She was jealous. *Jealous!* He felt the heady flood of triumph as he realised that now he had her exactly where he wanted her.

'And if she is?'

The instant denial she had been preying for had not materialised, but his ambiguous question did nothing but fuel the fire which was slowly building inside her.

'Yes, or no?'

'What's it to you, Lisi? Don't you like me having women friends?'

'No!' The word shot out all by itself before she could stop it.

He could see the tension building in her—he would build it and build it until it all came rushing out and she would be unable to stop it. His question was silky. 'Why not?'

Damn him! Was he going to make her beg? She wanted him, yes, but she would never, ever beg. Her breathing was so shallow and erratic that she could barely get the words out. 'You know why not.'

Oh, yes, he knew. He could tell just by looking at her. She shouldn't be able to appear so damned sexy—not in that dull, chain-store suit with her hair scraped right back off her face. Some men might have been turned on by Tricia's blonde, pampered perfection—but he wanted this complex, beguiling woman who could not disguise the hunger in her eyes.

'Come here,' he ordered softly.

Pride forgotten, she went to him, staring up at him with wide eyes, praying for him to take the next step and to pull her into his arms. But he did not touch her. Not straight away. His eyes were mocking her and enchanting her, his lips curved into a predatory smile.

'What do you want, Lisi? Tell me.'

Peace of mind, that was what she wanted—and she suspected that she would never get it with Philip Caprice in her life, in whatever capacity. She tipped her head to one side and wondered whether she could break *him*.

'Don't you know?' she responded shakily.

Something snapped inside him as he realised that he had wasted enough time. Tease her too much and she might just turn on her high heels and walk right out of here and he might never get another opportunity to discover whether she was as dynamic as he remembered, or whether time had distorted the memory and made it into something it wasn't.

He reached to her hair and removed the restraining clip and her hair tumbled free. 'Beautiful,' he murmured unsteadily as he pulled her into his arms and bent his head and she could feel his hot breath on her face.

'Are you jealous, Lisi?' he taunted. 'Jealous of Tricia?'

Jealous of every woman who might end up in his arms like this. 'Yes,' she whispered.

His laugh was a low sound of victory as he bent his mouth to hers, teasing it open with the elusive flicker of his tongue, and Lisi closed her eyes and gave into it, snaking her hands up to the broad shoulders as he levered her up close to him.

He could feel her breasts pushing against him—their fullness growing by the second—and something primal ex-

ploded inside him in a ferment of desire so blisteringly hot
that he shuddered in its power, scarcely aware of his actions
as he began to feverishly unbutton her suit jacket.

She knew exactly what he was doing, and that she ought
to stop him, that they shouldn't be doing this now, here,
but the moment his hand cupped at her breast Lisi knew
she was lost.

'Philip,' she cried.

Through the mists of wanting, her broken little cry pen-
etrated. 'What?'

She shook her head. 'Philip, Philip, Philip,' she said,
over and over again, and his name tasted as delicious as
the warm lips which were plundering hers so expertly, so
that she felt as if she were drowning in sheer forbidden
pleasure.

He pushed the jacket from her shoulders and it fell to
the floor, and then he unbuttoned her white blouse and
sucked in a shivering breath as he looked down at her
breasts. Rich, ripe breasts, covered by some washed-out
looking bra which had clearly seen better days. But none
of that mattered, not when each tight little bud was so
clearly defined.

With a small moan he reached his hand round her back
and unclipped the bra in a fluid gesture until it dropped
redundantly to join the jacket, and her breasts were free.

She jerked her head back with a moan as she felt the
first hot lick of his tongue teasing each nipple into near-
painful awareness. He was unbuttoning her skirt now and
sliding the zip down and she wanted him to, couldn't wait
for him to touch her where she so squirmingly needed to
be touched. The room was cool, but all she could feel was
the heat of his hands and his mouth as they trailed paths
of delight over the skin he was swiftly uncovering.

She was down to her panties and tights now, and Philip
pulled impatiently at his belt, silently groaning at the nec-

essary delay of getting free from this damned clothing. Her
fingers were scrabbling at his sweater and he momentarily
moved away from her so that he could haul it over his head,
and pulled her back again so that her breasts nudged so
enchantingly against his bare chest.

She was clumsily jerking at the zip now and he shook
his head, stilling her hand and moving it away while he
dealt with it, because he was so aroused that it needed a
man's hand to protect his straining hardness.

Shoes and socks and boxers were kicked and pulled off
and he unceremoniously hoicked her tights and panties off
before tossing them disdainfully into the corner. 'I'm going
to buy you stockings,' he promised unsteadily. 'From now
on you will wear nothing but stockings!'

She neither knew nor cared what he was intending to do,
apart from what lay in the immediate future.

'Are you still on the pill?' he was demanding.

She shook her head. 'Not any more.'

He grabbed his trousers and pulled a pack of condoms
out, thanking some merciful hand which had guided him to
buy some. 'I'd like you to slide this on for me, Lisi,' he
whispered as he ripped open the foil. 'Come on. Put it on
for me.'

She glanced down, and swallowed. She couldn't, not this
first time—it was too daunting, too intimate. 'You do it,'
she whispered back.

She felt him sliding the condom on, then heard him
swear softly, and when she opened her eyes to see what
was the matter he was glowering down at the bare floorboards with a look of disgust on his face.

'There's no bloody bed in the house yet!' he groaned,
and swiftly picked her up to carry her to the other side of
the room, out of view of the window.

'Wh-what are you doing?' She gasped as he leaned her

back against the wall and lifted her up, positioning her legs around his naked waist.

'What do you think I'm doing?' he ground out. His fingers moved down to find her slick and ready and he uttered silent thanks because he felt as if he would go insane unless he…he…

'Oh, Philip,' she sobbed as his great strength thrust into her, and she thought that nothing could ever feel this good, or this right. 'Philip,' she said again, on a long-drawn-out shudder.

Her pleasure only intensified his. He had never had to fight to maintain control quite so much as he moved inside her, watching her face as it bloomed, feeling her hot tightness encasing him in a moist, exquisite sheath.

He sought to distract himself with words rather than sensation. 'Tell me how it feels,' he urged throatily.

How to describe paradise in a sentence? she despaired with another helpless moan as he cupped her buttocks and thrust into her even deeper.

'Tell me!' he commanded.

'It's…it's…'

'It's what, Lisi?' he prompted, his voice a silken caress.

It's Philip, the father of my child, she thought as the unbelievable waves of orgasm crept unexpectedly upon her, sweeping her up in their swell, rocking her until she was left shuddering and weak, her tears spilling down like rain onto his shoulder.

Her tears confused him, acted as a temporary deterrent to his own fulfilment. For a second he almost wanted to lift her head and dry her tears away, demand that she tell him what had made her cry like that, but his own orgasm was too strong to be denied. Even as he began to frame the question he felt himself caught in its inexorable path, and he drove into her, pulled her closer still until his seed spilled out, and he was rocked with the force of it all.

Seconds—minutes?—later, he kissed the top of her head and felt her shiver.

'You're cold,' he observed. 'Better get dressed.'

So that was it. Wild and passionate sex up against the wall and all he could talk about was the temperature of the room.

Reminding herself that she had wanted it as much—if not more—than him, Lisi nodded and snuggled against his chest for one last precious moment of physical closeness, listening to the muffled thunder of his heart as it began to slow.

He could have stayed like this all day. Still inside her, with her naked body locked so indulgently around his and her hair spilling all over him—making everything black where it touched. He felt himself begin to stir again and knew that, if one of them did not begin to make an effort to get dressed, he would grow inside her to fill her again, and want to make love with the same sweet abandon as before.

'You acted like you really needed that,' he observed in a whisper.

She lifted her eyes to his and suddenly thought—tell him. Why not? 'It's...it's been a long time,' she admitted.

'How long?' he demanded, though his body tensed as it prepared itself for the stab of jealousy.

'Since that night with you,' she answered slowly and heard him suck in a disbelieving breath.

His eyes narrowed. 'Honestly?'

'There's no reason for me to lie, Philip.'

'I'm flattered,' he murmured.

Ridiculously disappointed by his reaction, she let her feet slide slowly to the ground. 'I have to get back to work,' she said.

He thought how matter-of-fact she sounded—still, if that was the way she wanted to play it, it was fine by him. At least there were to be no hypocritical words of love and affection, which neither of them would mean. 'There's hot water,' he offered. 'If you want to take a shower?'

Lisi blushed. She hadn't thought that she would have to go back all sticky and redolent of the scent of their sex—but she wouldn't, not really. Unlike last time, he had used a condom.

'Use the bathroom off the main bedroom,' he suggested. 'It's—'

'I know where it is, thank you, Philip,' she said impatiently, shaking her head. 'I used to live here, remember?' And then *she* remembered just which room they were in.

He felt her tense. 'What's the matter?'

She bit her lip as she reached for her underwear. 'This used to be *my* room,' she moaned. 'And soon it will be Tim's, and we've just…just…'

'Just had sex in it?'

Lisi turned away before he could see her face. He could not have termed it in a more insulting way. 'Yes,' she said tonelessly, and suddenly the desire and the passion which had made her want him so very badly—seemed like the worst idea she had ever had in her life.

'Lisi?'

Despairing at the hope which leapt up inside her, she turned around again. 'What?'

'Here!' He threw over her blouse and noted that she caught it like an athlete. 'There's nothing wrong with what we just did,' he said softly. 'It's as natural and as old as time. So what if it *is* going to be Tim's room—how can what we just did in here possibly harm him? It's how he got here in the first place, after all!'

'I don't need you to give me a basic lesson in sex education,' she said crossly, pulling her skirt up over her hips and zipping it up.

No, she certainly didn't. He had never met a woman so

free and generous in her love-making before. Still slightly reeling from learning that there had been no other lover, he came over and began to button up her blouse for her, tempted to lay the flat of his hands over the magnificent thrust of her breasts, but her unsmiling face told him not to bother trying.

'What's the matter?' he asked quietly. 'Are you regretting what just happened?'

There was no reason to be anything other than truthful—not now. Too much water had passed underneath the bridge for coyness or prevarication.

'A little. Aren't you?'

He shrugged as he slipped his shoes on. 'There's no point in feeling regret—you know it was inevitable.'

'I don't understand.'

'I think you do.' His eyes pierced her with their green light. 'Don't you think we *needed* that? To get rid of some of the tension between us?'

'You make it sound so...so...'

'So what, Lisi?''

'So *functional*.' She shuddered.

'Sometimes sex is. We were always going to have trouble creating the candlelight and roses scene, weren't we—what with Tim being around and your obvious low opinion of me?' He picked up his jacket. 'So what happened to make you change your mind about hating me? Was it purely jealousy—because you thought that I had something going with Tricia?'

'And do you?' she asked boldly. 'You never did answer that.'

The question angered him. 'You really think I would have just had sex with you, if I was involved with Tricia?'

She wanted to say that he had done once before, except that now she was beginning to look at that night differently. Could a man who was married to a woman who lay in a deep coma be considered married in the true sense of the word? She looked at him and shook her head, some bone-deep certainty giving her an answer she had not expected. 'No,' she said quietly. 'I don't.'

He expelled a long, pent-up sigh. 'Well, thanks for that, at least.'

'I have to go.' She straightened her jacket and at that moment felt almost close to him, though maybe that was just nature's way of justifying what they had just been do-ing. But she plucked up the courage to ask another ques-tion, one which had been praying on her mind for much longer. 'Philip?'

He narrowed his eyes. 'What?'

'What made you make love to me?' She saw the gleam in his eyes and hastily shook her head. 'No, not this time— last time. When you didn't really…know me…nor I you. Was it just lust? Me being in the wrong place at the wrong time?'

For a long time he had thought that it was simply lust— but if that were the case, then why hadn't he followed up one of the countless other invitations which had come his way? He remembered what Khalim had said, but then Khalim was a born romantic. He shook his head, knowing that he owed her his honesty. 'That's just it, Lisi—I don't know.'

It was not the answer she had wanted—but it was better than nothing.

'Listen,' he said, and she prayed for some sweetener, something to tell her that she wasn't just Lisi-the-body, but Lisi a woman who was entitled to a modicum of respect.

'What?'

'Can I come to the nursery with you later, when you collect Tim?'

It would be his first 'outing' as Tim's father and she knew that she could not refuse him—but he hadn't needed to make love to her first to ensure that she said yes. She nodded. The only way forward was with truth and honesty and no game-playing. She wasn't going to regret what she had been unable to resist, and neither was she going to use Tim as a pawn to try to make her feel better about her mixed-up emotions.

She smiled. 'Of course you can,' she said simply, but the smile cost her almost as much as the words to make.

CHAPTER TEN

MARIAN glanced across the office. 'Telephone, Lisi.' She smiled. 'For you. It's Philip.'

Lisi reached out for the phone. As if she needed to be told! Marian's gooey expression said it all, because her boss seemed to be labouring under the illusion that all was hunky-dory between the two of them.

She sighed. Maybe that was what it looked like to the outside world. He visited Langley nearly every weekend and he took the three of them to the zoo and to parks. Dragged them on long walks around the beautiful country-side. Tim liked it that way and so, stupidly, did she.

Philip had even started teaching Tim to play football and she had watched the bond between them grow and grow, happy for her son that it should be so, convincing herself that it did not mean that she was in any way marginalised.

But he had made no further attempt to make love to her again, and, while she didn't know why, she couldn't bring herself to ask him. She feared that once had been enough for him. He had got all the hunger out of his system and now he could move on. What choice did she have, other than to respect and accept that, even though in the long, restless nights her body ached for him?

She still wanted him like crazy, and she guessed that she always would—certainly no man had ever captured her quite so completely, neither before nor since. But sex complicated things and sex with Philip sent her whole world spinning into a vortex of confusion.

Sex with Philip made you long for the impossible—the

impossible in this case being his love. And in her heart she
knew she would never have that.

'Hello?'

'Hi. How are things?'

'Good.' He only ever rang her at the office, and part of
her wondered whether this was because this guaranteed her
polite courtesy towards him. Perhaps he thought that she
would not be nearly so compliant if she didn't have Marian
half listening in on the conversation. And if he thought that,
then he was a fool—because all the fight and hostility had
left her. Sex could complicate things, yes—but it could also
help define what was most important, and Lisi knew, rightly
or wrongly, that she loved him with a fervour which made
her ache for him.

'How's life in the big metropolis?' she asked.

'How long have you got?' he asked, with a short laugh,
thinking that the quiet village life of Langley was the one
true oasis in his high-powered life these days. 'It's busy,
crowded, pressured, competitive. Want more?'

Lots more. More than he would ever give her. She
laughed back. 'I think I get the picture.' She waited. Was
today's request going to be the one she most dreaded? That
he would ask if Tim could spend the night at The Old
Rectory with him alone, and the separation of their lives as
joint parents would begin? She had been astonished that he
hadn't asked already, when the bright yellow room with its
Mickey Mouse curtains had been ready for occupation
since mid-January, and they were now well into April.

'I was wondering whether you were free on Saturday?'
he asked.

'Saturday? Of course I am—why?'

He thought that most women might have pretended to
think about it. 'There's a ball I have to attend up here—
it's usually pretty good fun. I know it's short notice, but I
wondered whether you'd like to come?'

'As your guest?' she asked stupidly.

'I wasn't planning on asking you to be my chauffeur!' Had he been instrumental in heightening her insecurity? His voice softened. 'Of course as my guest!'

'I don't know whether I can get a babysitter for Tim, not this late. And anyway, I don't know if I'd want to leave him while I went up to London,' she added doubtfully.

'You wouldn't have to. I want you to bring him—an old friend of mine has offered to babysit. It's all arranged, if you're agreed?'

Her heart was pounding with excitement. Oh, for goodness' sake—calm down, Lisi! she told herself. Somebody else has probably let him down at the last minute.

'Well?'

She swallowed. 'Okay,' she replied, as casually as she could. 'I'd love to.'

'Good.' There was a pause. 'And I'd like to buy you something to wear.'

Lisi froze, and her fingers tightened around the receiver. 'I'm not sure that I understand what you mean,' she said icily.

'Something nice—a pretty dress. Whatever you like,' he amended hastily.

So he was ashamed of his country bumpkin, was he? 'What's the matter, Philip?' she asked sarcastically. 'Afraid that I'll turn up in something completely inappropriate and let you down?'

He sighed. Hadn't he anticipated just this response? She could be so damned *proud* about some things. Like her dogged insistence on paying her share whenever the three of them went out. Time after time she had infuriated him by letting him pay for Tim, but not her, and he worried about how much their outings were eating into her limited budget.

'That wasn't what I meant!' he protested.

'Well, that's what it sounded like!'

'Let's call it a Christmas present, then,' he said placatingly. 'Since I didn't buy you one.'

They had scarcely been able to be civil to one another at the time, so that was hardly surprising, but Lisi felt the slow pulse of anger ticking away inside her. Anything more designed to make her feel like a kept woman, she could not imagine!

'Thanks, but no thanks,' she said shortly. 'I'm sure that I can dig *something* suitable out!'

Philip sighed, recognising a stubbornness which would not be shifted, no matter how he played it. 'Okay, Lisi. Have it your own way. I'll arrange to have a car pick you and Tim up on Saturday afternoon—let's say about three. Does that suit you?'

'I can get the train!'

'Yes, you can—but you aren't going to,' he argued grimly. 'It'll take you for ever, and I'm sure that Tim would enjoy travelling in a big, shiny car.'

Yes, he would absolutely love it—of course he would. Philip could give Tim all kinds of expensive toys which she would never be able to. Perhaps that was why he always rang her at work—so that she would not be able to point out little home truths like that one.

'Shall we say three?' he persisted.

'Yes, Philip. We'll be ready. Goodbye,' and she put the phone down to find Marian watching her.

'What's happened?' she asked quickly.

'He's invited the two of us up to London. He's sending a car, he's arranged a babysitter for Tim and he's taking me to a ball.'

'Oh, for heaven's sake, Lisi!' exclaimed Marian. 'I thought he'd given you bad news! Why on earth are you sitting there with such a long face? What woman wouldn't give the earth for an invitation like that?'

Lisi forced a smile. If only it were as simple as Marian seemed to think it was. 'I'm sure it will be very enjoyable,' she agreed evenly and saw Marian shake her head in disbelief.

She told an excited Tim, and that night, after she had tucked him up in bed and read him his story, she went into her bedroom to survey the contents of her wardrobe.

Ballgowns were long and she had precisely two long dresses—one she had worn during her pregnancy and which now looked like a tent, while the other was flower-sprigged and hopelessly outdated. She zipped it up. And cheap.

Had she been out of her mind to refuse Philip his offer of a dress?

She pulled a grim face at the milk-maid image reflected back at her from the mirror.

No. She would not be in any way beholden to him. By hook or by crook she would make a transformation as total as Cinderella's had been.

She just wasn't sure how!

The next morning she left Tim with Rachel and Blaine while she went to the nearby town of Bilchester to investigate its ballgown possibilities, but after two hours spent solidly trudging from shop to shop she was approaching a state close to despair.

The kind of dress which an evening with Philip would require would create an impossibly huge hole in her tight budget.

'Why don't you hire?' suggested an assistant at her very last port of call.

Lisi shrugged, her naturally parsimonious streak baulking at paying out good money for a dress she would only get to wear once. 'I want something to show for my money,' she admitted.

The assistant grinned. 'Makes a nice change to get someone in here who isn't completely rolling in it!' She lowered her voice as the manageress drifted past in a heavy cloud of cloying perfume. 'Have you tried the thrift shops?' she questioned.

'Thrift shops?'

'Charity shops,' the assistant amended. 'There are two here in Bilchester, and it's such a rich area that you never know what you'll pick up. I shop there myself,' she confided. 'I get staff discount in here, but the stuff is way too expensive.'

'What a brilliant idea!' said Lisi, with a grateful smile. 'Thanks!'

In the second charity shop she could scarcely believe her luck, because she looked in the window and found her dream dress staring her right in the face.

It looked old—but fashionably old—as if someone had bought this dress many years ago and looked after it with loving care. It had a tight, strapless silk bodice from which the many-layered tulle skirt flared out like a black cloud. It was a fairy-tale dress.

An elderly woman behind the till saw her looking at it.

'Beautiful, isn't it?' She smiled.

'Exquisite.'

'Only came in this morning—must have cost someone a fortune.'

'Can I...can I try it on, please?' asked Lisi breathlessly

The woman wrinkled her nose. 'We're not really supposed to take it out of the window for a month.'

'Oh, please,' begged Lisi. 'Please.' And the next moment she found herself telling the woman all about Philip—well, not all, but the bit about going to the fancy ball and refusing his offer of a dress.

'How can I refuse after a story like that? I'll get it out of the window. But don't get your hopes up too much—it might not fit. The waist is absolutely tiny.'

But it did. Just. Lisi breathed in and knew a moment's anxiety as the assistant struggled slightly with the zip, but once up, it fitted as though it had been designed for her.

'I won't be able to eat a thing!' she groaned.

'You won't want to, I shouldn't think. Looking like that I doubt whether you'll leave the dance-floor all night!'

It was the most beautiful thing she had ever worn. Tiny sequins were dotted here and there over the skirt, so that they glittered and caught the light as she moved. 'I'll take it,' she said instantly. 'Provided that I can afford it!'

'I'll make sure you can!' The woman gave a dreamy smile. 'It's such a romantic story!'

If only she knew! Still, she was not going to dwell on what she hadn't got—she was going to enjoy what she had—and a ball with Philip sounded pretty near perfect.

The car arrived on Saturday at three o'clock on the dot— an outrageously luxurious vehicle, complete with a uniformed chauffeur, and Tim squealed in excitement, and chatted incessantly for the whole journey.

'Calm down, poppet,' murmured Lisi, thinking that if he carried on at this rate they would never get him settled for the night.

But when the car drew up outside a house situated in a quiet, leafy lane in Hampstead, Lisi very nearly asked the chauffeur to take them straight back home again.

She swallowed. She had known that Philip was rich, of course she had—but not *this* rich, because the house she glimpsed as the car purred its way up the drive was more the size of a small castle! And land in London was unbelievably expensive—so just how wealthy *was* he to be able to afford a plot this size?

'*Big* house, Mummy!' squealed Tim excitedly.

Why hadn't he told her? Prepared her? She twisted the strap of her handbag nervously. But what could he have said that wouldn't have sounded like boasting? And Philip was not a boastful man, she realised. He carried his obvious success with an air of cool understatement.

Nevertheless, her heart was still beating like a piston when he opened the door before she had a chance to knock and the sight of him on his home territory quite took her breath away, and drove all thoughts of his intimidating wealth away.

He was wearing black jeans and a soft blue cashmere sweater and his dark hair was ruffled and his eyes very green, if a little wary.

'I wasn't sure if you'd pull out at the last minute,' he admitted.

'At least I'm not wholly predictable!'

Predictable? Never, ever. He still hadn't got over that highly erotic scene in her old bedroom. He felt his heart accelerate and he silently cursed himself for breaking his self-imposed promise not to dwell on that. For once, with Lisi—he was going to make his head dictate events, and not his body.

'Hello, Tim,' he said softly and crouched down to smile on a level with the boy. 'Come on in.'

Tim was strangely silent, but he slid his little hand into Philip's proffered one and went inside.

Lisi was too excited and nervous to take much in except for the feeling of light and space and exquisite decor.

'Shall we have tea in the sitting room first?' Philip asked. 'You can have the guided tour later.'

Tea was all laid out on a table by a roaring log fire—a proper, old-fashioned tea with sandwiches and scones and cake and biscuits. Tim gave a little whimper of delight, which turned into a whoop when he spotted the wooden train-set which had been laid out beneath the window, and he dashed over to it immediately. It was just like the one he had at home, Lisi noted. Only bigger.

Wondering just how she would be able to bring him—

and her—back down to earth after an experience like this, Lisi gestured nervously towards the teapot.

'Shall I be mother?' she asked brightly.

'You *are* mother,' Philip responded softly. 'Aren't you?'

She sat down and busied herself with pouring the tea. She had gone so long without mixing with men that she was in danger of misinterpreting everything this particular one said.

She glanced up to find him watching her, the beautiful green eyes narrowed thoughtfully. 'Who's babysitting to-night?' she asked.

'It's a surprise.'

'I don't know that I really like surprises—and I think I ought to know, so that I can prepare Tim.'

Philip hesitated. Was he about to break an unwritten law of betraying an official confidence? But it *was* to Lisi, and Lisi he could trust.

He looked over at Tim, but Tim was oblivious to everything, save his exciting new train-set.

'Choo!' he crooned. 'Choo!'

Philip lowered his voice. 'It's Khalim,' he explained.

'Sorry?'

'Khalim,' he repeated.

'P-Prince Khalim?' Lisi gulped in disbelief.

'That's right. And his wife. Rose.'

Who just happened to be a princess! Lisi put the teapot down with a shaking hand. Her son was about to be looked after by the leading members of Maraban's royal family! 'Surely they're not *that* strapped for cash!' she joked, her voice rising with a very faint note of hysteria.

Philip gave her a rueful smile. 'It does tend to have that effect on people,' he admitted. 'Everyone was a bit taken aback when they first knew he was joining us at Cambridge—but only for a time. When you are young, these things seem to matter less. *Some* people liked him for all the wrong reasons, of course—but Khalim is adept at picking out falsehood. He is a consummate judge of character, despite the isolation his position inevitably brings.'

'What will I say to them?' moaned Lisi.

Philip smiled. 'Say what you would say to anyone. Just be yourself.'

Lisi handed him his tea and gave him a puzzled look. 'I can't understand why they want to spend their Saturday evening babysitting for someone else?'

Philip took the tea and gave her a noncommittal smile. There were some confidences which were not in his gift to break. 'Normality is what they crave above all else,' he said blandly. 'Somewhere where they can relax, and be themselves.'

After tea he showed Tim his room. It had obviously been decorated especially in his honour. There were bright walls and framed posters of cartoons and more toys.

'You're spoiling him,' protested Lisi weakly.

He shrugged. 'I have a lot of time to make up for.'

She walked quickly over to the window, his remark reminding her that he would never forget the secret she had kept from him all those years. But would he ever forgive her?

'Come on,' he said. 'I'll show you where you're sleeping. Next door to Tim—of course.'

It was surprisingly small and cosy, with a fire burning brightly in the grate.

'I know how much you like fires.' He smiled. 'And this is the only bedroom in house which has a fire, apart from mine, of course.'

Her heart gave a skip of disappointment. Of course he wasn't going to move her into *his* bedroom—why on earth should he, when the physical attraction between them had obviously died? For him, at least. But, oh, she knew one mad, wild moment of longing as she pictured herself in his arms, and in his bed.

'Shall I start to get dressed now?' she asked, with a glance at her watch. 'What time are they getting here?'

'Seven-thirty,' he said.

'I'll make sure I'm ready on time.' She smiled. 'Don't worry, Philip—I won't keep them waiting.'

He smiled back. Very astute of her to realise that, despite the fact that Khalim and Rose were as close to him as they were to anyone outside their family—the fact remained that they *were* different. Only a fool would keep them waiting and Lisi was no fool. 'I'll leave you to it.'

She showered, made her face up, blow-dried her hair and pinned it back with tiny, diamanté clips, but she couldn't do the damned zip of her dress up!

She sighed, knowing there was nothing else for it but to ask Philip—and there was absolutely no reason to be shy when he knew her body more intimately than any other man.

Nevertheless, she could feel her cheeks pinkening as she called along the corridor.

'Philip! Can you zip me up?'

Philip paused in the act of clipping on his cuff-links and grimaced. Yes, he *could* zip her up, but was there any worse torture for a man who had vowed not to lay another finger on her until the time was right?

'Philip?'

'Coming,' he replied, silently cursing himself for his poor choice of word.

She stood outside the door of her room, and shrugged her shoulders apologetically, trying desperately to distract herself from the magnificent sight he made in formal dinner clothes which set off his lean physique to perfection. 'I'm afraid that I have to be almost shoe-horned into it!' she babbled.

Shoe-horned? All he could think of was how stunning she looked in black, the stark colour setting off the paleness of her skin to perfection and reflecting the deep ebony of her hair.

She turned around so that her bare back was facing him, and he sucked in a raw breath to see that she was not wearing a bra, and that her magnificent breasts were to be held in place only by the clinging folds of heavy silk.

He caught hold of the zip as gingerly as if it had been a poisonous snake. He could feel the warmth radiating of her skin, and the drift of some sweet, subtle perfume invaded his senses.

The temptation not to close her dress up, but instead to lay his fingertips against the silky surface of her skin was so powerful that he felt the unwanted jerk of arousal. He wanted to lead her by the hand to his bedroom, and to slowly undress her and make love to her all night long, but he knew that he could not. And not just because Tim was up and awake.

Time seemed to have stood still, and Lisi felt the waves of longing as they washed heatedly over her skin. She could hear the very definite sound of his breathing and she wondered whether he was actually going to get round to doing her dress up, even while her body craved for him not to, but to turn her round and kiss her instead.

'How's that?' he ground out, using every atom of self restraint he possessed as he jerked the zip up.

'Fine! Thanks,' she gulped and fled back into the sanctuary of her room, hating herself for wanting him so badly but hating him even more for not wanting *her*. What could have happened to kill all his desire for her?

Her impulsive response might have turned him off. That eager and frantic bout of love-making might have prompted him into thinking that it was inappropriate behaviour for the mother of his child to act in such a free and easy way.

When she eventually emerged from her room, she found him waiting for her and thought that she heard a distant barking. 'Do you have a dog?' she asked in surprise.

He shook his head, pleased to be able to focus his mind on something other than how utterly irresistible she looked. 'That'll be Khalim's people.'

'People?'

'Bodyguards,' he explained. 'They'll have dogs patrolling the grounds, as well as a couple of people stationed out front and out back.'

Lisi nodded thoughtfully. 'It must be strange to live your life like that—always being monitored and never alone.'

'They have each other,' said Philip simply. 'Their love makes everything bearable.'

Lucky Rose, thought Lisi, with a painful leap of her heart. What wouldn't she give to have that kind of closeness with Philip?

'Let's take Tim downstairs and feed him, before they arrive,' he suggested, then added, almost as an afterthought, 'You look beautiful, by the way.'

'Thank you.' She gave a weak smile, wishing that he had said it as though he really meant it, rather than just subjecting her to the kind of cool, green gaze as if he had been admiring a particularly expensive piece of furniture.

They gave Tim boiled eggs and toast and then settled him down in one of the big armchairs, happily drinking a glass of milk and watching one of many videos which Philip must have bought specially. Lisi looked at them with interest. He had certainly gone out of his way to make sure that Tim felt at home here. She might hope in vain that he would be openly demonstrative to *her*, but there was no doubting the love and pride he felt for his son.

Khalim and Rose arrived at the appointed hour, and Lisi stood nervously at Philip's side while he introduced them.

'Should I bow or should I curtsy?' she had asked him moments earlier.

'Either will do.'

In the end she managed an odd mixture of the two, but she was more than slightly awestruck by the sight of the black-eyed prince and his exquisite, blonde-haired princess.

'So you are Lisi.' Rose smiled. 'And this must be Tim.'

On cue, Tim jumped excitedly to his feet, not seeming at all phased by his high-born child-minders. He gave a little bow just as Philip had taught him to, and Khalim and Rose both laughed in delight.

'Sweet,' murmured Rose, and a dreamy look came over her face.

'He has your profile, Philip,' said Khalim suddenly, and subjected Lisi to a blinding smile. 'And his mother's magnificent colouring.'

'He has many of his mother's qualities—and not too many of mine, hopefully,' responded Philip.

Lisi found Rose's eyes on her. 'Khalim?'

He turned to his wife immediately. 'Dearest?'

'Bring me some sweet mint tea, would you, my love? And take Philip with you, and Tim. Show them how domesticated you have become!'

The prince gave a rueful smile, looking a little like a tiger who had just been offered a saucer of milk. 'You see how she orders me around, Philip? That much at least has not changed!'

'Indeed,' came Philip's murmured response as he followed Khalim out of the room. It never failed to amuse him—the autocratic leader of Maraban's ruling family capitulating to his English wife's every whim!

Once they had left, Rose beckoned towards the sofa. 'Come and sit by me.'

Lisi waited until Rose was seated and then sat down next to her.

'Philip has told us much about you,' observed Rose softly.

Lisi bit her lip. 'Oh? May I ask what he said?'

'That you were an exemplary mother. And that you were very beautiful.'

Lisi hesitated.

'Do not be afraid to speak,' commanded Rose softly. 'We are not on ceremony here.'

'Did he tell you about…about…'

Rose shook her head. 'He told *me* nothing that you would not wish us to hear, I think—though he is naturally closer to Khalim. Just that the circumstances surrounding Tim's conception were not ideal.'

Which Lisi supposed was a fairly diplomatic way of putting it.

'But my romance with Khalim was not a simple, straight road either,' mused Rose. 'We encountered many rocky paths along the way. This is often the way of love, you know.'

Love, thought Lisi. And although her heart ached with longing, she knew that she could not confide in the princess and tell her that Philip did not love her, nor ever would. To the outside world their relationship might look close, and it was not her place to make the reality known to his friends.

Rose leaned back against one of the cushions and gave another dreamy smile. 'Now, tell me, Lisi,' she said softly. 'Is childbirth really as bad as they say it is?'

Lisi narrowed her eyes, but did not ask the obvious question. 'It's different for everyone,' she said slowly. 'Some women find it easier than others.'

'And you? Was it easy for you?'

Lisi stared into the princess's clear blue eyes. 'It was different for me,' she answered candidly. 'I was all on my own. There was no partner to hold my hand or massage my

back, or just to tell me that everything was going to be all
right.'

'I will be on my own, too,' sighed Rose and nodded in
answer to the silent query in Lisi's eyes. 'Yes, I carry the
prince's child. But Khalim will not be permitted to enter
the birthing chamber—it is not the Maraban custom for
fathers to be present. I will be attended to by his sisters and
my ladies-in-waiting, and with that I must be content.'

'I would buy every available book on the subject if I
were you,' advised Lisi. 'And practise breathing techniques
and relaxation—that can really help.'

Rose nodded, and then she laid her slim hand on Lisi's
hand. 'You know that Philip can be very hard on himself,
don't you?'

Lisi opened her mouth to ask her what she meant, but
the moment was lost when Philip, Khalim and Tim reappeared, carrying the tray of mint tea.

A car arrived to pick them up, and it wasn't until they
were speeding towards Hyde Park that Lisi turned towards
Philip's shadowed profile.

'Rose is pregnant,' she said. 'Did you know?'

The profile shifted so that he was facing her. 'She told
you that?'

Lisi nodded. 'Yes. You sound surprised.'

'I am. I would not normally expect such a personal admission from her, not on such a short acquaintanceship.'

'Actually, I'd kind of guessed.' She saw his eyes narrow.
'It's a woman thing—you can usually tell if another woman
is pregnant.'

'Khalim is over the moon,' he observed softly, looking
at the soft line of her lips and knowing that later he intended to kiss them. 'They both are.'

Lisi stared out of the window without really seeing anything. If only she could have had Philip's baby within the

context of a warm and loving relationship like Rose and Khalim's.

'Why did you invite me tonight, Philip?' she asked suddenly. 'Did somebody let you down at the last minute?'

He swore softly beneath his breath. 'If any question was designed to remind me that you continue to think the worst of me, then that one was. I asked you, Lisi, because I thought it would be a treat for you.'

'The country girl let loose in the Big City?'

He ignored her sarcastic tone. He didn't want to fight. Not tonight. 'I can assure you that tonight you look like the most sophisticated city slicker I've ever seen!'

'Shall I take that as a compliment?'

'You could try. Now stop frowning—you'll grow old before your time. Try smiling—we're here.'

The ball was lavishly spectacular and filled with beautiful people, yet Lisi did not feel out of place—though that probably had something to do with the fact that Philip did not leave her side all night.

He danced with her and introduced her to countless people. He fetched her food and idly fed her titbits with his fingers, and because she didn't want to make a scene she didn't stop him. Didn't want to stop him, if the truth be known.

Just after midnight, the party was still in full fling, and they had just finished dancing a very slow dance in the candlelit ballroom. Lisi was reluctant to move from his arms, and he seemed in no hurry to make her. She sighed, wanting to rest her cheek against his shoulder once more, to breathe in the heady masculine scent of him and to pretend for a while that they were real lovers as well as parents.

'Lisi?'

'Mmm?'

'Look at me—I want to ask you something.'

She glanced up, something in his voice telling her that this was not a perfunctory question about whether she would like another drink. 'Yes, Philip?'

His face was as emotionless as if he were asking her the time. 'Will you share my bed tonight?'

CHAPTER ELEVEN

'MUCH as I adore Khalim and Rose, I thought they'd never go,' whispered Philip as he drew her into his arms, and quietly closed the door of his bedroom behind them.

Part of Lisi had not wanted them to go. All during the drive back from the ball she had been a bag of nerves, sitting bolt upright in the seat and wondering if she had dreamt up his provocative question and her breathless agreement to sleep with him. But this was what she had wanted for much too long, wasn't it?

He had glanced at her set features on the journey home. He certainly hadn't been going to start making love to her there, with the interested eyes of the driver looking on. Not that he'd trusted himself. If he'd started, he couldn't imagine ever wanting or being able to stop, and tonight he wanted to do it properly—with a lazy and unhurried dressing and the comfort of his big bed awaiting them.

'Lisi,' he said softly now. 'Have you changed your mind?'

She shook her head.

'Scared, then?'

She nodded. 'A little apprehensive.'

'Well, don't be. There's nothing to be apprehensive about. Here.' He lifted her fingers to his mouth and slowly kissed them, one by one, and he felt a little of the tension melt away from her. Then he pulled the diamanté clips from her hair and it fell down around her pale shoulders in streams of dark satin.

With wide eyes Lisi stared up at him, and he thought that she looked like a trapped and cornered animal. 'Lisi,' he sighed. 'We don't have to do this, you know. I thought that you wanted it as much as I do.'

Her voice trembled. 'And I do. You know I do. It's just…'

'What?'

'You haven't come near me for weeks, nor shown the slightest inclination to. I thought that you didn't want me, not in that way.' She swallowed. 'So what's happened to change your mind?'

He gazed down at her with a mixture of dismay and disbelief. Not want her? He had never stopped wanting her! Was he really so difficult to read, or just a master at keeping his feelings disguised?

'I've always wanted you, Lisi,' he said quietly. 'But our passion always seems to spring up on us unawares. I didn't want to try to make love to you at your cottage, afraid that Tim might hear because he's next door.'

'He's next door now,' she pointed out.

'And the walls here are decidedly thicker,' he commented drily.

She wasn't going to get offended by that. He was merely stating a fact, not making a comparison between the basic structure of her little cottage and the luxurious proportions of his.

'I want to make love to you properly,' he whispered and began to trace the outline of her trembling mouth with the featherlight brush of his fingertip.

The glitter from his eyes made her glow from within. 'I always quite enjoyed it when you made love to me improperly,' she joked, and he leaned forward and dropped a kiss on her lips.

'That's better,' he murmured approvingly, and her arms went up around his neck and the kiss became extended. '*Much* better. Isn't it?'

'Mmm!' She swayed against him, her doubts banished

by the warmth of his mouth and the expert caress of his tongue.

'Shall I undress you, sweetheart?'

The term of endearment made her shakier than the kiss had, and she nodded, her heart beginning to pound as he slid her zip down and laid bare her breasts.

He bent his head to take each sweet nipple in turn, inciting them into instant life with the lazy flicker of his tongue as he slid the dress down over her hips and it fell with a sigh to the floor.

He looked down at her and sucked in a ragged breath. 'Stockings,' he said thickly. 'You're wearing stockings.'

Yes, she was. 'Y-you said that you liked them,' she said, almost shyly. And tights would have seemed all wrong beneath such a fairy tale of a dress.

He wanted to beg her to keep them on, to make love to him with those silken thighs pressed hard into his back, but he knew that there would be another time for that. Right now he wanted—no, needed—her to be completely naked, there to be nothing between the two of them except skin.

'Shall I take them off for you?' he questioned unsteadily.

'Yes, please.'

His hand was shaking as he unclipped the suspender and then took a deliberately long time sliding the gauzy silk down over every delicious centimetre of her legs, his face moving tantalisingly close to the dark, triangular blur of hair which concealed her most precious gift. He longed to bury his mouth in her most secret place, but resisted, fearing that he would only end up taking her on the floor.

He unhooked the suspender belt and it joined all the other garments on the carpet and then he lifted her up and carried her over to the bed, covering her up with a duvet, so that only her cute nose and those huge aquamarine eyes were showing, and the shiny fan of black hair lay all over his pillow.

He began to unbutton his shirt, never taking his eyes from her face. 'Want me to undress for you?'

Beneath the concealment of the duvet she felt herself melt. 'Y-yes.'

The shirt fluttered from his fingers and he began to undo his trousers. It was hard to reconcile this sweetly shy Lisi with the wild lover who had gripped his shoulders so ecstatically, her fingernails making tiny little nips into his skin, her back pressed up against the wall as he'd driven into her over and over again. He stifled a groan.

Her eyes growing wider by the second, Lisi wondered what had made him briefly close his eyes like that, or why suddenly he seemed to be having more than a little difficulty sliding his zip down.

Arrogantly, he kicked off the trousers and the silk boxers followed and he stood in front of her for a moment, wanting her to see what she did to him. How she could turn him on to this pitch without having laid a finger on him.

He pulled back the duvet and climbed in next to her, and pulled her into his arms, kissing the top of her head and enjoying its meadow-sweet scent. He would just hold her for a while, stop her trembling and make her feel safe.

But the trembling only seemed to get worse, and he pulled away from her, noting the look of acute distress which had creased her brow into a deep frown.

'What's the matter, sweetheart?' And then he saw that her eyes were almost black, they were so dilated. And her breathing was shallow and rapid, and he moved his hand down between her legs to feel her slick, inviting heat. He groaned. He had been planning to make this one last and last—but what the hell? They had all night.

But he had something he needed to tell her, something she deserved to know. 'You remember the last time we did this, that morning at the rectory?' he asked, in a low voice.

'I'm not likely to forget in a hurry.'

'And you told me that there had been no other lover since me?'

She nodded. Had she been mad to expose such obvious vulnerability?

He gazed down into her watchful eyes. 'Well, it was the same for me, Lisi. There had been no one else. No one.'

There was a short, breathless silence and she could have wept with the pleasure of discovering that. 'Oh, Philip,' she murmured, and held him very close.

Lisi lost count of the number of orgasms she had that night; her last reality check was drifting into sleep sometime in the early hours, when dawn was already beginning to bring a pale, clear light to the sky.

He woke her at six and made love to her again, and she knew that she really ought to get up and get out of there before Tim got up, when there was a little rap on the door, and Tim's voice calling.

'Daddy?'

Locked in each other's arms, they both froze and looked at one another, but Lisi knew immediately that there was no way around this without the whole situation being turned into some kind of farce.

She nodded at him and he understood immediately.

'In here,' he called back. 'Come in, Tim.'

Lisi held her breath, expecting shock or outrage or even—perhaps—a touch of early masculine jealousy from the male who had been in her life the longest, but Tim displayed none of these.

Instead, he ran over to the bed, carrying his night-time bunny, glanced over at the two of them and said happily, 'Oh, *good*! Now you're just like *Simon's* mummy and daddy!'

And Lisi didn't know whether to laugh or cry.

'Why don't you go downstairs and do me a drawing?' suggested Philip. 'And I'll come down in a minute and get you some juice while I'm making Mummy her morning coffee.'

'But Mummy has *tea* in the morning.' Tim pouted.

Philip nodded. 'Then I'll make her tea,' he said gravely. 'Okay!'

They heard him scampering down the stairs and their eyes met.

'That was easier than I had anticipated,' admitted Philip.

'You were expecting him to find us in bed, then, were you?'

He shrugged. 'Well, it had to happen some time, didn't it?'

How *sure* of himself he was—and how sure of *her*. But she wasn't going to be a hypocrite and feel badly about the most wonderful night of her life.

He gave her a quick kiss, and yawned. 'At least this makes things easier.'

Lisi stilled. 'How do you mean?'

'Well.' He paused and lifted her chin so that she could not escape the cool scrutiny of his eyes. 'How would it sound if I told you that I was moving to Langley?'

The words did not seem to make any sense. 'I don't understand.'

'I love the rectory,' he said softly. 'And I find myself increasingly frustrated at commuting down there every damned weekend, when I'd happily see Tim every day.'

Tim. Not her. Just Tim. 'Go on,' she said painfully.

'So I've decided to base myself in the village.'

'But what about your business?'

He smoothed a lock of hair away from her cheek, noticing that she shut her eyes very quickly. 'Technology has given people in my kind of work the freedom to work from anywhere.' He hesitated, drawing back from telling her the one really *big* bit of news.

She opened her eyes, sensing that something else was coming. 'What?' she questioned.

'I'm in the process of buying Marian Reece out.'

'You're *what*?'

'Don't look like that, Lisi.' He put his hand on her shoulder, but she shook it away and sat up in bed, her hair tumbling down to her waist, and he had to stifle the urge to start making love to her again. Tim was downstairs, he reminded himself, though he could see from the angry look on her face that an attempt at love-making *now* would not be particularly well received.

'You just didn't bother telling *me* that you're about to become my new boss?' she accused crossly. 'And neither, for that matter, did Marian!'

'It was tricky for her. She was undecided about whether or not she wanted to stay or go—she'd been thinking of it for some time, apparently.'

'But presumably you made her an offer she couldn't refuse?' she asked sarcastically.

'I gave her a good price, yes, but then I wanted—no, I *needed* a property base in Langley.'

'Perhaps you'll be pushing the existing staff out, and bringing in new people altogether!' she said, her voice rising on a note of hysteria. 'Or maybe I'll just hand my notice in—that might be best all round! Have you thought what it would be like if we were working together?'

He had thought of little else. 'I'm not going to make you do anything you don't want to, Lisi,' he said placatingly. 'I wasn't planning to be hands-on—particularly as I hoped we might be spending a lot more time together anyway.'

She stared at him uncomprehendingly. 'Because you'll be seeing more of Tim if you're living in the village, you mean?'

'Well, not just Tim. You, as well—that's if you agree to my next proposal.'

Proposal? Her hands had gone suddenly clammy. 'Your proposal being what, exactly?'

The words had gone round and round in his head countless times, but there was no guaranteed way of making sure that she would not take them the wrong way.

'I thought that you and Tim could come and live with me. At the rectory.'

Her heart stood still. *'What?'*

'It seems crazy for us to live in two houses on the same road, when the three of us seem to have forged a pretty good relationship.'

Pretty good relationship. How tepid and passionless that sounded!

'And last night proved something, didn't it?'

'What?' she asked shakily.

'That you and I are compatible in many, many ways.'

He meant, of course, that they were good in bed together. She guessed that it was intended as a compliment, so why did it make her feel distinctly uncomfortable?

Because sex without love was only ever second-best, that was why.

She wondered whether last night's magnificent seduction had all been part of his grand plan. Have her begging in his arms for more and she would not be able to deny him anything.

Least of all his son.

She supposed that she could toss her head back in a gesture of pride and thank him for his charming 'proposal', but tell him that she preferred what she already had.

But it would be a lie.

She had already decided that she couldn't bear for anyone else to have him and that she would settle for whatever he was offering. Hearts and flowers it was not, but perhaps it was the best she could hope for.

'What do you say, Lisi?' he asked softly. 'Will you and Tim come and live with me?'

She tried telling herself that for Tim's sake she could not refuse, but that would not be the whole picture. For her sake too, there was only one answer she could possibly give.

'Yes, Philip,' she answered quietly. 'We'll come and live with you.'

CHAPTER TWELVE

'No, MUMMY!'

'But, darling, you *need* a new pair of shoes—you know you do—and we're going to meet Philip's parents at the weekend. They have to see you looking your best, don't they?'

'Granny and Grandpa,' said Tim happily.

Lisi suppressed a sigh. Everything seemed to have happened so quickly. It seemed bizarre that a few short months ago it had been just her and Tim, and yet now he talked all the time about Daddy, and his grandparents and the uncle and aunt he was soon to meet.

One great big extended family—for him, at least—although Lisi still sometimes felt as though she was standing looking in from the sidelines. But her role was as Tim's mother and Philip's mistress, and she must never forget that.

The move from Cherry Tree Cottage to The Old Rectory had been seamless—practically, if not emotionally. She had been apprehensive about it at first, but her fears had been groundless and it had turned out to be nothing short of a delight to move into her old home, with all its happy childhood memories.

To the outside world they probably looked just like any other family—and, indeed, that was just how it felt most of the time. In every sense of the word.

After years of abstinence, Philip certainly wasn't holding back. He made love to her at every opportunity he got, and Lisi wasn't complaining. He took her to heaven and back every time, even if the words of love she longed for never materialised.

He was warm and tender when she lay in his arms, but he didn't let his defences down—nor she hers. He never told her whether he regretted that circumstances had forced them into this quasi-marriage, and she didn't dare ask. And he, like her, seemed happy enough to go along with the status quo. Either that, or he was a consummate actor.

He had persuaded Marian to stay on in a consultant capacity. She now worked mornings only, two new staff had been taken on, business was booming—and Lisi had been promoted to office manageress in the afternoons.

'Philip, I can't!' she had protested, when he had first mooted the idea. 'Everyone will say it's nepotism!'

'Then everyone will be wrong,' he had replied patiently. 'You've worked here for years, and you've worked damned hard. You're good—you know you are! You deserve it, Lisi—so enjoy it!'

And she did—especially so on the all-too-infrequent occasions when Philip himself was in the office. He had not exaggerated when he had told her that he did not plan to be too hands-on. He continued to travel around the countryside and, as often as not, chose to work from the beautiful study he had created at The Old Rectory, where he said the view made his heart sing, and Lisi had never thought she could be so jealous of a view!

Thank heavens she was essentially a practical person, determinedly enjoying what she had and not wishing for the impossible.

But the trip to meet his parents loomed. She wanted to make a good impression, and that meant a brand-new outfit as well as shoes for Tim.

'Let's leave Daddy a note, shall we?' she suggested. 'You can do him a little drawing while I load up the dishwasher before we go. Here.' She scribbled a few words down, resisting the desire to add hundreds of kisses. 'Have taken Tim to Bilchester to buy shoes and a dress for me—back in time for work. Love, Lisi.'

Tim grizzled from the moment she put him in the car, and Lisi wondered whether he was coming down with a cold.

'Don't *want* to go!' he screamed, and she looked at him.

Which was more important—a happy son, or a miserable son? His trainers weren't *that* bad—and surely Philip's parents would be more interested in seeing their grandson, than in analysing her choice of footwear for him! She glanced at the heavy clouds in the sky, and the thought of being caught in rain with an out-of-sorts Tim made her mind up for her.

'Tell you what,' she said as the car Philip had insisted on buying her bumped its way down the drive. 'We'll call in to see if Rachel's there. If she is and if she isn't too busy, we'll see if you can stay with her and Blaine, while Mummy goes to Bilchester on her own. How does that sound?'

'Hurrah!' cheered Tim.

Rachel seemed all too pleased to have him. 'That'll keep Blaine from under my feet.' She grinned. 'I have four tons of laundry to sort out, and all he wants to do is play!'

Bilchester was quiet, but Lisi suspected that the drizzle which had now turned into a torrential downpour had something to do with the lack of shoppers.

She managed to buy a flame-coloured dress and a sexy pair of suede shoes, but her umbrella did little to withstand the gathering gale, and by the time she got back in the car she was shivering.

Her progress back was slow and she found herself looking at her watch more than once, and she was just starting to get anxious when she felt the car pulling out of control, and she managed to steer it over to the side-verge before switching off the engine.

With the rain pouring down, she got out to investigate and her worst fears were confirmed when she looked down to see that her tyre was completely flat. To drive it would be madness, but how the hell did she get home?

She looked up and down the narrow lane, as if expecting a recovery vehicle to come roaring up to her aid, but the road was completely empty and she was miles from anywhere.

So did she sit in the car and wait, and hope to flag down a passing motorist who might just turn out to be a homicidal maniac?

Or should she start walking home—or at least to the nearest phone-box? Philip would be home and he could drive out and pick her up.

Her raincoat already almost soaked through, she took her bags and set off as icy mud spattered up the sides of her legs and the heavens continued to unleash their downpour.

It took for ever to find a phone-box, and by then she felt that there was not one part of her body which wasn't cold and wet.

With chattering teeth she inserted a coin and dialled home, but the phone rang and rang and she remembered with a sinking heart that she had not put the answering machine on before she had left.

She replaced the receiver with a sigh of resignation. Nothing else for it but to carry on walking.

Never had a journey seemed quite so long or so arduous. Two cars passed her, but she let them drive on by—she was nearly into Langley now. A little way more wouldn't kill her.

It was almost two o'clock when she trudged past the duck pond and down the lane towards The Old Rectory. With frozen fingers she was fumbling around in her bag for her doorkey when the door flew open and there stood Philip, his face so white and furious that she hardly recognised him.

'Where the hell have you been?' he exploded, although the frantic racing of his heart abated slightly.

She was taken aback by the dark fury in his eyes. 'Well, that's a nice way to greet someone,' she managed, but her teeth were chattering so much that her words sounded like gobbledygook.

'I've been worried sick! Worried out of my head! You left a note saying that you'd gone out with Tim and I thought...I thought...' he heaved in a shuddering breath '...I thought that something had happened to you!'

Lisi pushed past him into the hall, suddenly understanding his distress. He was out of his mind with worry, but it had been Tim who had been the cause of his concern, not her. Of course it had.

'Why do you have to be so damned stubborn?' he demanded. 'Why wouldn't you let me buy you a mobile phone?'

'Because I don't need one! I've never had one before now, and I'm not going to start now just because I have the good fortune to be living with a rich man!'

'How charmingly you put it!' he snarled.

'Well, it's the truth!' She had never seen Philip quite so het-up before. Never. She glared at him. 'Why haven't you even bothered to ask me where Tim is, as you're so worried about him?'

'I know where he is!' he snapped. 'He's at nursery! I've just taken him there. Rachel rang here to find out where you were because you hadn't collected him, and I told her that I didn't know. You didn't ring—'

'Yes, I did! There was no reply—'

'I was out collecting Tim, that's why. Did you bother to put the answering machine on this morning?'

'Did *you*?' she countered. 'Anyway, there's nothing to worry about now, is there? Tim's safe, and that's all that matters!'

'All that *matters*?' he said incredulously.

'Yes!' she snapped.

He went very still, and his face took on an implacable look she had never seen there before. 'Take that coat off,' he said suddenly. 'You're soaking.'

She attempted to undo her coat, but her fingers were shaking so much that they slipped ineffectually at the buttons and Philip reached across to help her. She tried to swat him away. 'G-go away!'

He ignored her. 'Now go and get changed,' he ordered. 'And then come down to my study. I've lit a fire.'

She had had enough. Too tired and cold and shaken to care about what she said, she shot him a look of defiance. 'Stop sounding like a bloody headmaster!'

'Then stop behaving like a naughty schoolgirl!'

His rage was both intimidating and yet oddly exciting. 'And if I don't come down?'

He gave a grim smile as he slipped the sopping coat from her shoulders. 'Don't stretch my patience, Lisi—I've taken just about as much as I can stand from you this morning.'

There was something about his stance and his attitude which made all the rebellion die on her lips. Of course he had been worried—wouldn't she have been out of her mind herself in the same situation?

She changed into jeans and a big, thick sweater and towel-dried her hair, and when she walked into his study, not only did he have a glorious fire blazing, but he had also made tea, and a large bowl of soup sat steaming on the tray.

He handed her the soup. 'Eat that,' he commanded.

There was something so unimpeachable about the expression on his face that Lisi took the bowl from him obediently and began to drink it, while he stood over her making sure she did.

When she had finished the soup and drunk some tea, and the colour was beginning to seep back into her pale cheeks, he sat down in the chair opposite hers beside the fire.

Lisi pouted. The least he could have done was to have taken her upstairs and to have brought complete warmth back into her body by making love to her.

Philip saw the way her eyes darkened and the way her lips had softened. He knew what she wanted, but she was damned well going to have to wait! For too long now, he realised, he had allowed the intimacy of the bedroom to help shield him from confronting *real* intimacy.

'Did you really think that it was only Tim I was concerned about?' he demanded. 'Didn't it enter your pretty little head that I might be worried sick about *you*?'

She met the accusatory green glitter of his eyes. So he wanted the truth, did he? Then the truth he would have. 'Not really, no.'

'Lisi.' His voice was incredulous. 'Why on earth do you think that you're here, living with me the way we have been? Why do you think I asked you to move in?'

'Because that way you can have Tim full-time, and a sex life into the bargain!'

He stared at her. 'You honestly think that?'

'What else am I to think? You've never told me anything apart from the fact that I'm a great mother and a great lover. Oh, and a great cook.'

'And that isn't enough?'

She wasn't going to ask him for anything he couldn't offer freely. 'It's obviously enough for you.'

There was a moment of fraught silence. 'Oh, but it isn't,' he said softly. 'Not nearly enough.' This kind of thing didn't come easy to him, but he was going to have to try.

'You see, what I want more than anything else is your love, Lisi.'

She stared at him. 'Why?'

She needed to ask him *why*? He shook his head impatiently. Didn't she *know*? 'Because I'm finding that I can't hold back my love for you. Not for much longer. I love you, Lisi—hadn't you begun to even guess?'

She didn't respond for a moment. When you had spent so long wishing that something would happen, you didn't believe the sound of your own ears when it seemed as though something just had. 'You don't have to say things like that to make me feel better.'

'I'm not,' he said patiently. 'But what if saying them makes *me* feel better? What if I told you that I don't know when I started loving you, but I do, and not just because you're mother and lover and cook, but because you make me laugh and you make me mad, and I can't imagine the world without you. And the only unknown factor in this equation is that I don't know how you feel about me.'

She felt hope—delirious, impossible hope—begin to beat out a rapid thunder in her heart. 'You must do,' she said weakly.

'Why must I? You never tell me what's going on inside your head, do you, Lisi? At night you never whisper anything more tender than the fact that I'm a bit of a stud in the bedroom.'

'And what about you?' she countered. 'You're the master of disguising your feelings! If, as you say, you love me—then why didn't you tell me before? Why didn't you make that a part of asking me to move in here with you, instead of leaving me feeling like a mistress-cum-mother?'

'Is that what I made you feel like?'

She nodded.

He sighed. 'Because I didn't know how much I loved you until you became a part of my life,' he admitted. 'It kind of crept up on me slowly, like a sunny day at the end of winter.'

Curled up in her chair, Lisi felt some of the tension begin to leave her. 'Something still stopped you, though, even when you realised?'

'I was scared,' he said simply.

'Scared?' Lisi smiled. 'Oh, no! That really *would* be stretching credibility too far—I can't imagine you being scared of *anything*, Philip.'

'Scared that it would all sound too pat. That you wouldn't believe me—and why should you? I thought you would begin to see for yourself, only…'

'Only what?' she prompted, her heart in her mouth.

He shook his head as he read the doubts and fears in her eyes. 'It was like you had erected a barrier between us, and sometimes you would lower it down, but only so far—so I didn't have a clue whether you knew how I felt. Or how you felt about me,' he finished, a question in his eyes.

He had been about as honest as it was possible to be, and she knew that, to Philip, such admissions did not come easily. It was time to make her own.

'I was scared, too,' she whispered. 'Only my fear was that the love I felt for you might frighten you away. Falling in love wasn't supposed to be part of the deal, even if that's what I wanted more than anything.'

A slow smile began to transform his face into the most carefree Philip she had ever seen. 'Come here,' he whispered.

She didn't need asking twice, just went and sat on his lap, and he wrapped his arms tightly around her waist while her head fell onto his shoulder and she fought to keep the stupid and irrational tears away.

'Don't cry, Lisi,' he soothed as he felt her tremble. 'There's nothing to cry about. Not any more.'

She thought about how far she had come to reach this

moment, and, despite his words, the tears spilled over onto his sweater and soaked right through it.

He didn't say another word, just held her very, very tight until a last little sniff told him that she was all cried out, and he lifted her head and gave her the kind of tender smile she had always dreamed of. 'Better?'

'Mmm.'

'Need a hanky?'

She bit her lip and actually giggled. 'I used your sweater, thanks.'

He smiled as he brushed a last stray tear away. 'You once asked me whether that first night had just been lust,' he said softly. 'And I said that I didn't know.' He paused. 'That wasn't quite true.'

She stilled. 'What do you mean?'

It was time at last to make sense of all his vague suspicions. 'I talked to Khalim about it—I told him the whole story, and he said that such uncharacteristic behaviour on my part meant far more than I perhaps realised.' He smiled as he touched her lips, just for the hell of it. 'I told you that Khalim was a romantic, but he would prefer to describe himself as a realist. He said that I was being too hard on myself and that my subconscious was telling me that you were—or could be—very important to me. How right he was.' He kissed her tenderly. 'How right he was!'

'Oh, Philip!' She snuggled even closer to him.

'And one more thing.' He kissed her again. 'I'm sick of not letting the world know how I feel about you. I want to marry you, Lisi—just as soon as you like, *if* you like.'

'Mmm! I can't think of anything I'd like better!' She kissed him back. But not for a while. She wanted to enjoy what she had never had with Philip—a loving courtship with no pressures.

'But let's take it step by step,' she whispered. 'Better get

your parents used to having a grandson before we announce
that you're getting married!'

His mouth trailed a lazy line down her cheek and he felt
her shiver. 'Nervous about meeting them?' he questioned.

'A little.' She pressed herself closer, revelling in the
knowledge that there were no secrets or taboo between
them now. Love, she realised, was a very liberating emotion. 'We've done everything the wrong way round, Philip.'
She sighed. 'Haven't we?'

'It certainly hasn't been a text-book love-affair,' he
agreed. 'And I need to take you to bed,' he added softly.

She felt the raw need and tension in his body, but there
was one other thing she needed to say to him. 'You must
never forget Carla,' she whispered. 'I don't want you to.
Let all the guilt go now and remember all good times—she
would want that for you, having loved you. I would.'

There was a moment of silence. 'That's about the
sweetest thing you could have said,' he said shakily, and
right then he needed her as he had never needed her before.
He gave a slow smile. 'We'll have to go and collect Tim
in an hour, you know.'

'I know. And?'

A finger was grazed carelessly around the outline of her
lips. 'Any idea how you'd best like to fill the time?'

She felt the invasive tug of desire and gave him a be-
witching smile, loving the predatory and possessive darkening of his eyes. 'One or two,' she said demurely.

'Me, too. Let's say we swop notes. Upstairs,' he purred,
lifting her up into his arms and slanting a provocative smile
down at her.

She opened her eyes very wide. 'You're going to *carry*
me to bed?'

'That depends.'

'On what?'

'On whether we make it to the bedroom!'

EPILOGUE

SOMEONE was banging a spoon against an empty wineglass and the excited chatter of the guests began to die away.

It had been the most wonderful wedding imaginable. Lisi stole a glance at her new husband and let out a small sigh of contentment. She almost didn't want it to end, except that the night ahead beckoned her with such erotic promise.

Philip slowly turned his head, as though he had known she was watching him, and mouthed 'I love you' with an expression on his face which made her heart feel like spilling over with happiness.

'May I just say a few words?' The banger of the spoon was Philip's father, who was now rising to his feet.

Charles Caprice was a poppet, thought Lisi fondly. Tall and distinguished, his hair brushed with silver, he had given her a very pleasing insight into how her darling Philip would look when he was older.

Philip's mother had been equally welcoming—embracing her as if she were the daughter she had never had, and both of them were absolutely besotted by their grandson. In fact, Tim was going to stay with them while they were away in Maraban for their honeymoon.

She looked around the room. Langley had never seen a wedding like it—but maybe that wasn't so surprising. When a small English village was invaded by the leading members of the Maraban royal family and their entourage, then excitement was pretty much guaranteed!

Prince Khalim had stood as Philip's best man, and an ecstatic Rose had proudly carried the infant Prince Aziz, who had lain contentedly in her arms throughout the ceremony.

'I do not know why Rose has brought along a nanny,' Khalim had remarked drily to Philip. 'She guards him so jealously—like a tiger!'

'And would you have it any other way?' Philip had smiled.

'Never!'

Philip looked down at the jet-dark hair of the baby Aziz, and ruffled it. He had never seen his own son as a baby, and Lisi had cried and cried about denying him that right on more than one occasion, but he had urged her to let it go, as he now had. 'There'll be more babies,' he had whispered.

'Wh-when?' she had questioned shakily.

'Whenever you like. I think Tim would like a brother or a sister, don't you?'

And she had nodded and then kissed him, too full of emotion to speak for a moment or two.

Philip's father was now clearing his throat. 'I know that it isn't conventional for the *groom's* father to speak,' he began, and then sent Lisi a gentle smile across the table. 'But Lisi has become like a daughter to my wife and I— actually, she *is* our daughter, as well as my son's wife. And that's really what I want to say to you all.' His voice faltered a little. 'I would like you all to raise your glasses in a toast. To Lisi, beautiful, sweet Lisi—who has put a smile on my son's face again, and for which I will always be grateful.'

Champagne glasses were lifted and waved in the direction of the top table, but Lisi was so choked that she didn't dare look up for fear that everyone would see her eyes brimming over with tears.

'To Lisi!' they all echoed.

Beneath the table, Philip squeezed her hand. 'Look at me, my darling,' he urged softly.

She lifted her face to his, seeing the corresponding glitter of his own eyes and immediately understanding why. His father's emotional words had reinforced that a bright, new future lay ahead and that the past was now behind them. And in a way, Philip had been saying goodbye to Carla, she guessed, and squeezed his hand back, very tightly.

'It's okay to cry at weddings, you know, sweetheart,' he whispered.

She wobbled him a smile. 'But my mascara will run!'

He laughed. She was everything to him—his passion and his soul mate—the woman who had brought the light back into his life. 'I love you very much, Mrs Caprice,' he told her simply, because he did.

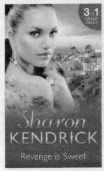

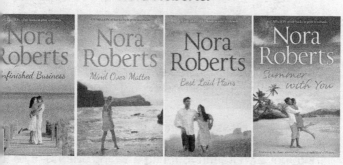

MILLS & BOON®

It's Got to be Perfect

*IT'S GOT
TO BE
Perfect*

UNCORRECTED
PROOF COPY

HALEY HILL

* cover in development

When Ellie Rigby throws her three-carat engagement ring into the gutter, she is certain of only one thing. She has yet to know true love!

Fed up with disastrous internet dates and conflicting advice from her friends, Ellie decides to take matters into her own hands. Starting a dating agency, Ellie becomes an expert in love. Well, that is until a match with one of her clients, charming, infuriating Nick, has her questioning everything she's ever thought about love…

**Order yours today at
www.millsandboon.co.uk**

MILLS & BOON®

The Thirty List

* cover in development

At thirty, Rachel has slid down every ladder she has ever climbed. Jobless, broke and ditched by her husband, she has to move in with grumpy Patrick and his four-year-old son.

Patrick is also getting divorced, so to cheer themselves up the two decide to draw up bucket lists. Soon they are learning to tango, abseiling, trying stand-up comedy and more. But, as she gets closer to Patrick, Rachel wonders if their relationship is too good to be true…

Order yours today at
www.millsandboon.co.uk/Thethirtylist

MILLS & BOON®

Want to get more from Mills & Boon?

Here's what's available to you if you join the exclusive **Mills & Boon eBook Club** today:

- ✦ *Convenience – choose your books each month*
- ✦ *Exclusive – receive your books a month before anywhere else*
- ✦ *Flexibility – change your subscription at any time*
- ✦ *Variety – gain access to eBook-only series*
- ✦ *Value – subscriptions from just £3.99 a month*

So visit **www.millsandboon.co.uk/esubs** today to be a part of this exclusive eBook Club!